Y0-AAX-975

The Control
of Nuclear Activity

PRENTICE-HALL INTERNATIONAL, INC., *London*
PRENTICE-HALL OF AUSTRALIA, PTY. LTD., *Sydney*
PRENTICE-HALL OF CANADA, LTD., *Toronto*
PRENTICE-HALL OF INDIA (PRIVATE) LTD., *New Delhi*
PRENTICE-HALL OF JAPAN, INC., *Tokyo*

The Control of Nuclear Activity

A symposium held under the auspices of
The Society of General Physiologists
at its annual meeting at
The Marine Biological Laboratory,
Woods Hole, Massachusetts, August 31–
September 3, 1966

Lester Goldstein, *Editor*

Prentice-Hall, Inc.
Englewood Cliffs, New Jersey

Library of Congress Catalog Card Number: 67-15171

Printed in the United States of America
-C-

Dedicated to
Professor Merkel H. Jacobs
on the
Twentieth Anniversary
of
The Society of General Physiologists
of which
He was a Founder

Preface

Of the unknowns that confront biologists in 1966, none is more tantalizing than the processes that control nuclear activity. This is especially true, of course, for biologists who study cells (cukaryotes) in which the nuclear material is separated from the rest of the cell by a nuclear envelope. Part of the tantalization results from the knowledge that genetic control mechanisms in bacteria (prokaryotes) have become, by contrast, relatively well understood in recent years. The reasons for the differences in the knowledge about the two cell types—thought until recently to be due to differences in complexity of cellular organization—may be discernible in the following pages but, aside from the presence of eukaryotic cell functions that are clearly absent from prokaryotic cells, the reasons are not strikingly apparent. The symposium that led to this volume was planned with the notion that at this time the discoveries of bacterial regulatory phenomena might be sufficiently advanced and refined to provide insights that would enable a gathering of eukaryotic cell workers to interact effectively in their efforts to comprehend control mechanisms in higher organisms. However, the symposium proceedings probably emphasized more strongly than ever the differences between the two cell types—but may have accelerated progress, nevertheless, by dispelling some of the seemingly hypnotic influence cast by the elegant bacterial work. That cells with defined nuclei may have unique regulatory mechanisms is a divisive possibility that should be faced.

The symposium, entitled "Cytoplasmic and Environmental Influences on Nuclear Behavior," was held in conjunction with the annual meeting of *The Society of General Physiologists* at Woods Hole from August 31 to September 3, 1966. It was organized into sections different from those into which this volume is ordered. After the final manuscript material was assembled, the arrangement given here seemed more reasonable, since the symposium, after all, was planned only on the *anticipated* content of the reports. Some of the papers still do not fit perfectly into the sections assigned here, but to have had a precise classification would have made the sections almost as numerous as the chapters. A. L. Judin was unable to attend the symposium but did submit a manuscript for publication.

I had remarkably good cooperation from the authors on most particulars but of unusual noteworthiness is the fact that most manuscripts were submitted at the symposium and all were submitted within a month of that event. I am deeply grateful for the participants' efforts. With the help of Prentice-Hall, Inc., the efforts of the authors are expected (at the time of this writing) to lead to a publication date less than six months from the time of actual symposium proceedings. As part of the procedure for achieving early publication a sacrifice was made in the method of composing the book, but this we feel is a minor discomfort. A possibly more serious circumstance is that some authors had no opportunity to correct proof properly before we went to press; this also was necessary to insure timely publication. In view of these procedures, the responsibility for errors should fall on the editor and not the authors.

From the viewpoint of the organizer (the undersigned), the planning and proceedings of the symposium went magnificently. Directly responsible were many able individuals, and my warmest gratitude is expressed to: the officers of *The Society of General Physiologists* (especially Dr. David W. Bishop, president; Dr. Eloise Clark, secretary; Dr. Timothy Goldsmith, treasurer; and Dr. Leonard Nelson, chairman of the local committee); the chairmen of the various sessions (Drs. Teru Hayashi, Seymour S. Cohen, James Lash, Howard Holtzer, and Paul R. Gross) whose execution of their functions fulfilled our most optimistic expectations; Drs. David M. Prescott and Irving Finger, who at various times during the planning of the symposium offered wise advice, none of which included nominating themselves as symposium speakers. Mrs. Karen Meadow excellently performed numerous editorial services that did much to facilitate the publication of this book. The travel expenses of the symposium participants were paid for from a grant generously provided by the National Science Foundation.

LESTER GOLDSTEIN

Philadelphia, Pennsylvania

Contents

Section iii. The Exchange of Material between Nucleus and Cytoplasm

Section iv. The Control of Gene Expression

Section v. Conclusion

Section I

Chromosome and Cell Reproduction

*Nucleocytoplasmic Interactions in the Control of Nuclear Reproduction and Other Cell Cycle Stages**

Lester Goldstein

Department of Biology
University of Pennsylvania
Philadelphia

and

David M. Prescott

Institute for Developmental Biology
University of Colorado
Boulder

Progress through the cell life cycle is almost certainly based on a continuum of causally linked, biochemical and physiological events. The schedule of some events is clearly defined - e.g., the initiation and termination of DNA synthesis and nuclear and cellular division - but much of the continuum is undefined. The basis for the existence of the G_1 and G_2 periods, measurable in most cells, represents major information gaps. The transition from the pre-DNA synthesis state into DNA synthesis is of special interest because the cycle's primary off-on switch is apparently associated with the events of this change. The control of DNA synthesis remains one of the central, unsolved problems of molecular biology.

*Supported by a grant from the National Science Foundation to David M. Prescott and a grant from the U.S. Public Health Service to Lester Goldstein.

By altering nuclear-cytoplasmic relations in Amoeba proteus at known parts of the cycle, we hope to gain some insight into the character of the events that govern its progress. With several types of manipulations, experimental cells can be constructed that combine cytoplasm of particular cycle ages with nuclei of particular cycle ages. For example, the nucleus of a cell in DNA synthesis can be transplanted into a late G_2 cell that itself has just been enucleated. The reciprocal transplant can also be carried out, and the experiments can be varied by retaining the original nucleus of the recipient cell to form a mixed binucleate.

Experimental results of this general type have proven more complicated than anticipated, but also more instructive. In this paper we shall report our progress to date.

MATERIAL AND METHODS

The cells used in all our experiments were free-living amebae, Amoeba proteus (4). Nuclei were transplanted from cell to cell by the usual method (3): a nucleus is pushed, without exposure to extracellular media and with no detectable transfer of cytoplasm, from one cell to another with a microprobe. If desired, a cell was enucleated in the same manner, except that the nucleus was pushed into the external medium.

Nuclei were isolated by drawing cells in and out of a narrow-tipped pipet in a medium of 1 ml Triton X-100 (a Rohm and Haas detergent) and 2 mg spermidine-HCl per 200 ml until the nuclei were free of all traces of cytoplasm (4).

Incorporation of radioactive material by cells was detected by liquid emulsion autoradiography (6). Binucleated cells were prepared by placing amebae in early stages of division into a concentrated solution of crystalline bovine albumin for about 45 min to block cytokinesis. Such cells became binucleate because mitosis is completed normally.

RESULTS AND DISCUSSION

The Normal Cell Cycle

In *A. proteus*, as in other cell types, the generation time varies within certain limits that must be accounted for experimentally. At 23°C, the generation time for most cells falls between 36 and 40 hr and at 17°C, between 48 and 55 hr.

The stages of the cell cycle were determined in a traditional manner. Several hundred cells were synchronized by manual selection of dividing cells from a growing culture, and small groups of such cells were incubated in ^{3}H thymidine (^{3}H-TdR) for short intervals at various times after cell division. At the end of each incubation period, nuclei were isolated, affixed to slides, treated with 1 N HCl at 25°C for 5 min, rinsed with water, and autoradiographed to determine ^{3}H-TdR incorporation.

The results show that the G_1 period, if it exists at all, occurs in less than 15 min immediately following cytokinesis (less than 1% of a generation time). If the end of telophase, rather than the completion of cytokinesis, is adopted as the time for the beginning of G_1, then certainly no G_1 exists in ameba, because telophase is not finished until 10 to 15 min after cytokinesis. This finding indicates that under normal conditions of continuous growth, the initiation of DNA synthesis in *A. proteus* is causally linked to some event occurring during the immediately preceding mitosis. Both under normal growth conditions and under experimentally altered conditions, this relationship between mitosis and initiation of DNA synthesis has remained absolutely constant. When dividing cells are transferred to nonnutrient conditions, DNA synthesis begins on schedule in the daughter cells in the absence of new food intake. Amputation of 50% of the cytoplasm from a dividing ameba does not interfere detectably in the initiation of DNA synthesis at the normal time in the two, abnormally small, daughter cells. Complete inhibition of cytokinesis with a bovine albumin solu-
does not disrupt the schedule of DNA synthesis in the

two nuclei of the resulting binucleate cell. Apparently, then, the initiation of DNA synthesis has been firmly programmed by the time mitosis is in progress.

A G_1 period is also absent for the micronucleus cycle in some ciliates (5, 7), in the slime mold Physarum (1), and in grasshopper neuroblasts (2). Of greater significance is the absence of G_1 in a line of hamster cells derived from a population showing the usual G_1 period of several hours (8). Whether the elimination of G_1 stems from a genetic change cannot yet be decided, but in this case, G_1 as a measurable time interval is clearly an expendable part of the cell life cycle.

DNA synthesis is not inalterably linked temporally to mitosis, for amebae starved several days immediately start to synthesize DNA when refed. (Mitosis does not occur until many hours later.) Since DNA synthesis has been found to occur invariably following mitosis, the starving amebae must have been in the G_2 state at the beginning of the imposed starvation. Starvation, therefore, allows the ameba to lapse into a condition that resembles G_1, inasmuch as DNA synthesis begins immediately with refeeding. Presumably such cells undergo two rounds of DNA synthesis between the pre- and post-starvation divisions.

The duration of the S period is a remarkably brief portion of the cell cycle; for a 36 hr cycle, the period of DNA synthesis occupies no more than 6 hr and perhaps as little as 3 hr immediately following cell division. This brevity may be related to the unusually small amount of DNA for such a large cell, plus the fact that the DNA is packaged into a large number of very small chromosomes.

The remainder of the cycle, 30 to 33 hr, is G_2. During G_2, some amebae incubated in ^{3}H-TdR incorporate a very low level of radioactivity into an acid-insoluble form. The rate of such incorporation is no more than 1% of the rate during S, and at least 95% of the incorporation of radioactivity occurs during S. The activity incorporated during S is almost completely removed by deoxyribonuclease treatment, but some and perhaps all of the minor activity incorporated during

G_2 is not so removed.

Cytoplasmic Influence on the Initiation of DNA Synthesis

We approached this question in ameba by observing the influence of S phase cytoplasm on the ability of a G_2 nucleus to incorporate ^{3}H-TdR. Table 1 gives the

TABLE 1

Effect of cytoplasm on ^{3}H thymidine incorporation*

G_2 nuc → S cyto	G_2 nuc → G_2 cyto	S nuc → S cyto	S nuc → G_2 cyto
+++	0	+++	0
+++	+	+++	+
0	0	+++	0
0†	0	+++	0
++	+	+++	++
+§	0	0†	+
++	0	+++	+
+	0	+++	+
++	+	+++	+++
+	0	0§	0
	0	+++	
	+	+++	
	0	++	
	0	+++	
	0	+++	

*The heading for each column shows the nature of the experimental cell. Thus, the left-hand column shows the data for cells that were composed of a G_2 nucleus grafted into S cytoplasm.

†These two nuclei were in the same cytoplasm.

§These two nuclei were in the same cytoplasm.

Scale of Autoradiographic Activity

0 = 5-25 grains
+ = 26-45 grains
++ = 46-75 grains
+++ = > 75 grains

data for one such experiment. When a late G_2 nucleus (in the last quarter of the cell cycle) is grafted into an S cell, DNA synthesis is initiated in this G_2 nucleus. In the control experiment, a G_2 nucleus is grafted into a G_2 cell; in such cases DNA synthesis is not initiated. Since the original nucleus of the recipient S phase cell was checked for ^{3}H-TdR incorporation, we have direct knowledge of whether any given cell was still in an S condition when it received the G_2 nucleus. In two of the cases in Table 1, the presumed S cell apparently had entered G_2, because the original cell nucleus as well as the grafted G_2 nucleus did not incorporate ^{3}H-TdR.

From these observations on G_2 nuclei, we conclude that the normal, tight, temporal coupling between mitosis and the initiation of DNA synthesis is not mandatory. The incorporation of a substantial amount of ^{3}H-TdR into a G_2 nucleus in S cytoplasm clearly demonstrates a cytoplasmic role in the initiation of DNA synthesis. This experiment, and the observation that starving amebae begin DNA synthesis when refed, therefore show that a nucleus need not undergo mitosis to enter DNA synthesis.

A striking feature of the cytoplasmic influence is the suddenness with which it appears. By definition, the G_2 cytoplasm is not concerned with supporting DNA synthesis; yet within a matter of minutes in ameba - no more than the time required for mitosis - the cytoplasm becomes abruptly amenable to DNA synthesis in the newly divided nuclei. A more dramatic demonstration of the suddenness of the change is evident when a G_2 nucleus begins DNA synthesis upon implantation into a cell that had been blocked in division (by albumin treatment) and then had both daughter nuclei removed before the G_2 nucleus was introduced. In this case, cell division and the new, postmitotic surface-volume relations of nucleus and cytoplasm are eliminated as factors involved in the initiation of S. The new experimental cell in many ways resembles a G_2 cell, different primarily because mitosis has taken place, although the mitotic participants are gone. Possibly, then, mitosis does not influence directly the chromosomes to commence S, but rather effects a change in the cytoplasm that enables the cell to support DNA synthesis.

Cytoplasmic Influence on the Cessation of DNA Synthesis

From these experiments we conclude that an event (or events) normally coinciding with mitosis in ameba brings about alterations in the cytoplasm (and perhaps in the nucleus) which in turn lead to DNA synthesis. The question is then raised whether the cytoplasmic alteration is an absolute requirement for nuclear DNA synthesis or whether, in fact, the nuclear alteration is sufficient. The problem is translated into experiment by determining whether an S phase nucleus grafted into the cytoplasm of a G_2 cell continues DNA synthesis without diminution or delay. The data in Table 1 show that ^{3}H-TdR incorporation declines for an S nucleus in G_2 cytoplasm. The experiment does not distinguish between active inhibition by the cytoplasm and failure to provide essential support, but the results do show that a correct cytoplasmic condition is necessary for full DNA synthesis. What meager information is now available on the extent of replication under various conditions would favor the interpretation that the transfer of an S nucleus into G_2 cytoplasm deprives the nucleus of specific initiators of DNA synthesis. The decline in DNA synthesis in the G_2 cytoplasm may reflect completion of replication of DNA units initiated before transfer, as well as the failure of unreplicated units to undergo initiation of synthesis on schedule. Such an interpretation is consistent with the observation that in mammalian cells the replication of DNA units follows a sequential pattern.

We do not know, in fact, whether G_2 cytoplasm shuts off an S phase nucleus completely for a time or only slows it down. Whatever the effect of G_2 cytoplasm on DNA synthesis, such cells eventually divide and behave normally if allowed to grow - an indication that an adjustment is reached that ultimately permits the completion of DNA synthesis. Recall that starving cells supposedly in G_2 (since all cells go through DNA synthesis following the last division before starvation becomes effective) shift to a DNA synthesis upon refeeding - i.e., a cell need not undergo mitosis to convert from G_2 to S.

In many of these experiments it would be extremely useful to know in precise quantitative terms how much DNA was initially present in a nucleus or how much DNA has been synthesized during an experiment. Unfortunately, we have currently no practical method for measuring the small amount of nuclear DNA in ameba.

Before we turn to other aspects of the cell cycle, we should note - to reemphasize the influence of the cytoplasm on S - that when nuclei of different cell cycle stages are in the same cell, their ability to incorporate ^{3}H-TdR is always influenced in the same direction.

Nucleocytoplasmic Interactions at Other Stages of the Cell Cycle

We have begun an investigation of the nature of G_2 in ameba, hoping to provide some information about the relative role of the nucleus and the cytoplasm in the events underlying this part of the cell cycle. We have tried to determine whether G_2 is concerned primarily with cytoplasmic or nuclear events. It was immediately suggested that G_2 is not devoted exclusively to nuclear affairs because a late G_2 nucleus placed into S cytoplasm (original S nucleus removed) does not divide unless fed and allowed to grow. Apparently some "maturation" of the cytoplasm must occur during the normal G_2 as part of division preparation. Conversely, however, a cell with an S nucleus and a late G_2 cytoplasm is not able to reach division unless it is fed and allowed to grow.

Examining the situation further, we find that if these two kinds of experimental cells are permitted to grow under the same nutrient conditions, the cell with the S nucleus and G_2 cytoplasm divides appreciably before the cell with the G_2 nucleus and S cytoplasm (compare curves in Figure 1 marked "S nuc in G_2 cyto" and "G_2 nuc in S cyto"). Since the first cell to

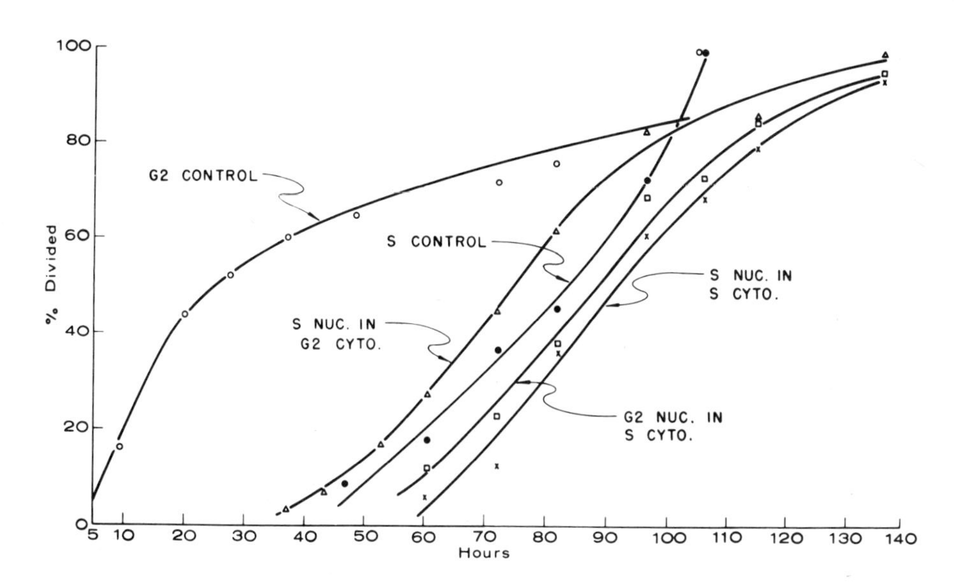

Figure 1. Demonstration of rate of division for various kinds of cells. "G_2 controls" were from a relatively synchronous population of cells that also furnished cells which were the source of G_2 nuclei and G_2 cytoplasm for the experimental cells. "S controls" were the counterparts to the G_2 controls. "S nuc in S cyto" were controls for the effect of the microsurgery, if compared to the "S controls." "S nuc in G_2 cyto" are enucleate G_2 cells that underwent S nucleus implantation. "G_2 nuc in G_2 cyto" are enucleate S cells that underwent G_2 nucleus implantation. All cells were fed continuously from "0" hours. All curves were drawn by eye.

divide is the one with the more advanced cytoplasm (G_2 cytoplasm) rather than the more advanced nucleus (G_2 nucleus), it is argued that progress through the cycle, most of which is G_2 , depends upon cytoplasm maturation. The argument that cycle progress may depend only on nuclear events does not seem tenable because the transfer of a G_2 nucleus into S cytoplasm might possibly be more disruptive to nuclear activities than is a transfer of an S nucleus into G_2 cytoplasm. As we shall show (curve "G_2 nuc → enucleated binuc" in Figure 3), under appropriate circumstances a G_2 nucleus in S cytoplasm is in no apparent way disturbed. Since the S nucleus - G_2 cytoplasm cell is larger, we might argue that a mere mass increase is all that is required for the G_2 nucleus - S cytoplasm cell to be ready for division, as long as the G_2 nucleus was prepared for mitosis. If that were so, the latter cell should not be delayed, relative to the former, but the S nucleus - G_2 cytoplasm cell might be expected to divide later because its nucleus would need to complete the G_2 maturation process.

Both types of mixed cells are accelerated over the control transfer of an S nucleus into S cytoplasm; the cell with a G_2 nucleus in S cytoplasm divides about 5 hr sooner, and the cell with a G_2 cytoplasm and an S nucleus is accelerated 16 to 17 hr. Figure 2 illustrates another version of this experiment, which again suggests that G_2 is devoted in a major way to cytoplasmic matters. A comparison has been made between a cell containing late G_2 cytoplasm and an S nucleus and a control cell of late G_2 cytoplasm that has received a late G_2 nucleus by transplantation. The experimental cell (S nucleus into G_2 cytoplasm) takes only about 10 hr longer to reach division than the control (G_2 nucleus into G_2 cytoplasm). Perhaps the additional 10 hr is merely the time required for the S nucleus to finish DNA synthesis in the G_2 cytoplasm. The experiments in Table 1 show that DNA synthesis is slowed by G_2 cytoplasm, which would explain the 10 hr value instead of 6 hr, the maximum length of normal S.

The experiments just described have introduced us to new ways of thinking about the cycle, but much of the interpretation is speculative. We have continued the general approach by using two new experimentally derived cells: the enucleated binucleate (EB) and the mononucleated binucleate (MB). The EB ameba is prepared by inhibition of cytokinesis with an albumin solution and microsurgical removal of both nuclei from the resulting binucleate. The MB cell is similar with only one of the two nuclei removed. With this material

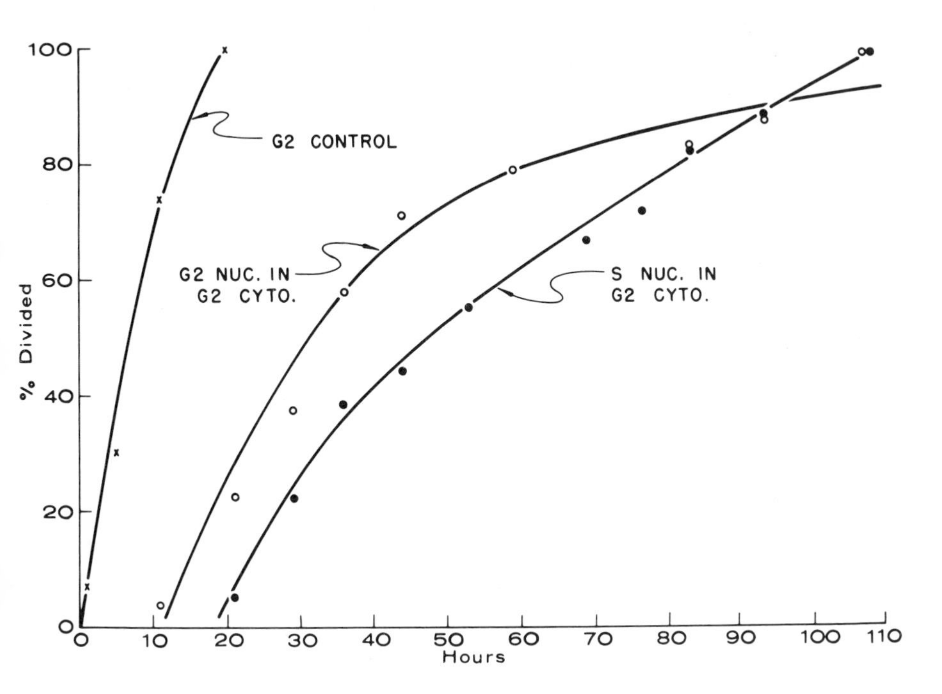

Figure 2. Demonstration of role of nucleus in determination of division rate. "G_2 controls" are the same as described in Figure 1. "G_2 nuc in G_2 cyto" are G_2 cells that had their nuclei exchanged for nuclei from other G_2 cells. "S nuc in G_2 cyto" are enucleate G_2 cells into which were grafted S nuclei. All curves were drawn by eye.

we have compared the time three types of cells need to reach division:

1. a cell with late G_2 cytoplasm that has had its nucleus exchanged for another from a G_2 cell;
2. an EB cell that has received a late G_2 nucleus;
3. an MB cell.

Of these three types, we might expect the cell prepared by combining G_2 cytoplasm with a G_2 nucleus to divide first, because both cell compartments are well advanced toward division. Remarkably, however, the G_2 nucleus in the EB cell (S cytoplasm) divided earlier than the other two (Figure 3). It is difficult

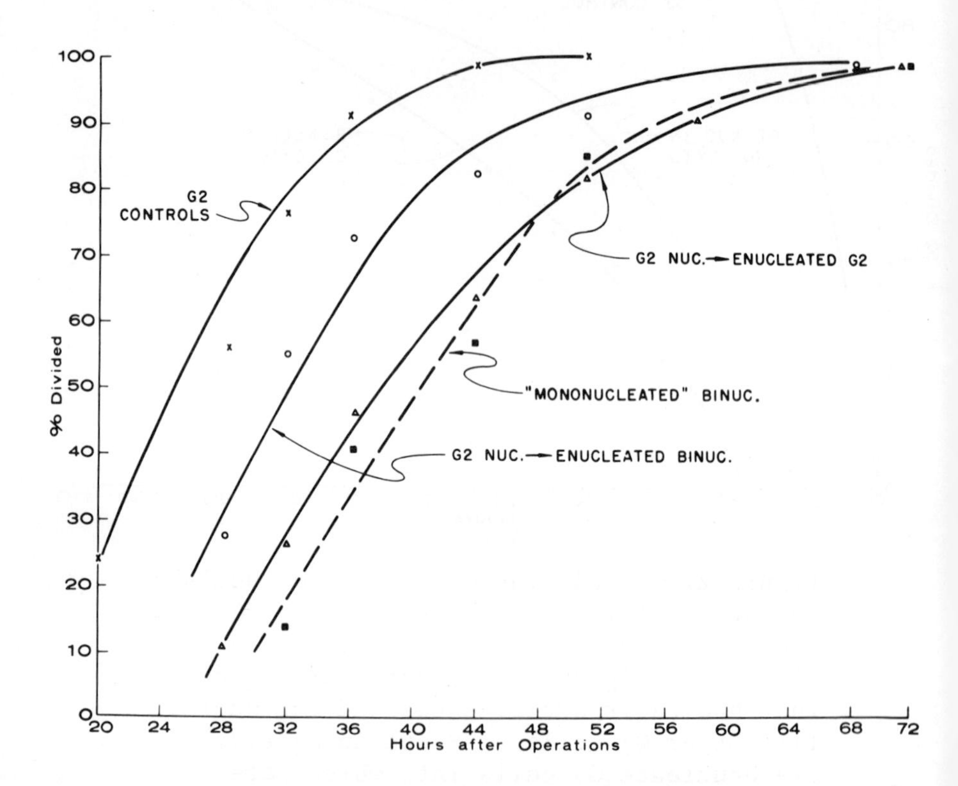

Figure 3. Effect of cytoplasm and of nucleus on division rate. Information in legends for Figures 1 and 2 also applies here, where appropriate. "mononucleated binuc" is a cell the cytokinesis of which was blocked by albumin, and, after the completion of mitosis, had one nucleus removed. "G_2 nuc → enucleated binuc," was a cell in which cytokinesis was blocked by albumin, and which, after the completion of mitosis, had both nuclei removed and a G_2 nucleus implanted.

to explain why this should happen, unless we speculate that early S cytoplasm has not changed in certain properties in the hour or two since it was, in fact, G_2 cytoplasm, and therefore it is more readily prepared to enter another division when given a late G_2 nucleus than are the other cells. Also, the amount of "division" cytoplasm in the EB cell may facilitate rapid adjustment with a late G_2 nucleus. The binucleated cell allowed to retain one nucleus (in normal S) divides only slightly after the cell with G_2 cytoplasm and a transplanted G_2 nucleus, but is ca. 7 to 8 hr behind the EB cell with the G_2 nucleus. The latter difference may reflect directly the time the nucleus requires to finish a round of DNA synthesis.

The results are more complicated than we anticipated. We might have concluded that a cell with a late G_2 nucleus and S cytoplasm has only to achieve cytoplasmic progress through the cycle in order to reach division (the late G_2 nucleus is nearly there). A G_2 nucleus in S cytoplasm begins DNA synthesis again, however, and we have not eliminated the possibility that this conversion to DNA synthesis retards the nucleus in the cycle such that some intranuclear events (after DNA synthesis is over) would be required to bring it again to its original late G_2 condition. Since the S cytoplasm must go through a long process to reach the division stage, the nuclear events may be inconsequential when we are studying only the division time.

There is a seeming contradiction in some of our observations. Earlier, we said that a cell with an S nucleus grafted into a late G_2 enucleate could not divide unless fed and permitted to grow. Later, we implied that an MB cell could enter division without additional feeding. Both statements are indeed true; the MB cell, therefore, is potentially very interesting. It begins with a completely immature nucleus and continues to divide in the apparent absence of growth.

In our second experiment with MB cells, we noted that for division to be reached, some food reserves - in the form of food vacuoles for amebae - acquired before the albumin blocked division, were needed. The amount of these reserves is at least an order of magnitude less than that needed for a normal daughter cell to reach division. The amount of growth is small, but some anabolic processes dependent on vacuole nutrients are essential. Thus, the MB cell may be very favorable for studying metabolic events exclusively concerned with division preparations, because it is almost free of the "noise" of other metabolic events.

In these experiments, we also noted that there is a decay in the MB cell's capacity to divide (unless additional food is provided). If MB cells are created by removal of one nucleus from a binucleate 20 hr after the blocked division, the capacity of the resulting MB cell to reach division (without additional food) is lost.

Our information gathered so far does not permit us to make sharp and definitive conclusions, but it does guide us to design succeeding experiments. Finally, while we have attempted to analyze separately nuclear and cytoplasmic progress through the cycle, the data have forced us to realize that the conditions of both compartments are highly interdependent, and that any change in one compartment probably alters the other in a major way.

REFERENCES

1. Braun, R., C. Mittermayer, and H.P. Rusch. 1965. Sequential temporal replication of DNA in _Physarum polycephalum._ Proc. Natl. Acad. Sci. U.S. 53: 924.
2. Gaulden, M.E. 1956. DNA synthesis and X-ray effects at different mitotic stages in grasshopper neuroblasts. Genetics 41: 645.
3. Goldstein, L. 1964. Nuclear transplantation in ameba. In "Methods in Cell Physiology," D.M. Prescott, ed. Academic Press, N.Y. Vol. I., 97.
4. Goldstein, L., and D.M. Prescott. 1967. Proteins in nucleocytoplasmic interactions. I. The fundamental characteristics of the rapidly migrating proteins and the slow turnover proteins of _Amoeba proteus_. (Submitted to J. Cell Biol.)
5. McDonald, B.B. 1962. Synthesis of deoxyribonucleic acid by micro- and macronucleus of _Tetrahymena pyriformis_. J. Cell Biol. 13: 193.

6. Prescott, D.M. 1964. Autoradiography with liquid emulsion. In "Methods in Cell Physiology," D.M. Prescott, ed. Academic Press, N.Y., Vol. I, 365.
7. Prescott, D.M., R.F. Kimball, and R.F. Carrier. 1962. Comparison between the timing of micronuclear and macronuclear DNA synthesis in *Euplotes eurystomus*. J. Cell Biol. 13: 175.
8. Robbins, E. Personal communication.

Proliferation and Differentiation in the Immune Response[*]

Richard W. Dutton and Robert I. Mishell

Scripps Clinic and Research Foundation
La Jolla

Despite the rapid advance in our knowledge of the structure of γ-globulin molecules, we are still far from a complete understanding of the genetic control of antibody synthesis or the control of cellular proliferation and differentiation by which it is preceded or accompanied. This paper will first consider the evidence concerning antigen-induced proliferation in

*Publication 178 from the Department of Experimental Pathology, Scripps Clinic and Research Foundation, La Jolla, California. This work was supported in part by United States Public Health Service grant 7007-01 and in part by American Cancer Society grant E-395. Dr. Dutton is supported by a Dernham Fellowship of the California Division, American Cancer Society. Dr. Mishell is supported by a United States Public Health Service Special Fellowship.

the immune response, and second, describe two experimental models we are currently using to investigate this problem.

EVIDENCE CONCERNING ANTIGEN-INDUCED PROLIFERATION

Antibody is synthesized by certain specialized cells of the lymphoid system. These, the plasma cells and related forms, are highly differentiated cells and contain all the cytoplasmic equipment normally associated with protein synthesis. This population is not present in the unstimulated animal and only arises after antigenic stimulation. We shall discuss three questions:

1. Do the plasma cells arise by proliferation from, or transformation of, a precursor cell population?
2. What is the nature of the precursor cell population?
3. How does the antigen bring about this change?

Before we discuss these questions, we should stress that the phenomenon is considerably more complex than already indicated. First, the "anamnestic" or "secondary" response to antigen is, in general, much more intense and long lasting than the "primary" response. Besides the obvious quantitative differences, there are possible qualitative differences also, especially in the nature of the antibody molecule synthesized. Therefore, there may be a distinct operational difference in the way antigen acts in the primary and secondary response. It is also possible that there is, in a sense, no such thing as a primary response and that all antibodies are synthesized in minute amounts before experimental antigen stimulation (48). Such synthesis might be either the consequence of stimulation by environmental antigens or simply the phenotypic expression of genetic information in the complete absence of any antigenic stimulation. It is inappropriate to evaluate the data bearing on this question here, except to note that the problem is unresolved. It is necessary, however, to retain the terms primary and secondary antigenic stimulation as operational descriptions of an experimental protocol and to be aware of the possible implications.

The second complication is that of antibody heterogeneity. At least three to seven distinct classes of antibody are synthesized in the species investigated so far. The three major classes are γG (7S), γM (19S) and γA (7-17S). (For general reviews see Cohen and Porter (13), Fudenberg (38), and Fleischman (35).) All three types of molecule consist of a four-chain structure of two light chains (MW, 22,000) and two heavy chains (MW, ca. 50,000). γM and γA molecules are made up of polymers containing up to five such four-chain units. Antigenic analysis has shown that the light chains are common in structure to all three classes of molecules, although two distinct types of light chains exist. Antigenic variation representing structural differences in the heavy chains form the basis for the classification into the globulin classes, γ chains in γG, μ chains in γM, and α chains in γA. The different light and heavy chains clearly represent the products of different genes. In general, antibody molecules of all three classes are synthesized in response to a single antigenic substance (43, 31, 30), although some restrictions have been noticed in certain instances (60, 2). A further order of heterogeneity exists within each class on the basis of:

1. more subtle structural differences (allotypy) (54, 94, 38);
2. the avidity with which individual antibody molecules bind antigen (29, 78);
3. electrophoretic mobility (13).

The genetically determined isoantigens or allotypes have been described for markers on both light and heavy chains and appear to be largely unrelated to antibody specificity. (Experimentally, they provide a useful tool for establishing the donor of the gene controlling the synthesis of a given product in experiments involving cell transfer from one individual to another or in in vitro experiments where two cell populations are incubated together.)

The existence of several distinct classes of antibody molecules raises three important questions:

1. Do the products of different genes have antibody-combining sites of the same specificity?
2. If they do, how does this come about?
3. Are antibodies of different classes synthesized in separate cells, or are they synthesized, perhaps sequentially, in the same cell?

All three questions are unresolved but have considerable bearing on the cellular events that occur in the immune response. Thus, several hypotheses have been made in which the genetic information that controls the synthesis of the peptide chain containing the antibody-combining site becomes linked to each of the three separate genes that define the three separate globulin classes. Smithies (83), for instance, has suggested that "antibody viruses" may transfer the gene controlling the synthesis of the site from one locus to another by mechanisms analogous to lysogeny and transduction in phage-infected bacteria.

Many attempts have been made to determine how far the capacities of individual antibody-forming cells are limited to a single antibody specificity - to globulin molecules of a single class, or to molecules of a single allotype specificity (for a review see Cebra, Colberg, and Dray (10)). The results have been somewhat conflicting but do seem to indicate a considerable restriction in the range of phenotypic expression in a mature differentiated cell, at least at the moment the observation was made (10). It would seem likely either that individual antigens stimulate several parallel populations of cells, which proliferate, differentiate, and synthesize their separate populations of antibody molecules, or that more multipotential stem cells are caused to differentiate along several divergent lines. Other possibilities, as we have indicated previously, cannot be excluded.

The third complication is the possibility that a second cell type may be involved in conveying the stimulus of the antigen to the precursor cell. Morphological evidence has been presented by Thiery (90) and by others (97, 96). The second cell may in some way process the antigen before transmitting it to the precursor cell, (36, 4), or it may manufacture and transmit some "messenger" substance entirely separate from the antigen (33, 34). Current evidence seems to favor the former possibility. Macrophage cells may somehow produce a "super" antigen, possibly in the form of an RNA-antigen complex (7, 76). There is no conclusive evidence that such intervention by a second cell is mandatory, and the antigen may also act directly on the precursor cell.

As long as we remember these aspects, we may return to our original problem - the origin of the antibody synthesizing cell - and consider it in terms of a simplified model. The questions involved are summarized in Figure 1.

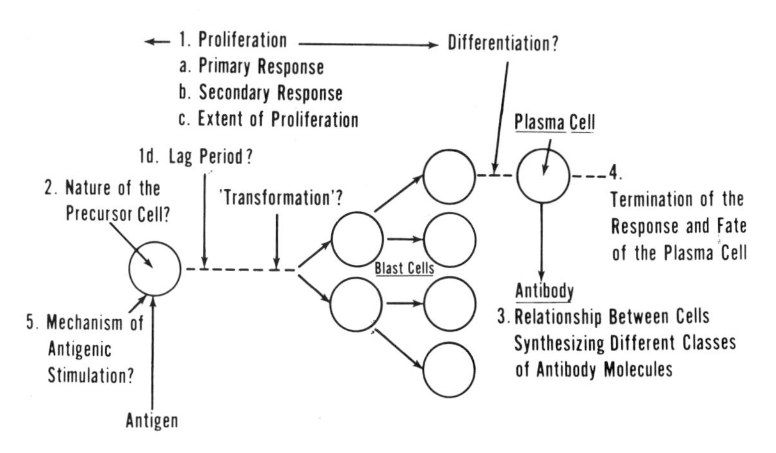

Figure 1. Schematic indication of the possible mechanisms involved in the development and regulation of the antibody-forming cell and the principal questions that are raised. Numbers and letters refer to the corresponding sections in the text.

1. Proliferation or Transformation

Historically, there appeared to be considerable resistance to the idea that proliferation played a major role in providing the population of cells that form antibody. More recently, however, convincing evidence has been obtained that this is, indeed, the case. We can summarize the evidence as follows.

A. Proliferation in the secondary response. It had long been recognized that a considerable cell proliferation occurred in lymph nodes and other organs following antigenic stimulation, but the relationship between these cells and plasma cells remained in dispute. Leduc, Coons, and Connally (56) were the first to provide convincing evidence that the antibody-forming cells were derived from a proliferating population of undifferentiated cells. Using the fluorescent antibody staining technique, they showed a steadily increasing content of antibody in the dividing cells as they began to differentiate into mature plasma cells. Further evidence was obtained when specific inhibitors of DNA synthesis were shown to prevent antibody formation in vitro (27, 16, 68), and when the transfer of antibody-forming capacity by lymphoid cells was shown to have the same sensitivity to X-irradiation ($D37 = 70$ rad) as does cell division (59).

Schooley (79) and Nossal and Mäkelä (65) traced the proliferation of thymidine labeled cells, following antigenic stimulation, and the differentiation of labeled blast cells into plasma cells. The latter results, although subject to some criticism (40), nevertheless indicated that the precursor cell divided many times, giving rise to a population 1000 times larger than that initially present. Antigen-dependent stimulation of cell division was also demonstrated in in vitro systems (26, 9, 58, 22, 75).

Conclusive evidence for cell division came from the demonstration of radioactive label in individual antibody-forming cells in animals exposed to radioactive thymidine between antigenic stimulation and the detection of antibody in the cell in a variety of experimental models (6, 57, 93, 12).

B. The primary response. Almost parallel evidence has been obtained for the origin of antibody-forming cells in the primary response. Antibody has been detected in proliferating blast cells (56). Blast proliferation following antigenic stimulation has been demonstrated using thymidine label in vivo (65) or in vitro (8, 64). Antibody synthesis by transferred cells was shown to have the same high sensitivity to X-irradiation as in the secondary response (59, 52), and inhibitors of DNA synthesis suppress the initiation of antibody formation (37, 61, 88).

In addition, it has been shown that serum antibody titers show an exponential rise following antigenic stimulation which we can extrapolate backward almost to zero time by using sensitive techniques for antibody detection (92). Similarly, the increase in the number of hemolytic plaque-forming cells measured by the Jerne technique (49) shows as exponential rise (50, 51, 85, 55, 42). The doubling time has been calculated to be as short as 7.5 hr (53).

Again, the crucial evidence is the demonstration of thymidine label in the antibody-forming cells when thymidine was administered between antigenic injection and the time the animal was sacrificed (51, 85, 53, 89), although Tannenberg interpreted his data differently.

It is thus clear that most, if not all, antibody-forming cells arise from (at least one) division of a precursor cell. This observation is true of both the secondary response and the primary response, including the cells synthesizing 19S antibody molecules. It is true of the response to soluble and particulate antigens and also of the homograft response, at least as manifested in the graft versus host response studied by Gowans and McGregor (40), and in the in vitro responses described by Bain, Vas, and Lowenstein (5), Chapman and Dutton (11), Dutton (18, 19), and Dutton and Mishell (23), between cell populations obtained from two unrelated individuals of the same species. We know little of the origin of cells that mediate delayed hypersensitivity reactions.

C. The extent and rate of cell proliferation. It is clear that in the studies of Schooley (79) and Nossal and Mäkelä (65), the cell population increased up to 1000-fold. Similar conclusions were reached for a study of the rise in the number of plaque-forming cells following antigenic stimulation. Estimates of the mean generation time have varied from 12 to 24 hr to 7.5 hr (53). Koros and her colleagues showed that 55% of the plaque-forming cells were labeled by a single pulse of labeled thymidine and calculated an S period of 4 hr. Similar data have been obtained by Sterzl et al. (85) and by others.

D. The existence of a lag period following administration of antigen. The time lapse between antigen injection and the first appearance of measurable antibody in the serum led to the concept of lag period. In cellular terms, a time gap was postulated between contact with antigen and the onset of proliferation or antibody synthesis. Recently, it has become clear that much of the lag period before the detection of antibody in the serum results from the insensitivity of the methods employed for antibody detection. Thus, for example, Uhr, Finkelstein, and Baumann (92), using a sensitive assay for antibody to ΦX174, were able to detect a rise in antibody titer only 24 hr after the primary injection of antigen, while Svehag and Mandel (86) found a rise in antibody to polio virus 8 to 12 hr after the antigen injection. The exponential rise in the number of hemolytic plaque-forming cells extrapolates backward to zero time (51, 55, 42).

Concerning the lag before proliferation begins, it has been shown that increases in the rate of DNA synthesis can be detected as soon as 8 hr after the addition of antigen to spleen cell suspensions from previously immunized donors. The kinetics of the increase appear to extrapolate backward to zero (28). These observations argue against the existence of a significant lag period. Similarly, Capalbo, Makinodan, and Gude (9), using an in vitro system, showed that the autoradiographic grain count of previously labeled cells fell 4-fold in the first 24 hr on exposure to antigen, and that the rate of fall extrapolated backward to zero time.

Others, however, have presented evidence showing that DNA synthesis and cell division do not begin until as much as 18 hr after antigen injection. Thus, neither thioguanine (37) nor FUdR (61) inhibit the primary reponse when given simultaneously with antigen, but they completely suppress the response if given 24 hr after antigen. These agents, however, actually stimulate the immune response when given at the early time, which makes the interpretation of this finding somewhat equivocal. O'Brien and Coons (68) showed that BUdR suppressed a secondary in vitro response when added 2 or 3 days after antigen, but had less effect if present during the first 24 hr.

Cohen and Talmage (12) were unable to demonstrate much thymidine incorporation into cells subsequently shown to synthesize antibody when the label was present as a pulse 24 hours after the antigen in the secondary response. Similarly, Sterzl (85) could show little thymidine incorporation in the first 24 hr after primary antigenic stimulation. In both these experiments, we could argue that thymidine label incorporated at this stage of the response would be so heavily diluted by subsequent cell division that it would be lost by the time the antibody-synthesizing cells were harvested and examined.

Several workers have studied the effect of anitgen on peripheral leukocyte cultures from immune human donors (73, 20). Large numbers of proliferating blast cells are found present 3 to 5 days after antigen addition, and investigators have generally concluded that the cells arise by a transformation of a substantial population of small lymphocytes and that proliferation begins only after the transformation is complete. Much of the evidence is open to criticism (20). The question of the existence of a lag period before the onset of DNA synthesis is clearly still unresolved.

2. Identification of the Precursor Cell

The cell populations obtained from spleen, lymph nodes, or other immunologically competent tissues are all heterogeneous and consist of cells fulfilling a variety of biological functions. Since there is no method available for taking a single, morphologically identifiable cell and determining whether it is capable of a response to antigen, the only evidence for the nature of the precursor cell is indirect. Essentially, the biological activity of a cell population in a given experimental system is determined and related to the major component of the cell mixture.

In this way, populations of cells consisting of more than 99.8% small lymphocytes have been shown capable of transferring the capacity to give both primary and secondary responses to a variety of antigens and of effecting a graft versus host reaction (40). The biological activity of such populations does not seem to vary with variations in the amount of the minor component cell type, and when the total cell population is labeled, labeled cells have taken part in the recipient's immune response. Thus, very strong circumstantial evidence exists that the small lymphocyte is the immunocompetent cell in the primary response, or the memory cell in the secondary response. This population of cells does not synthesize DNA in the unstimulated animal and is shown to contain long-lived cells.

Nossal and Mäkelä (65) and Mäkelä and Nossal (57), however, pulse labeled animals with tritiated thymidine prior to antigenic stimulation and found the principal cells labeled were large undifferentiated cells. On antigenic stimulation, this population proliferated rapidly and antibody-synthesizing cells were shown to contain thymidine label. These results indicate that the precursor cell is a blast cell and proliferates before antigenic stimulation. The experiments have been criticized on the grounds that label is released from the preantigen labeled cells and reutilized during subsequent proliferation. It seems improbable that this could account for all the label observed, however, and the evidence and its implications cannot be completely dismissed. Cohen and Talmage (12) using in vitro labeling in a cell-transfer experiment, could demonstrate no incorporation of label into the cells subsequently shown to contain antibody when they were exposed to thymidine prior to antigenic stimulation.

Jerne (48) proposed a natural selection theory for the mechanism of antibody formation and suggested that the capacity to respond to a given antigen resided in different cells. He further proposed that each cell synthesized minute amounts of its specific antibody prior to antigen stimulation. With the advent of a hemolytic plaquing technique for the detection of individual antibody releasing cells (49, 47), it has been shown that such cells are already present at approximately 1 cell to 10^6 spleen cells prior to experimental antigen (erythrocyte) stimulation. Investigators have suggested these cells may represent the precursor cell (51). Since cell differentiation does occur during the immune response, it would seem more likely that these cells represent the progeny derived from a small population of nonantibody forming cells. Sterzl et al. (85) have argued against this concept; they believe these plaque-forming cells only arise after antigenic stimulation, because they cannot be detected in the spleens of piglets reared under sterile conditions on a nonantigenic diet.

Estimates for the size of the precursor cell population made by several workers (64, 50, 51) have ranged as low as 1 cell in 10^6. Under these circumstances and with the presently available means, it is virtually impossible to exclude any cell type as candidate for the precursor cell. There may also possibly be more than one type of precursor cell, each giving rise to a separate series of cells mediating the immune response.

3. Relationship Between the Different Classes of Antibody and Regulation of Antibody Synthesis

In general, the antibody detectable early in the primary response is a 19S macroglobulin molecule; the antibody detected later consists predominantly of 7S molecules. It has been suggested that specific antibody adsorbed onto or incorporated into potential antibody-forming cells may inhibit these cells from making antibody by some homeostatic or feedback mechanism (74). Furthermore, 7S antibody may be involved in some mechanism controlling the change from 19S to 7S antibody production (77). A similar cessation of antibody formation on administration of passive antibody has been noted (32, 63), but it was concluded that the passive antibody produces its effect by neutralizing or removing antigen necessary for continued stimulation of antibody synthesis. In producing the effect, 7S antibody was found to be much more effective than 19S antibody, but it is not clear whether this difference is correlated with some property of the different antibody classes (γG versus γM) or whether it merely reflects the higher avidity of antibody synthesized later in the response. It is clear that antibody once formed may act to regulate further antibody synthesis and prevent hyperimmunization, but it seems doubtful whether it is involved in some switch mechanism to "turn off" the 19S genes and "turn on" the 7S genes. There is good evidence that the fall in the synthesis of 19S early in the response results from the lack of antigen, since a second injection of antigen results in a resumption of 19S antibody synthesis (91, 87, 42).

The principal question concerning us here is whether the synthesis of both molecules occurs sequentially in the same cell or whether two independent cell populations are involved; we have no conclusive evidence on this point. It has been claimed that single cells synthesizing both antibodies are detectable when the change from 19S to 7S occurs (66). This most important observation should perhaps be accepted with some reservation, because the technique for measuring antibody synthesized by a single cell may measure antibody synthesized by other cells and only secondarily associated with the cell under consideration.

Svehag and Mandel (87) have described several differences in the characteristics of the 19S and 7S response to antigen, suggesting that the two responses are made by different cell populations. Thus, they stated that 19S and 7S antibody formation differed in antigen dose requirements for induction and maintenance of synthesis, kinetics of the response, retention of immunological memory, and sensitivity to prior X-irradiation. Other studies (10) have also indicated a remarkable differentiation at the cellular level with respect to the type of molecule produced.

4. Termination of the Antibody Synthesis and the Fate of the Plasma Cell

The exponential increase in the number of antibody-forming cells (51) or the synthesis of antibody molecules (14) ends quite abruptly, and the mature plasma cells rapidly disappear. It has been postulated that some control mechanism exists to prevent unlimited proliferation and to terminate antibody synthesis (59). It has been debated whether the plasma cell represents the end product of a suicidal path of differentiation or whether it transforms into another cell type (such as the small lymphocyte) which persists as a memory cell. There is, as yet, little experimental evidence bearing on these questions.

5. Mechanisms of Antigenic Stimulation

We know extremely little of the mechanism of antigenic stimulation. The evidence is conflicting on the crucial point as to whether antigen is broken down into smaller fragments carrying individual determinants (7) or whether its activity depends upon the tertiary or even quaternary structure of the antigen molecule as many studies suggest.

A variety of substances which react with components of lymphoid cell surfaces will stimulate cell proliferation. These include phytohemagglutinin (67, 45), streptolysin S (44), heterologous antisera (41), and homologous antisera (80-82, 39). Antiserum to certain antigens of the sea urchin egg (71) will stimulate sea urchin eggs to divide, and PHA will also stimulate amoeba (1). Hirschhorn and colleagues (46) have suggested that PHA initiates cell transformation and division by disrupting lysosomal membranes with the release of a variety of hydrolytic enzymes (3).

It has been suggested by analogy that antigen reacts with a specific receptor molecule on the surface of the lymphoid cell, a process which leads to the proliferative response. One obvious condidate for such a receptor molecule would be antibody itself.

We can summarize by saying the concept that extensive cell proliferation occurs in the immune response is an established fact but the questions concerning the extent, kinetics, and control of this proliferation, and the nature of the precursor cell, remain unresolved.

EXPERIMENTAL SYSTEMS

In the second half of this presentation, we shall describe, rather briefly, two experimental systems we are using to study some of these problems.

1. Antigen Specific Stimulation of DNA Synthesis

Spleen or lymph node cell suspensions are prepared from immune or nonimmune rabbits, mice, or rats, and are incubated in a tissue culture medium for 48 hr. During this period, the rate of DNA synthesis is measured by the rate of incorporation of radioactive thymidine into the cell suspension - i.e., the total incorporation in a standard time.

In the absence of antigen, there is a rapid initial fall in the rate of DNA synthesis in cell suspensions from immune or nonimmune donors which levels off at about 24 hr. Addition of antigen to cells from immune animals stimulates DNA synthesis (Figure 2). Responses can still be obtained if the antigen addition is delayed until as late as 48 hr. The stimulation is antigen specific and proportional to the log of the antigen concentration. There is no response to antigen in cells from nonimmune animals.

Increases in the rate of DNA synthesis can be detected as little as 12 hr after antigen addition, and increases in the rate of RNA synthesis are evident even sooner. The kinetics of the response suggest there is little or no lag between antigen addition and the onset of the response. A further analysis of this problem is in progress.

Autoradiographic analysis of the antigen-stimulated

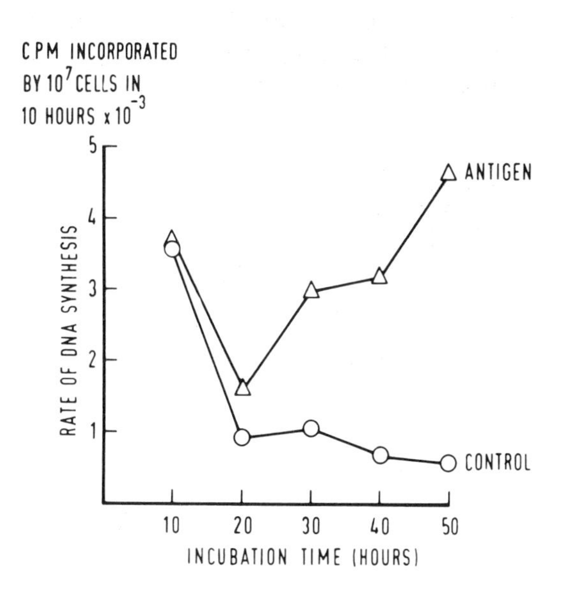

Figure 2. The rate of DNA synthesis in spleen cell suspensions from a previously immunized rabbit was measured in the presence and absence of antigen by the uptake of radioactive thymidine in standard incubation periods. o represents no addition, and Δ, specific antigen added at time zero.

suspensions at 48 hr established that 2 to 4% of the cells take part in the response. These and other observations are described in more detail in previous publications (26, 28, 22, 21, 24, 17, 25). Attempts were made to analyze the mechanism of the antigenic stimulation by determining the effect of chemical and physical modification of the antigen on its stimulatory activity. It was shown that aggregated antigen was more active than the soluble form and that the physical alteration of the molecule is more important than the chemical. Further analysis of the effects of chemical modification was precluded by the overriding effect of accompanying physical alteration (70).

Attempts were also made to determine whether a second cell type was involved in conveying the stimulus from antigen to the dividing cell. Additional autologous macrophages were added to spleen cell suspensions,

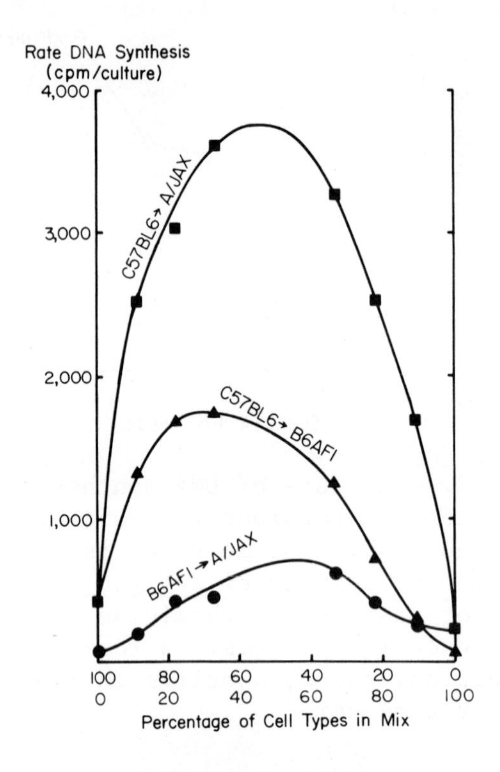

Figure 3. Proliferative responses between parental and F_1 hybrid strains of mice. Cell suspensions were obtained from two parental strains, C57BL/6 and A/J, and the F_1 hybrid B6AF1. The cell suspensions from the two parents, or one parent and the F_1 hybrid, were incubated together in various proportions, as the X axis indicates. The rate of DNA synthesis of each mixture (Y axis) was measured by the uptake of radioactive thymidine during the 24 to 48 hr period after incubation started.

but these merely inhibited DNA synthesis for some reason not understood (69).

Proliferative responses are also obtained when lymphoid cell populations from unrelated individuals of the same species are incubated together. These responses take place in the absence of any prior experimental immunization (11). This response is directed towards histocompatibility antigens, as shown in studies using inbred strains of mice (18, 19, 23).

Parent-F_1 hybrid combinations give less stimulation than the corresponding parent-parent mix (Figure 3). If we can accept that this interaction follows the normal conventions for an immunological reaction, we can assume that the F_1 hybrid does not respond to the parent cells and that the effect observed results wholely from the parent cell responding to the foreign antigens present in the F_1 hybrid. Conceivably, however, the stimulus to proliferation is mediated through a diffusible nonspecific intermediate. Hopefully, further analysis of this model using chromosomal markers to determine whether the F_1 hybrid cells do participate in the response may help solve this problem.

2. In Vitro Response to Sheep Erythrocytes

Cell suspensions prepared from the spleens of unimmunized mice are incubated under somewhat different experimental conditions from those employed in the system already described; they are stimulated by the addition of small numbers of sheep erythrocytes. The response is measured by assaying the number of hemolytic plaque-forming cells present after various periods of incubation. This technique measures cells releasing γM antibody. The plaque count increases several hundred fold from an initial background of one cell per million to an average of 400 or more per million at 4 days (Table 1). This response is about half that obtained in the whole animal (Figure 4). It is obtained with cells from unimmunized spleen donors and is, in this sense, a primary response. Hemolytic antibody can be recovered from the culture fluids, and the response is antigen specific.

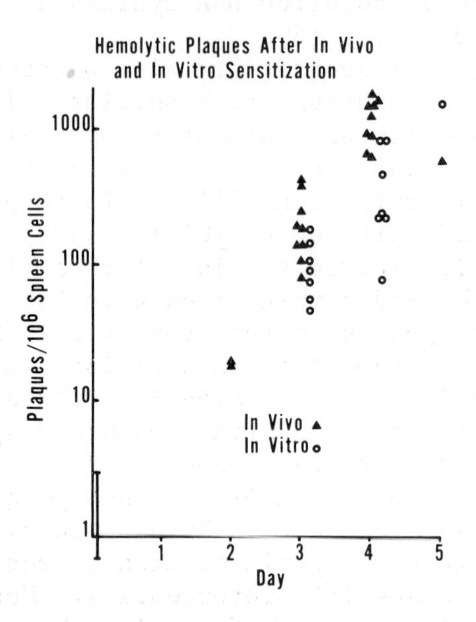

Figure 4. Hemolytic palques per million spleen cells against sheep erythrocytes. In vivo: Mice injected intravenously with 0.2 ml 10% red cells. In vitro: 1-ml cultures contained 2 × 10^7 spleen cells and 1 to 2 × 10^5 sheep red cells. Background plaques (indicated by bar at day zero) equal 0.3 to 3.0 per 10^6 spleen cells. (From Mishell and Dutton (62).)

There is a much smaller but still considerable increase in the plaque count in the absence of sheep erythrocytes (Table 1). It is believed that this rise represents stimulation by components of the fetal calf serum contained in the medium (such as "J" substance) which cross react with components of the sheep erythrocyte used in the assay. No such rise is seen in a similar response against pig erythrocytes, and fetal calf serum contains an antigen that reacts with mouse antisheep erythrocyte sera (R.I. Mishell, unpublished observation). Distinctive features of the culture conditions are high cell density, shaking of the cell suspension, low oxygen tension in the gas phase, and

TABLE 1

Sensitization of normal mouse spleen cells with sheep erythrocytes in vitro*

2×10^7 spleen cells cultured	Day 3†	Day 4†
In fetal calf serum only	21 (12-41)	63 (7-112)
In fetal calf serum with sheep erythrocytes (1×10^5)	99 (46-187)	476 (79-879)

*Seven consecutive experiments.
†Hemolytic plaques per 10^6 spleen cells. Mouse strains: BDF_1, CAF_1, C57BL/6, DBA/2. (Background plaques, 0.3 to 3.0 before culturing.)

daily feeding of the culture with a nutritional cocktail, but it is not known which of these factors are critical. The experimental details of this system have been previously described (62).

Modifications of the Jerne hemolytic plaque technique have been developed for the detection of cells synthesizing γG antibody (84, 15) and other classes of globulin (95). It should therefore be possible to investigate the development of γG antibody-forming cells in this system. Hopefully, techniques will be developed to identify the progeny of proliferating cells, either by immobilization in a semisolid medium or by cloning, and thus permit the study of the relationship between cells forming anitbody of different globulin classes.

The role of antigen and other factors in the maintenance of proliferation and the termination of the response can also be studied. Correlation of the cell separation studies with the biological function of the resulting population may illuminate the properties of the precursor cell and the possible role of a second cell type in antigen stimulation.

REFERENCES

1. Agrell, I.P.S. 1966. Phytohemagglutinin as a mitotic stimulator on sea-living amoebae. Exp. Cell Res. 42: 403.
2. Allen, J.C., H.G. Kunkel, and E.A. Kabat. 1964. Studies on human antibodies. II. Distribution of genetic factors. J. Exp. Med. 119: 453.
3. Allison, A.C., and L. Mallucci. 1964. Lysosomes in dividing cells, with special references to lymphocytes. Lancet ii: 1371.
4. Askonas, B.A., and J.M. Rhodes. 1965. Immunogenicity of antigen-containing ribonucleic acid preparations from macrophages. Nature 205: 470.
5. Bain, B., M. Vas, and L. Lowenstein. 1964. The development of large immature mononuclear cells in mixed leukocyte cultures. Blood 23: 108.
6. Baney, R.N., J.J. Vazquez, and F.J. Dixon. 1962. Cellular proliferation in relation to antibody synthesis. Proc. Soc. Exp. Biol. Med. 109: 1.
7. Campbell, D.H., and J.S. Garvey. 1963. Nature of retained antigen and its role in immune mechanisms. Advan. Immunol. 3: 261.
8. Capalbo, E.E., and T. Makinodan. 1964. Doubling time of mouse spleen cells during the latent and lag phases of primary antibody response. J. Immunol. 92: 234.
9. Capalbo, E.E., T. Makinodan, and W.D. Gude. 1962. Fate of H^3-thymidine labeled spleen cells in _in vivo_ cultures during secondary antibody response. J. Immunol. 89: 1.
10. Cebra, J.J., J.E. Colberg, and S. Dray. 1966. Rabbit lymphoid cells differentiated with respect to α-, γ-, and μ-heavy polypeptide chains and to allotypic markers Aa1 and Aa2. J. Exp. Med. 123: 547.
11. Chapman, N.D., and R.W. Dutton. 1965. The stimulation of DNA synthesis in cultures of rabbit lymph node and spleen cell suspensions by homologous cells. J. Exp. Med. 121: 85.
12. Cohen, E.P., and D.W. Talmage. 1965. Onset and duration of DNA synthesis in antibody-forming cells

after antigen. J. Exp. Med. 121: 125.
13. Cohen, S., and R.R. Porter. 1964. Structure and biological activity of immunoglobulins. Advan. Immunol. 4: 287.
14. Dixon, F.J., P.H. Maurer, W.O. Weigle, and M.P. Deichmiller. 1956. Rates of antibody synthesis during first, second and hyperimmune responses of rabbits to bovine gamma globulin. J. Exp. Med. 103: 425.
15. Dresser, D.W., and H.H. Wortis. 1965. Use of an antiglobulin serum to detect cells producing antibody with low hemolytic efficiency. Nature 208: 859.
16. Dutton, R.W. 1961. Importance of cell division for antibody production in an _in vitro_ system. Nature 192: 462.
17. Dutton, R.W. 1964. The effect of antigen on the proliferation of spleen cell suspensions from tolerant rabbits. J. Immunol. 93: 814.
18. Dutton, R.W. 1965. Further studies of the stimulation of DNA synthesis in cultures of spleen cell suspensions by homologous cells in inbred strains of mice and rats. J. Exp. Med. 122: 759.
19. Dutton, R.W. 1966a. Spleen cell proliferation in response to homologous antigens studied in congenic resistant strains of mice. J. Exp. Med. 123: 665.
20. Dutton, R.W. 1966b. Symposium on _In Vitro_ Studies of the Immune Response. II. Significance of the reaction of lymphoid cells to homologous tissue. Bacteriol. Rev. 30: 397.
21. Dutton, R.W., and H.N. Bulman. 1964. The significance of the protein carrier in the stimulation of DNA synthesis by hapten-protein conjugates in the secondary response. Immunology 7: 54.
22. Dutton, R.W., and J.D. Eady. 1964. An _in vitro_ system for the study of the mechanism of antigenic stimulation in the secondary response. Immunology 7: 40.
23. Dutton, R.W., and R.I. Mishell. 1966. Lymphocytic proliferation in response to homologous tissue antigens. Symposium: Recent Advances on the Biology and Function of the Lymphocyte. Federation

Proc. (In press.)

24. Dutton, R.W., and G.M. Page. 1964. The response of spleen cells from immunized rabbits to cross-reacting antigens in an in vitro system. Immunology 7: 665.
25. Dutton, R.W., and R.M.E. Parkhouse. 1965. Studies on the mechanism of antigenic stimulation in the secondary response. In "Molecular and Cellular Basis of Antibody Formation," J. Sterzl, ed. Czechoslovak Academy of Science Press, Prague, p. 567.
26. Dutton, R.W., and J.D. Pearce. 1962. Antigen-dependent stimulation of synthesis of deoxyribonucleic acid in spleen cells from immunized rabbits. Nature 194: 93.
27. Dutton, R.W., A.H. Dutton, and J.H. Vaughan. 1960. The effect of 5-bromouracil deoxyriboside on the synthesis of antibody in vitro. Biochem. J. 75: 230.
28. Dutton, R.W., J.D. Eady, and H.N. Bulman. 1963. The antigenic stimulation of DNA synthesis in spleen cells from immunized rabbits. In "Conceptual Advances in Immunology and Oncology." Sixteenth Annual Symposium on Fundamental Cancer Research, Houston, Texas, p. 98.
29. Eisen, H.N., and G.W. Siskind. 1964. Variations in affinities of antibodies during the immune response. Biochemistry 3: 996.
30. Fahey, J.L., and H. Goodman. 1964. Antibody activity in six classes of human immunoglobulins. Science 143: 588.
31. Fahey, J.L., J. Wunderlich, and R.I. Mishell. 1964. The immunoglobulins of mice. I. Four major classes of immunoglobulins: $7S\gamma_2$-, $7S\gamma_1$-, γ_{1A} (β_{2A})-, and $18S\gamma_{1M}$-globulins. J. Exp. Med. 120: 223.
32. Finkelstein, M.S., and J.W. Uhr. 1964. Specific inhibition of antibody formation by passively administered 19S and 7S antibody. Science 146: 67.
33. Fishman, M, and F.L. Adler. 1963. Antibody formation initiated in vitro. II. Antibody synthesis in X-irradiated recipients of diffusion chambers containing nucleic acid derived from macrophages incubated with antigen. J. Exp. Med. 117: 595.

34. Fishman, M., J.J. van Rood, and F.L. Adler. 1965. The initiation of antibody formation by ribonucleic acid from specifically stimulated macrophages. In "Molecular and Cellular Basis of Antibody Formation," J. Sterzl, ed. Czechoslovak Academy of Science Press, Prague, p. 491.
35. Fleischman, J.B. 1966. Immunoglobulins. Ann. Rev. Biochem. 35: 835.
36. Friedman, H.P., A.B. Stavitsky, and J.M. Solomon. 1965. Induction in vitro of antibodies to phage T2: Antigens in the RNA extract employed. Science 149: 1106.
37. Frisch, A.W., and G.H. Davies. 1962. Inhibition of hemagglutinin formation by thioguanine: Dose time relationships. Proc. Soc. Exp. Biol. Med. 110: 444.
38. Fudenberg, H.H. 1965. The immune globulins. Ann. Rev. Microbiol. 19: 301.
39. Gell, P.G.H., and S. Sell. 1965. Studies on rabbit lymphocytes in vitro. II. Induction of blast transformation with antisera to six 1gG allotypes and summation with mixtures of antisera to different allotypes. J. Exp. Med. 122: 813.
40. Gowans, J.L., and D.D. McGregor. 1965. The immunological activities of lymphocytes. Progr. Allergy 9: 1.
41. Gräsbeck, R., C.T. Nordman, and A. de la Chapelle. 1964. The leucocyte-mitogenic effect of serum from rabbits immunized with human leucocytes. Acta Med. Scand., Suppl. 412: 39.
42. Hege, J.S., and L.J. Cole. 1966. Antibody plaque-forming cells: Kinetics of primary and secondary responses. J. Immunol. 96: 559.
43. Heremans, J.F., J.P. Vaerman, and C. Vaerman. 1963. Studies on the immune globulins of human serum. J. Immunol. 91: 11.
44. Hirschhorn, K., and R.R. Scheibman. 1964. The action of streptolysin S on peripheral lymphocytes of normal subjects and patients with acute rheumatic fever. Proc. Natl. Acad. Sci. U.S. 52: 1151.
45. Hirschhorn, K., F. Bach, R.L. Kolodny, I.L. Firschein, and N. Hashem. 1963. Immune response and mitosis of human peripheral blood lymphocytes in vitro. Science 142: 1185.

46. Hirschhorn, R., J.M. Kaplan, A.F. Goldberg, K. Hirschhorn, and G. Weissmann. 1965. Acid phosphatase-rich granules in human lymphocytes induced by phytohemagglutinin. Science 147: 55.
47. Ingraham, J.S., and A. Bussard. 1964. Application of a localized hemolysin reaction for specific detection of individual antibody-forming cells. J. Exp. Med. 119: 667.
48. Jerne, N.K. 1955. The natural-selection theory of antibody formation. Proc. Natl. Acad. Sci. U.S. 41: 849.
49. Jerne, N.K., and A.A. Nordin. 1963. Plaque formation in agar by single cell antibody-producing cells. Science 140: 405.
50. Jerne, N.K., A.A. Nordin, and C. Henry. 1963. The agar plaque technique for recognizing antibody-producing cells. In "Cell Bound Antibodies," B. Amos and H. Koprowski, eds. Wistar Institute Press, Phila., Pa., p. 109.
51. Jerne, N.K., A.A. Nordin , C. Henry, H. Fuji, and A. Koros. 1965. (Personal communication, Immunopathology I.E.G. No. 46.)
52. Kennedy, J.C., J.E. Till, L. Siminovitch, and E.A. McCulloch. 1965. Radiosensitivity of the immune response to sheep red cells in the mouse, as measured by the hemolytic plaque technique. J. Immunol. 94: 715.
53. Koros, A.M.C., H. Fuji, and N.K. Jerne. 1966. Kinetics of proliferation of clones of antibody-producing cells. Federation Proc. 25: 305.
54. Kunkel, H.G., J.C. Allen, and H.M. Grey. 1964. Genetic characters and the polypeptide chains of various types of gamma globulin. Cold Spring Harbor Symposia on Quantitative Biology 29: 443.
55. Landy, M., R.P. Sanderson, and A.L. Jackson. 1965. Humoral and cellular aspects of the immune response to the somatic antigen of _Salmonella enteritidis_. J. Exp. Med. 122: 483.
56. Leduc, E.H., A.H. Coons, and J.M. Connolly. 1955. Studies on antibody production. II. The primary and secondary responses in the popliteal lymph node of the rabbit. J. Exp. Med. 102: 61.

57. Mäkelä, O., and G.J.V. Nossal. 1962. Autoradiographic studies on the immune response. II. DNA synthesis amongst single antibody-producing cells. J. Exp. Med. 115: 231.
58. Makinodan, T., and J.F. Albright. 1963. Cytokinetics of antibody response. In "Immunopathology, Third International Symposium," P. Grabar and P.A. Miescher, eds. Schwabe and Co., Basel, p. 99.
59. Makinodan, T., M.A. Kastenbaum, and W.J. Peterson. 1962. Radiosensitivity of spleen cells from normal and preimmunized mice and its significance to intact animals. J. Immunol. 88: 31.
60. Mannik, M., and H.G. Kunkel. 1963. Localization of antibodies in group I and group II γ-globulins. J. Exp. Med. 118: 817.
61. Merritt, K., and A.G. Johnson. 1965. Studies on the adjuvant action of bacterial endotoxins on antibody formation. VI. Enhancement of antibody formation by nucleic acids. J. Immunol. 94: 416.
62. Mishell, R.I., and R.W. Dutton. 1966. Immunization of normal mouse spleen cell suspensions in vitro. Science 153: 1004.
63. Moller, G., and H. Wigzell. 1965. Antibody synthesis at the cellular level. Antibody-inducing suppression of 19S and 7S antibody response. J. Exp. Med. 121: 969.
64. Nettescheim, P., and T. Makinodan. 1965. Differentiation of lymphocytes undergoing an immune response in diffusion chambers. J. Immunol. 94: 868.
65. Nossal, G.J.V., and O. Mäkelä. 1962. Autoradiographic studies on the immune response. I. The kinetics of plasma cell porliferation. J. Exp. Med. 115: 209.
66. Nossal, G.J.V., A. Szenberg, G.L. Ada, and C.M. Austin. 1964. Single cell studies on 19S antibody production. J. Exp. Med. 119: 485.
67. Nowell, P.C. 1960. PHS - an initiator of mitosis in cultures of normal human leucocytes. Cancer Res. 20: 462.
68. O'Brien, T.F., and A.H. Coons. 1963. Studies on antibody production. VII. The effect of 5-bromodeoxyuridine on the in vitro anamnestic antibody

response. J. Exp. Med. 117: 1063.

69. Parkhouse, R.M.E., and R.W. Dutton. 1966. Inhibition of spleen cell DNA synthesis by autologous macrophages. J. Immunol. (In press.)
70. Parkhouse, R.M.E., and R.W. Dutton. The effect of physical and chemical modifications on antigen in the secondary response in vitro. (In preparation.)
71. Perlmann, P. 1959. Immunochemical analysis of the surface of the sea urchin egg - an approach to the study of fertilization. Experientia 41: 485.
72. Pernis, B., G. Chiappino, A.S. Kelus, and P.G.H. Gell. 1965. Cellular localization of immunoglobulins with different allotypic specificities in rabbit lymphoid tissues. J. Exp. Med. 122: 853.
73. Robbins, J.H. 1964. Tissue culture studies of the human lymphocyte. Science 146: 1648.
74. Rowley, D.A., and F.W. Fitch. 1964. Homeostasis of antibody formation in the adult rat. J. Exp. Med. 120: 987.
75. Sado, T., and T. Makinodan. 1964. The cell cycle of blast cells involved in secondary antibody response. J. Immunol. 93: 696.
76. Saha, A., J.S. Garvey, and D.H. Campbell. 1964. The physicochemical characterization of the ribonucleic acid-antigen complex persisting in the liver of immunized rabbits. Arch. Biochem. Biophys. 105: 179.
77. Sahiar, K., and R.S. Schwartz. 1964. Inhibition of 19S antibody synthesis by 7S antibody. Science 145: 395.
78. Schlossman, S.F., and E.A. Kabat. 1962. Specific fractionation of a population of antidextran molecules with combining sites of various sizes. J. Exp. Med. 116: 535.
79. Schooley, J.C. 1961. Autoradiographic observations of plasma cell formation. J. Immunol. 86: 331.
80. Sell, S., and P.G.H. Gell. 1965a. Studies on rabbit lymphocytes in vitro. I. Stimulation of blast transformation with an anti-allotype serum. J. Exp. Med. 122: 423.
81. Sell, S., and P.G.H. Gell. 1965b. Studies on rabbit lymphocytes in vitro. IV. Blast transformation of the lymphocytes from newborn rabbits induced by

anti-allotype serum to a paternal lgG allotype not present in the serum of the lymphocyte donors. J. Exp. Med. 122: 923.

82. Sell, S., D.S. Rowe, and P.G.H. Gell. 1965. Studies on rabbit lymphocytes _in vitro_. III. Protein, RNA, and DNA synthesis by lymphocyte cultures after stimulation with phytohemagglutinin, with staphylococcal filtrate, with an anti-allotype serum, and with heterologous antiserum to rabbit whole serum. J. Exp. Med. 122: 823.
83. Smithies, O. 1965. Antibody induction and tolerance. Science 149: 151.
84. Sterzl, J., and I. Riha. 1965. Detection of cells producing 7S antibodies by the plaque technique. Nature 208: 858.
85. Sterzl, J., J. Vesely, M. Jilek, and L. Mandel. 1965. The inductive phase of antibody formation studies with isolated cells. In "Molecular and Cellular Basis of Antibody Formation, " J. Sterzl, ed. Czechoslovak Academy of Science Press, Prague, p. 463.
86. Svehag, S.E., and B. Mandel. 1964a. The formation and properties of poliovirus-neutralizing antibody. I. 19S and 7S antibody formation: Differences in kinetics and antigen dose requirements for induction. J. Exp. Med. 119: 1.
87. Svehag, S.E., and B. Mandel. 1964b. The formation and properties of poliovirus-neutralizing antibody. II. 19S and 7S antibody formation: Differences in antigen dose requirement for sustained synthesis, anamnesis, and sensitivity to X-irradiation. J. Exp. Med. 119: 21.
88. Syeklocha, D., L. Siminovitch, J.E. Till, and E.A. McCulloch. 1966. The proliferative state of antigen-sensitive precursors of hemolysin-producing cells, determined by the use of the inhibitor vinblastine. J. Immunol. 96: 472.
89. Tannenberg, W.J.K. 1966. Dissociation of proliferation and 19S antibody synthesis. Federation Proc. 25: 370.
90. Thiery, J.P. 1960. Microcinematographic contributions to the study of plasma cells. in "Cellular Aspects of Immunity," Ciba Foundation Symposium,

G.E.W. Wolstenholme and M. O'Connor, eds. Little, Brown and Co., Boston, Mass., p. 59.

91. Uhr, J.W., and M.S. Finkelstein. 1963. Antibody formation. IV. Formation of rapidly and slowly sedimenting antibodies and immunological memory to bacteriophage ΦX174. J. Exp. Med. 117:457.
92. Uhr, J.W., M.S. Finkelstein, and J.B. Baumann. 1962. Antibody formation. III. The primary and secondary antibody response to bacteriophage ΦX174 in guinea pigs. J. Exp. Med. 115: 655.
93. Urso, P., and T. Makinodan. 1963. The roles of cellular division and maturation in the formation of precipitating antibody. J. Immunol. 90: 897.
94. Warner, N.L., L.A. Herzenberg, and G. Goldstein. 1966. Immunoglobulin isoantigens (allotypes) in the mouse. II. Allotypic analysis of three γG_2-myeloma proteins from (NZB × BALB/c) F_1 hybrids and of normal γG_2 globulins. J. Exp. Med. 123: 707.
95. Weiler, E., E.W. Melletz, and E. Breuninger-Peck. 1965. Facilitation of immune hemolysis by an interaction between red cell-sensitizing antibody and γ-globulin allotype antibody. Proc. Nat. Acad. Sci. U.S. 54: 1310.
96. Williams, G.M. 1966. Ontogeny of the immune response. II. Correlations between the development of the afferent and efferent limbs. J. Exp. Med. 124: 57.
97. Williams, G.M., and G.J.V. Nossal. 1966. Ontogeny of the immune response. I. The development of the follicular antigen-trapping mechanism. J. Exp. Med. 124: 47.

*Chromosome Behavior During Development of Meiotic Tissue**

Herbert Stern and Yasuo Hotta

Department of Biology
University of California
La Jolla

INTRODUCTION

In all organisms, meiotic tissue is derived from somatic cells. In animals, a "germ line" is usually laid down early in development; in plants, the tissue from which meiocytes derive differentiates at various stages of development according to the flowering characteristics of the particular species. Common to all organisms however, is the fact that every meiotic cell is a product of a mitotic division. Differences between meiotic and mitotic cells encompass more than their respective patterns of chromosome segregation, but, for obvious reasons, these patterns have been a major focus of attention. Cytological details of mitosis

*These studies were supported by Grant GB-3902 from the National Science Foundation.

and meiosis abound, but relevant information on biochemical properties is in short supply. We have no grasp of the biochemical mechanisms which account for the differences in behavior between meiotic and mitotic chromosomes.

Cytologically, the distinguishing features of meiosis are chromosome pairing and delayed centromere division. Usually, the paired chromosomes, each with an undivided centromere, are separated at anaphase I, and the chromatids are separated at anaphase II. Were it possible to identify the mechanisms which lead to chromosome pairing and those which govern the timing of centromere division, our understanding of meiosis would be much improved. In this discussion, therefore, we shall consider recent experiments in our laboratory that reveal information about the mechanism of chromosome pairing and provide a few hints about the regulation of centromere division.*

GENERAL ANALYSIS OF THE PROBLEM

Although chromosome pairing and delayed centromere division have been identified as the distinctive events in meiosis, neither of these events is unique to meiotic cells. Somatic pairing in _Drosophila_ is very well known, and the timing of centromere division is as essential a feature of mitosis as it is of meiosis. What stands out in any comparison of meiotic with mitotic cells is the temporal relationship of these events to other processes in the chromosome cycle. Theoretically, if not actually, pairing could occur in every mitotic cycle, but if such pairing were entirely unstable, the functional result would be the equivalent

*Most of the studies reported here were conducted in collaboration with Dr. Michio Ito presently with the Department of Biology at the University of Nagoya, Japan. Preliminary accounts of the action of protein inhibitors are from the current studies of Dr. L.G. Parchman. Studies of fine structure are being conducted by Dr. T.F. Roth.

of no pairing. Therefore, a basic question to which we must address ourselves is whether the component events of pairing and of centromere division in meiosis are the same or different from those occurring in mitosis. If they are the same, then an understanding of the mechanisms underlying the two types of chromosome cycles will depend upon our success in identifying the distinctive sequences in which the mechanisms function. Such an approach to the problem is hardly novel. It was formulated more than 30 years ago under the title, "The Precocity Theory of Meiosis" by C.D. Darlington (4). The theory had all the attributes of excellence except proof, and, since its mainstay was the postulate that chromosome reproduction was delayed in meiotic cells, recent autoradiographic evidence for DNA synthesis during premeiosis has destroyed the theory along with its excellence. With the hindsight now available from our experiments, we can say that the doctrine was right even though its details were wrong. The distinctive features of meiosis do appear to lie in the temporal pattern of events rather than in the events themselves.

EXPERIMENTAL STUDIES

A. General Observations

A prominent physiological characteristic of meiotic cells is the relatively long duration of the prophase interval. In lily, for example, microsporocytes take about 9 to 10 days to complete meiosis from the leptotene stage, whereas the microspores undergo mitosis within several hours. Under certain conditions, which we shall discuss later, premeiotic microsporocytes can be induced to undergo a mitotic division. In such a population of cells, the peak frequency of metaphase is reached within 3 days. By contrast, comparable cells at only a slightly later stage of development take about 12 days to reach metaphase I if they enter into a meiotic rather than a mitotic cycle. An obvious explanation of the long duration of meiotic prophase is that a set of distinctive biochemical events must occur to effect the correspondingly distinctive cytological events.

Various biochemical and cytochemical studies have been made of cells in meiotic prophase. The general conclusion drawn is that RNA and proteins are synthesized mainly in the nucleus during this interval (6, 11, 16). The specific nature of the macromolecules formed and their role in the meiotic process remain open questions. Inhibitors of RNA or protein synthesis certainly affect chromosome segregation if applied during the prophase interval, but the specific mechanisms which are the targets of these agents need to be identified. On the whole, the information thus far obtained with respect to protein and RNA synthesis does not point in any direct way to the phenomenon of principal interest, the pairing of chromosomes.

A few analyses have been made of the histone composition of meiotic cells to determine whether the unique features of chromosome behavior might be correlated with special types of histones. A preponderance of lysine-rich histones in synaptic chromosomes has been found by histochemical analysis (1), but the observation has not been pursued far enough to illuminate the nature of synapsis. In a different study, histones were extracted from meiotic cells at different developmental stages, and their respective patterns were compared by disc electrophoresis (15). A slow-moving histone band that was not found in mitotic cells appeared in the meiotic cells at about the time of premeiotic DNA synthesis. This band persisted until well after the completion of meiosis; however, no obvious differences in band pattern were found between the different stages of meiosis. The significance of the novel histone band remains obscure. The progression of cytological events during the meiotic cycle could not be correlated with any set of corresponding changes in histone composition. Failure to identify specific protein changes may, however, be a result of inadequacy of present techniques for analyzing chromosomal proteins. The role of such proteins in meiotic development must therefore remain an open question.

The one component which has not been intensively studied during meiotic prophase is DNA. From a purely theoretical standpoint, a coincidence of pairing and DNA replication would provide a good basis for rationalizing synapsis. However, the abundant evidence that meiotic chromosomes are replicated during premeiotic interphase would seem to rule out this possibility (10, 19). Yet, on the basis of cytological evidence, Darlington's postulation of such a coincidence has considerable force. Leptonema threads, unlike the chromosomal threads in mitotic prophase, appear to be single; when doubleness becomes apparent in pachynema, the chromosomes are already paired. The theory is matchless in its simplicity, and against other labored hypotheses of chromosome pairing, its gracefulness is most inviting. For these reasons, if no other, it remained the theory of choice until, as we have mentioned, autoradiographic studies made it unacceptable.

The technique of autoradiography has some limitations which could prove serious in certain types of analysis. If a very small amount of DNA synthesis occurred outside the conventional S-period, its detection by autoradiography would be difficult. The presence of very few silver grains over nuclei cannot be interpreted with a great deal of confidence, especially if the interval between the presumed synthesis and the S-period is short, or if some of the thymidine label is incorporated into other macromolecular components, as is the case in the microsporocytes we have studied. Using autoradiographic techniques, Wimber and Prensky (20) obtained evidence for thymidine incorporation into DNA during meiotic prophase. They interpreted the results cautiously, but the evidence has been more or less disregarded. Chemical analysis does not obviate the difficulty of identifying a very small amount of DNA synthesis if it occurs close to a major interval of DNA synthesis, but it does make possible qualitative as well as quantitative comparisons. In combination, these comparisons can remove much of the ambiguity that arises when only rates of synthesis are compared. The question which must obviously follow this discussion of the limitations of autoradiography is what bearing it has on the problem of replication, the Achilles' heel of Darlington's theory.

An essential argument in the Precocity Theory is the singleness of the leptotene chromosome. It is easy to gloss over the chain of events between the gross doubling of DNA content in a nucleus and the partition of a chromosome into two functional chromatids. That the two phenomena are not different aspects of a single process is evident in polytene chromosomes. Some set of events must determine when a chromosome which has doubled its original DNA content becomes two chromatids. It is this question which has generally been disregarded in appraising the cytological evidence that leptotene chromosomes are single. Of course, there are no a priori grounds on which to predict the nature of the components that must be altered to effect chromatid formation. Our studies of DNA behavior during meiotic prophase did not arise from a profound analysis of this question, but it is important that the results obtained are relevant to it.

B. Synthesis of DNA during Meiotic Prophase

In our initial studies, intact flower buds of lily and Trillium were exposed to ^{32}P phosphate over a period of time when the microsporocytes were in meiotic prophase (5). DNA isolated from the microsporocytes had a very low level of radioactivity compared with that of cells labeled during premeiotic S-phase. From the standpoint of providing evidence for DNA synthesis during meiotic prophase, the results were at best ambiguous, and they would have remained so were it not for two additional observations. In comparing the behavior of microsporocytes at different stages of meiotic prophase, we found that cells exposed during leptonema or after pachynema had negligible amounts of radioactive DNA, unlike those exposed during zygonema-pachynema. Moreover, when labeled DNA obtained from zygotene-pachytene cells was characterized by equilibrium density centrifugation in a solution of CsCl, its distribution in the gradient was very different from

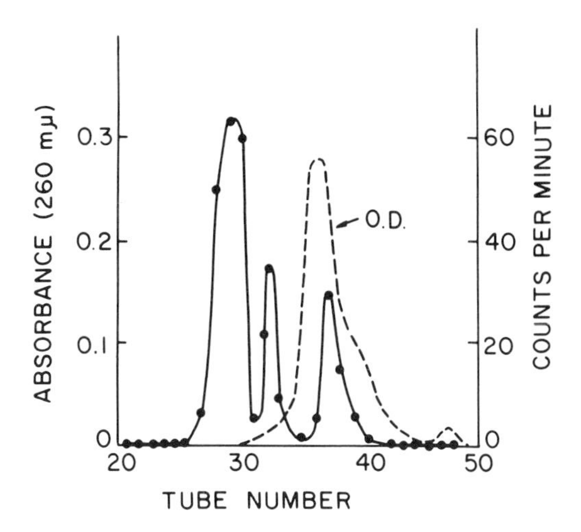

Figure 1. Density profile of DNA labeled during zygonema. Cultured microsporocytes of Lilium longiflorum (var. Nellie White) were exposed to ^{32}P phosphate during zygonema. The dotted line represents the density profile of the total DNA. This figure is one of a series obtained by exposing microsporocytes to this isotope during five different intervals of meiotic prophase. All preparations were centrifuged in CsCl solution until equilibrium was attained. The lower tube numbers contain the denser fractions. (Data from studies by Hotta, Ito and Stern (5).)

the bulk of the DNA (Figure 1). By contrast, DNA labeled during the premeiotic S-period had a distribution identical with the total DNA of the cells. The apparent absence of labeling in leptotene cells was consistent with the interpretation that the observed DNA labeling represented a discrete event and not the tail-end of a premeiotic synthesis. The distinctive density pattern encouraged the conclusion that prophase DNA synthesis was a real meiotic phenomenon.

A more thorough examination of prophase labeling was undertaken with cultured meiotic cells, much more suitable for these studies. The results of this examination may be summarized as follows:

1. Cultured microsporocytes showed the same pattern of DNA synthesis as did those which were labeled in the intact flower bud.
2. The labeled DNA was nuclear.
3. The labeled DNA was double stranded, but it had a lower sedimentation value than that of the total DNA.
4. DNA labeled during successive but brief periods of zygonema-pachynema showed progressive changes in density characteristics. The major component of the DNA synthesized during early zygonema had a density considerably higher than the average density of the total DNA (Figure 1). During pachynema, one of the major components synthesized was virtually identical in density with the total DNA.
5. The label in the DNA persisted at least until after the formation of the four haploid division products.
6. DNA prepared from somatic nuclei hybridized with prophase-labeled DNA to the same extent and with the same kinetic characteristics as it did with DNA labeled in somatic tissue or with DNA labeled during the premeiotic S-phase.

We may draw several conclusions from the results of these biochemical studies. A discrete period of DNA synthesis clearly exists during meiotic prophase. The total amount of DNA synthesized is approximately 0.3% of the total nuclear DNA. Not only is this DNA synthesized during a separate interval of the meiotic cycle, but it is also distinctive with respect to base composition and molecular size. The meaning of the size difference is unclear since the molecules are undoubtedly sheared in the course of isolation. Nevertheless, the fact that this difference was observed in all the preparations analyzed may be considered as additional evidence for the distinctiveness of prophase DNA synthesis. The hybridization experiments permit the conclusion that the DNA synthesized during meiotic prophase has an identical counterpart in somatic nuclei. These experiments rule out the possibility that the DNA synthesized is unique to meiotic cells.

Evidence for the replication of a small portion of the total DNA during meiotic prophase may be interpreted in one of two ways: such synthesis either represents a delayed replication of a DNA component in the chromosome, or it is a product of repair mechanisms associated with crossing-over. The chemical data alone do not provide adequate grounds for a choice, but the particular meiotic stages during which synthesis occurs do provide some pointers. Synthesis begins in early zygonema; therefore, it is coincident with the initiation of pairing. If repair mechanisms were the only source of synthesis, we would expect an increase in the rate of synthesis as pairing progressed with a maximum being reached in pachynema. This is not the case. The differences we have observed between zygonema and pachynema with respect to DNA synthesis are qualitative ones and could be reconciled with the view that a delayed replication occurs during zygonema and that repairs occur during pachynema. We shall examine the correctness of this view in the light of other studies.

C. Cytological Consequences of Inhibiting DNA Synthesis during Early Prophase

Implicit in all speculation about the role of DNA synthesis during mieosis is the assumption that such synthesis must have a functional significance. Nevertheless, the chemical evidence does not prove the validity of this assumption. We can obtain proof, however, by testing the responses of meiotic cells to inhibitors of DNA synthesis. Synchronously developing cells may be explanted at different stages of meiosis into media which permit normal meiosis. By challenging the explanted cells with appropriate inhibitors, some aspects of the relationship between DNA synthesis and meiotic development should be revealed (7, 8).

One problem we encounter in interpreting the effect of various DNA inhibitors is their possible lack of specificity. This problem can be overcome partly by using inhibitors presumed to be specific and by comparing the effects produced by such inhibitors with those produced by inhibitors of RNA or protein synthesis. By this comparison, we rule out the possibility, distant though it may seem, that the presumed inhibitors of DNA synthesis are acting on protein or RNA rather than on DNA.

Without entering a detailed analysis of the effects produced by inhibitors of protein or RNA synthesis, we can make the general statement that these effects do not mimic those produced by inhibitors of DNA synthesis. The combination of using inhibitors which act selectively on DNA synthesis and of observing effects which are more or less unique to these inhibitors, assures us that the experiments reported are real tests of the role of DNA synthesis in meiotic prophase.

Among the inhibitors tested, deoxyadenosine (ADR) was found to be the most useful. Not only does it inhibit DNA synthesis preferentially, but its action may be reversed by other deoxynucleosides. The mechanism by which ADR inhibits DNA synthesis is not fully understood, but it is believed to act at the substrate level and to impede the normal flow of precursors into DNA (12). In most of our experiments, we used 0.004 M ADR. At this concentration, DNA synthesis is inhibited by about 60% in a mixture of cells at different stages of meiotic prophase. We suspect that initiation of DNA synthesis is more sensitive to ADR than its continuation, but we have not made any chemical measurements of ADR action at the different stages of prophase.

The earliest observable effect of ADR occurs in cells exposed to this agent during the early zygotene stage. Cells so treated do not develop beyond zygonema, and most of them die after about 5 days in culture. How far cells can progress through zygonema and remain sensitive to arrest by ADR is difficult to determine precisely, but the interval is definitely short. In lilies, meiotic development is correlated with bud length, and it is only at the shortest bud length which marks the beginning of zygonema that this effect has been observed. Usually, even at this bud length, no more than 50 to 60% of the cells are arrested, the remainder showing the symptoms characteristic of a later stage.

The complete arrest of meiosis during prophase by an inhibitor of DNA synthesis would appear to be unusual against the background of our information about mitotic cells. Although the mitotic cell cycle may be interrupted at the S-phase by inhibiting DNA synthesis, or mitotic chromosomes may be damaged by the action of inhibitors such as ADR or FUDR during the end of the S-period (3, 13, 18), no evidence exists for an arrest of mitosis by the action of DNA inhibitors during mitotic prophase. Such a difference in response between meiotic and mitotic prophase must reflect a major difference in respective metabolic patterns.

The most obvious explanation of this observation is that ADR interferes with a meiotic event which normally occurs in early zygonema and without which meiosis cannot proceed. Cytologically, the major event recognized in early zygonema is the initiation of pairing. If this event is the target of ADR action, supporting evidence should be obtainable from an examination of the ultrastructure of zygonema cells. Such an examination has been carried out in our laboratory by Roth and Ito (14). In control cells, the synaptinemal complex can be identified readily; in cells treated before pairing is initiated, it cannot be found. Thus, to the extent that the presence of a synaptinemal complex reflects the occurrence of pairing, evidence suggests that initiation of DNA synthesis is necessary to the initiation of pairing. Whether the initiation of DNA synthesis is also a sufficient condition for the initiation of pairing cannot be decided from these experiments. The important conclusion is that one distinctive feature of meiosis - chromosome pairing - can be correlated with a distinctive biochemical event - the initiation of DNA synthesis during early zygonema.

D. Cytological Effects of Inhibiting DNA Synthesis During Zygonema and Pachynema

Cells exposed to ADR at stages following early zygonema show various types of chromosomal abnormalities. On the whole, the action of ADR correlates with the chemical data (Figure 2). The most severe cytological effects are observed in cells which are exposed from mid-zygonema to early pachynema. By mid-pachynema, when DNA synthesis has progressed beyond the half-way mark, the cells show fewer cytological abnormalities on exposure to ADR. By late pachynema, the cells are virtually resistant to ADR action, even at a concentration of 0.01 M. Thus, meiotic cells respond to DNA inhibitors only during the interval of zygonema-pachynema when DNA synthesis is occurring demonstrably, and the severity of their response decreases as they progress through the interval of DNA synthesis. By contrast, inhibitors of protein and RNA synthesis are effective beyond pachynema and at least

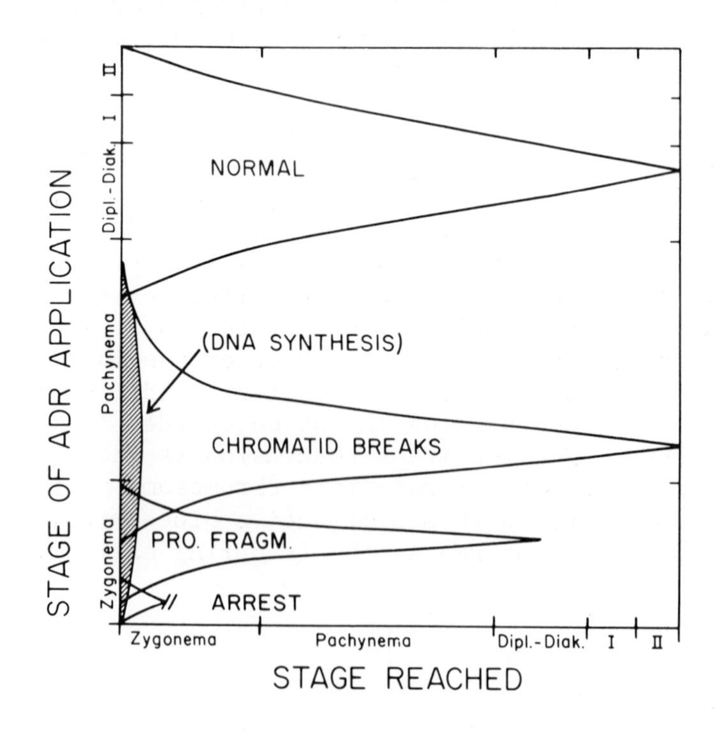

until diakinesis.

The evidence is sufficient to establish the general conclusion that prophase DNA synthesis has a functional role in meiosis. Further definition of that role is more difficult. The difficulty, as we shall see, arises from the deep-seated consequences of DNA inhibition. Primary and secondary effects are not easily sorted out; inferences drawn from the observed cytological abnormalities are at best crude approximations. Even so, they should contribute to our understanding of the complexity of the meiotic process.

E. Chromosomal Abnormalities Produced by ADR

The principal events in meiosis which might be dependent on DNA synthesis are chromosome pairing and contraction, crossing-over, centromere function, and organization of the spindle body. On the basis of our observations, we may eliminate chromosome contraction and spindle body organization as events which depend directly upon prophase DNA synthesis. In general, chromosomes undergo a more or less normal cycle of

---

Figure 2. (Opposite page.) A diagrammatic summary of ADR effects on cultured microsporocytes in relation to the meiotic stage at which they were first exposed to the agent. The ordinates indicate the meiotic interval at which the cultures were begun in the presence of ADR. The abscissae indicate the stages of meiosis the treated cells reach after 6 or more days in culture. The interval of prophase DNA synthesis is shown by the shaded area. Aberrations other than breakage are not shown, but they occur with chromatid breaks or prophase fragmentation. Two points are important: meiotic arrest occurs only in cells exposed to ADR in early zygonema; no abnormalities occur in cells exposed to ADR from late pachynema. The areas enclosed by the two lines defining each category of effect have no quantitative significance. They are drawn to indicate the stage cells reach in culture if exposed to ADR during the designated meiotic interval. (Results based on studies by Ito, Hotta, and Stern (8).)

contraction and extension in the presence of ADR. Metaphase, and ultimately interphase, configurations are the rule rather than the exception in cells exposed to ADR. Although aberrant chromosome segregation often occurs in treated cells, we infer the continued functioning of the spindle elements from the fact that anaphase I and II figures are common. Much, but not all, of the aberrant segregation is directly attributable to acentric fragments or to "sticky" chromosomes. We prefer to invoke a failure of centromere function as a cause of segregation anomalies, but the only argument we can advance in favor of our preference is that ADR does not induce aberrant segregation patterns in cells with undamaged chromosomes, although it does induce chromosome damage without any apparent effect on segregation.

The damaging effect of ADR on chromosome structure is evident in almost all cells exposed to it during mid- and late zygonema and early pachynema (Figure 3). The kinds of abnormalities and their frequency of occurrence vary according to the time of exposure, the stage of the cells at the beginning of exposure, and the species of plant from which the cells have been derived. The feature common to all abnormalities is a distortion of chromosome structure such that chromosomes either fragment, become sticky, or form anaphase bridges. Although these effects would appear to be very different in nature, we consider the differences trivial from the standpoint of the primary action of ADR. Our reasons become apparent in discussing the behavior of microsporocytes derived from the variety of lily known as "Nellie White."

The two varieties of lily we have studied most extensively are "Cinnabar" and "Nellie White." Our results with Nellie White are better suited for analysis because, at a concentration of 0.004 M ADR, chromosome breakage and stickiness are both prominent, whereas in Cinnabar, breakage is much less frequent. In Nellie White microsporocytes exposed to ADR from mid-zygonema to late zygonema, "prophase fragmentation" is virtually universal. We define prophase fragmentation as a breakage of chromosomes in cells which have

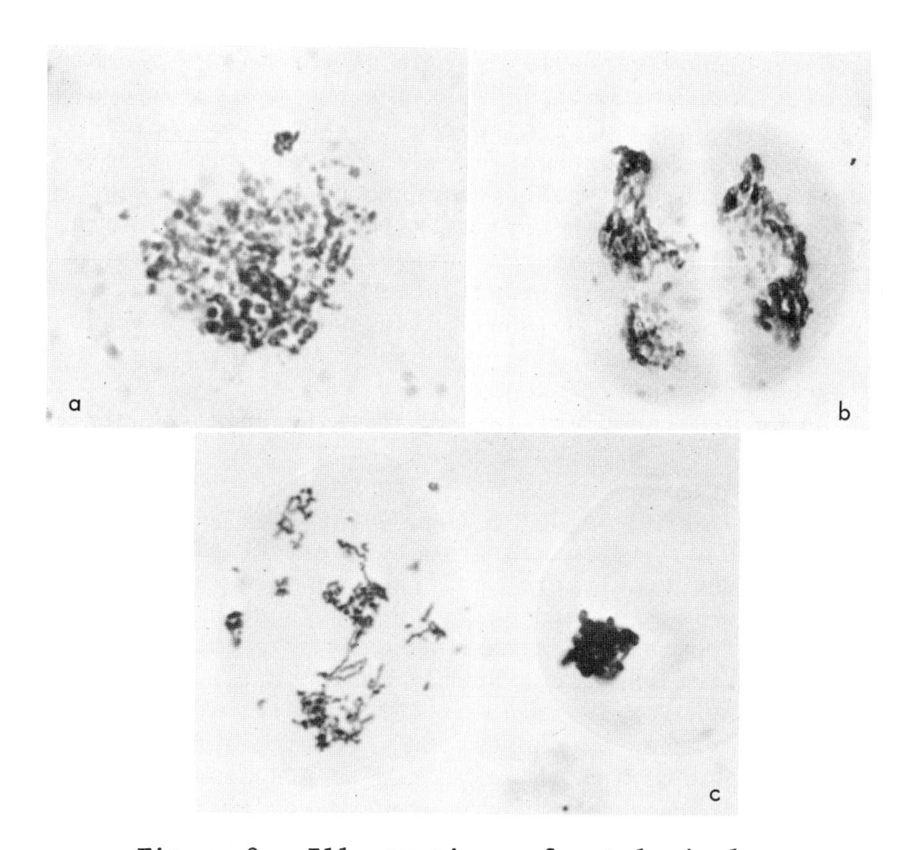

Figure 3. Illustrations of cytological abnormalities induced by treating meiotic cells with ADR. (a) Prophase fragmentation in microsporocytes of Nellie White. (b) Sticky anaphase II cell in Cinnabar microsporocyte. (c) Sticky metaphase I and anaphase II in Nellie White microsporocyte. Note the fragmentation in the anaphase cell. (Photographs prepared by Dr. Michio Ito.)

not progressed beyond diakinesis. Indeed, the fragmentation is so extreme that in most cases stage identification is impossible. The interval of prophase during which cells are susceptible to prophase fragmentation is short, and it is rarely encountered in cells exposed to ADR after mid-zygonema (Figure 2). Cells exposed to ADR from late zygonema through early pachynema show variable degrees of chromosome breakage at diakinesis or metaphase I, but the most prominent effect is observed at anaphase II when chromosome breakage becomes extensive. In general, for any particular culture of cells, the frequency of cells with broken anaphase II chromosomes is at least ten times that of cells with broken metaphase I chromosomes. "Sticky" chromosomes are also common, but, except for special conditions we shall discuss shortly, stickiness is less frequent in Nellie White than in Cinnabar microsporocytes (Figure 3).

As we mentioned earlier, it is difficult to attribute a particular significance to each type of chromosomal abnormality observed. Prophase fragmentation, which might be considered the most extensive form of damage, is a delayed response to ADR action. This may be deduced not only from the fact that few breaks are seen if cells are examined 1 to 2 days after exposure, but also from the fact that damage may be averted if cells are returned to a normal medium after being exposed to ADR for 24 to 48 hr (Figure 4). The existence of a lag between the appearance of chromosome breaks and the time of initial exposure to ADR is even more apparent in cells which are exposed to ADR in late zygonema and which progress through the first division with few broken chromosomes. For reasons which we shall not elaborate here, the lag in response cannot be satisfactorily explained by assuming a lag in ADR penetration. The most probable explanation is that the appearance of breakage results from secondary processes which act on a primary lesion in chromosomes exposed to ADR. Our main interest, therefore, is in identifying this lesion by evaluating the data on chromosome abnormalities.

To interpret the abnormalities observed, we must make some assumptions regarding DNA metabolism and chromosome organization. We must focus on DNA at the molecular level, because it is the target of ADR action. Because that action is an inhibition of DNA synthesis, we infer that its immediate effect would be

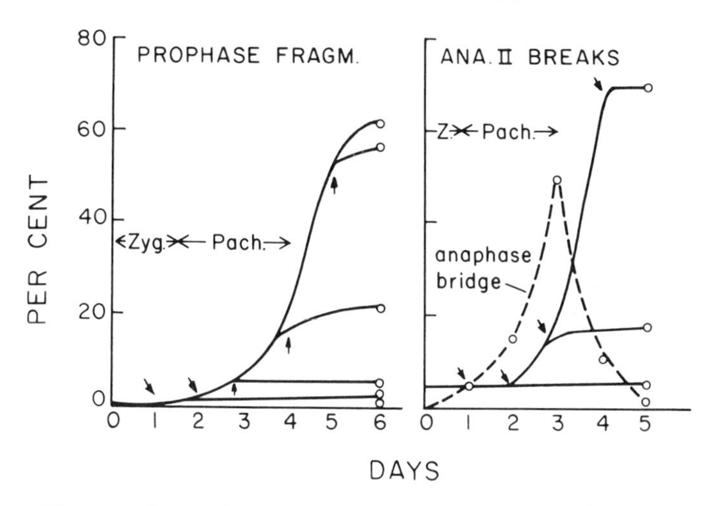

Figure 4. The reversal of ADR action by thymidine. Microsporocytes were explanted in media containing 0.004 M ADR. Arrows indicate the number of days the cells remained in ADR media prior to being transferred to a medium containing 0.004 M thymidine. All cultures were examined 6 days after explantation. Data on prophase fragmentation were obtained from microsporocytes explanted in early to mid-zygonema. Anaphase II breaks were scored in cultures which began with cells in late zygonema. The duration of zygonema and pachynema of the cultured cells is shown in the figures. Note that thymidine is ineffective in antagonizing the action of ADR once the cells have completed pachynema. Another significant point, discussed in the text, is the appearance of anaphase bridges in cells which had been transferred to a thymidine medium after 3 days of exposure to ADR. The ordinates indicate the percentage of cells affected as a function of the total number of cells in that stage. (Data from studies by Ito, Hotta and Stern (8).)

to leave gaps in the DNA chain which would not be present if synthesis proceeded normally. If so, we must take into account three processes which would affect the magnitude of the gaps. We assume that the degree to which DNA synthesis is inhibited would set an upper limit on the extent of damage produced. This relationship would explain the fact that zygonema cells show more extensive prophase fragmentation in 0.01 M than in 0.004 M ADR. However, we must also assume that repair enzymes may be present, and, if they are, the number of lesions produced would be decreased in proportion to the rate of repair. We have no evidence for the presence of special repair enzymes, but we do infer their presence from knowledge that cells in late zygonema which have been transferred to a thymidine medium after 3 days of exposure to ADR show an appreciable decrease in the number of anaphase II breaks but considerable increase in the number of anaphase bridges (Figure 4). If, as seems possible, several types of enzymes mediate DNA synthesis, and each of these responds differently to ADR concentration, the outcome of ADR treatment on the integrity of the DNA chain would be a product of the interaction of these enzymes.

However, as is evident from the observation just described, repair need not lead to a restitution of normal structure. If a rejoining of free ends occurs between homologous or sister chromatids rather than within the chromatid itself, bridges will form at either anaphase I or anaphase II. Considering the paucity of our information about the enzymes which act on DNA during meiosis, and about the levels of endogenous substrates which might affect the action of inhibitory agents, we can do little more than speculate about the interaction of these three metabolic factors. Clearly, under the conditions of these experiments, breakage or cross-linking of chromosomes is unlikely to reflect distinctive differences in the primary action of ADR.

To rationalize the cytological abnormalities, we must somehow relate breaks in the DNA filament to chromosome structure. We make two assumptions about chromsome organization for which there is a great deal of evidence.

1. The linear integrity of the DNA filament is essential to the linear integrity of the chromosome.
2. Chromosomes replicate by a semiconservative mechanism so that each chromatid inherits one intact strand.

From these assumptions we may conclude that an inhibition of DNA synthesis per se cannot cause a complete break in either chromosome or chromatid. Breakage, if it occurs, must be the consequence of rupturing an internucleotide linkage. Such rupture might be brought about either by special nucleases which cause breaks in order to make crossing-over possible, or by enzymes which attack single-stranded DNA. Regions of single-stranded DNA would be expected to occur if, as previously postulated, part of prophase DNA synthesis represents a delayed replication of certain regions in the chromosome. If the replication is interrupted by ADR, sections of the old DNA filament would lack a complementary strand. How quickly these hypothetical single-stranded regions of DNA would be cleaved is unclear. In observing broken chromosomes through the light microscope, we have frequently noted thin strands connecting the apparent pieces. Whether these connecting strands are often severed in the course of fixation or whether they are eventually destroyed within the living cell is uncertain. There is no doubt, however, that the regions in which such strands occur are structurally abnormal.

Thus, the most important single question concerns how to explain the origin of gaps in the DNA. ADR can only prevent a healing of gaps; it cannot produce them. Any answer to this question must account for the fact that fragmentation can occur in all the chromosomes and at many points over the entire length of the chromosome. Yet, as already stated, the amount of DNA synthesized during the entire prophase interval is about 0.3% of the total DNA. From our previous assumptions about chromosome structure, we can postulate two conditions under which breaks could originate: either comparatively short regions of DNA interspersed along the entire length of the DNA filament are delayed in their replication until zygonema, or breaks occur randomly along the chromosome during the zygotene-pachytene stages in association with crossing-over. By inhibiting DNA synthesis during these stages, interrupted DNA strands would result because of either incomplete replication or incomplete repair. From the standpoint of cytogenetic data, we cannot exclude the second alternative. The question we wish to raise is whether the first alternative can be included.

Two pieces of evidence (and one other we shall discuss later) favor the inclusion of delayed replication as a source of chromosome breaks. The results cited earlier - inhibition of DNA synthesis at the time of its initiation leads to a failure of synapsis and to an arrest of meiosis - are extremely difficult to reconcile with the postulate that prophase DNA synthesis is exclusively concerned with repair of breaks. If repair were the sole function of prophase DNA synthesis, we would expect many breaks rather than no pairing as a consequence of ADR treatment. But, to the extent that we can correlate cytological stage with DNA synthesis and with sensitivity to ADR, we have to conclude that breaks occur only if ADR is added _after_ the initiation of DNA synthesis.

The second piece of evidence which favors the idea of delayed replication is the relationship between cytological stage and susceptibility to breakage. Prophase fragmentation is most extensive between early and mid-zygonema, yet pairing is rarely complete before the end of zygonema or early pachynema. If we assume crossing-over between homologs occurs in paired regions, we would expect a higher frequency of fragmentation at the end of zygonema. This is not the case. Cells exposed to ADR in late zygonema show very little prophase fragmentation. To argue that most breaks are made and repaired before late zygonema would only introduce other difficulties, for if it is assumed that DNA synthesis represents only a repair of breaks associated with crossing-over, the occurrence of DNA synthesis at a time when homologs have just begun to pair is difficult to explain. Most breaks would have had to precede pairing. Since DNA synthesis continues through late zygonema as well as pachynema, and since ADR induces chromosomal abnormalities at least until mid-pachynema, the logical explanation would be that breaks associated with crossing-over originate during late zygonema and pachynema. This interpretation, and the observations that meiotic development may be arrested by ADR and that the composition of DNA synthesized during zygonema differs from that synthesized during pachynema, lead us to conclude that part of all of zygonema synthesis represents a delayed replication of an essential DNA component.

For want of a better understanding of chromosome organization, we picture the DNA filament of the chromosome to be interrupted by relatively small lengths of DNA which do not replicate during the premeiotic S-phase (17). Since the failure of these regions to replicate would block the formation of two functional chromatids, we denote these regions as "axial elements." In normal meiotic cells, replication of these elements is initiated with the formation of the synaptinemal complex. We presume that the two processes are so related in early zygonema that inhibition of the one leads to an inhibition of the other. We attribute prophase fragmentation, which occurs after initiation of DNA synthesis, to the incomplete replication of the axial elements. If the gaps in the DNA filament resulting from an interrupted synthesis are not repaired, the structure of the chromosome would be abnormal in the region of the gaps, and breakage could occur by the action of hydrolytic enzymes. If repair occurs by a random linking of free ends, sticky chromosomes - such as are frequently found in Cinnabar microsporocytes - would result. The drop in frequency of prophase fragmentation after mid-zygonema occurs because axial replication has progressed far enough to render the chromosomes stable. The different pattern of chromosome damage which occurs in cells exposed to ADR during late zygonema or early pachynema may reflect the shift from axial replication to crossing-over.

F. Events During the Premeiotic G-2 Phase

Our principal inference from these studies is the existence of a primary difference between a meiotic and mitotic cell at the termination of the S-period. In meiotic cells, we visualize some regulatory mechanism which prevents a replication of the axial DNA element until the cell has reached the zygotene stage. In mitotic cells, we consider it probable that this hypothetical axial element is replicated either at the end of the S-period or in the G-2 phase. Such G-2 synthesis, virtually undetectable by autoradiography, would explain reports of chromosome breakage by DNA inhibitors during the G-2 period (3). However, the precise time of axial replication in mitotic cells is less relevant to the present discussion than the disparity in time of its replication between meiotic and mitotic systems, which implies that the ordering of events in the G-2 phase is different for each of the systems. If this implication is correct, some

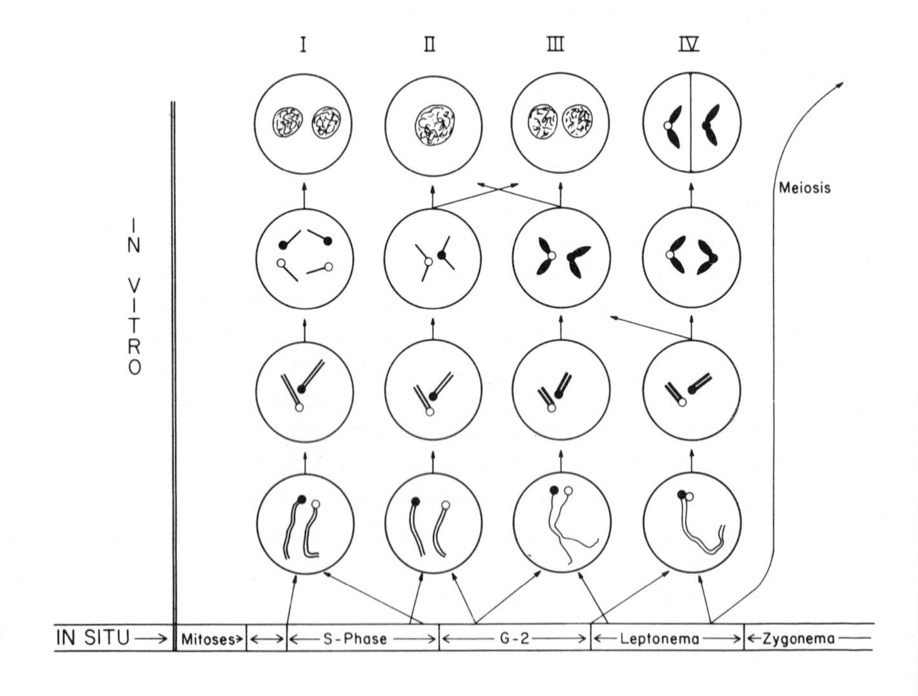

supporting evidence should be obtainable from studies of cells in premeiotic interphase. A few such studies have been made on cultured meiotic cells (9), and although they throw some light on the nature of events during the G-2 phase, they also reveal an unexpected complexity in regulatory pattern (Figure 5).

Cells explanted either just preceding or during the premeiotic S-phase undergo normal mitotic divisions after 2 to 3 days in culture. Periodic examination of the cultures over an interval of 90 days revealed no signs of meiosis. The process of explantation must have upset normal regulatory mechanisms, such that cells which would have entered meiosis under in situ conditions, enter a normal mitotic cycle in vitro. If, as supposed, one of the regulatory mechanisms required for meiosis is a delay in axial replication, then we are compelled to assume that explantation has induced completion of DNA synthesis.

Additional experiments reveal, however, that even if the assumption is correct, other events critical

---

Figure 5. (Opposite page.) The behavior of microsporocytes explanted into culture media at various stages of premeiosis. The bottom line shows the stages at which cells were explanted; vertical rows illustrate their subsequent development in vitro. I, Normal mitosis. II, Normal mitosis but with nondividing centromeres. III, Abnormal meiosis with little, if any, pairing. IV, Abnormal meiosis with bivalents which usually fall apart at, or before, metaphase I. In some cells, a true anaphase I may occur. More often, we find a mixture of univalents and bivalents which segregate abnormally. Eventually, chromosomes in all types return to an interphase condition, some cells having a single nucleus and others with two or more. Where two arrows are drawn to indicate the course of meiotic development, cells have been observed to follow either of the two courses. Thus, in the category labeled "Type IV", some cells undergo anaphase I whereas others revert to an interphase condition without an anaphase separation following the metaphase stage. (Based on studies by Ito, Hotta, and Stern (9).)

to meiosis must also occur at about the same time. If cells are explanted shortly after S-phase and examined 2 to 3 days later, mitotic figures are again evident, but the centromeres do not divide and anaphase separations do not occur. Eventually, the cells revert to an interphase condition as either uninucleate or multinucleate cells. This behavior is probably significant, because repression of centromere division at first metaphase is a characteristic of meiotic division. At the cytological level of analysis, "centromere fixation" appears to be the first irreversible change following the premeiotic S-period.

The complexity of G-2 events becomes strikingly evident in cells explanted during the interval remaining between the time of centromere fixation and the appearance of the leptotene stage. Such cells invariably enter some form of abnormal meiosis. One major difference between these cells and those explanted at a prior stage is the duration of prophase. Cultures which revert to mitosis reach metaphase within about 3 days; those which enter meiosis, however abnormal the process becomes, reach metaphase within about 12 days. The abnormalities which develop also depend upon the interval of explantation. Those explanted close to the interval of centromere fixation show little, if any, pairing, even though the chromosomes have a typical meiotic appearance. Whatever pairing does occur is abortive, so that bivalents are rarely seen at diplonema or diakinesis. By contrast, those explanted close to leptonema or even in early leptonema appear to be fully paired, but the pairing is still unstable. At metaphase I, most cells show a mixture of bivalent and univalent chromosomal aggregates. Undoubtedly, the medium into which the cells are explanted lacks certain essential components, but the progressive changes in the behavior of cultured cells that correlate with the stage of explantation must surely reflect a sequence of changes which is occurring in situ.

We may summarize the sequence of changes by the following explanation. At the termination of premeiotic DNA synthesis, the centromere region of the chromosome becomes so modified that it will not divide when the cells reach metaphase. Since cells explanted at this stage behave in all other respects like mitotic cells, we infer that other modifications of the chromosome which anticipate meiotic requirements either have not yet occurred or, if they have occurred, are unstable under the conditions of culture. The first evidence for changes during premeiosis ultimately leading to pairing is found in cells just after the interval of centromere fixation. The fact that the pairing is unstable in cultured cells leads us to conclude the mechanisms required for pairing are different from those required for stabilization. The significance of our finding that pairing becomes more stable as cells are explanted at later intervals of G-2 is unclear. The lack of stability may be a secondary consequence of disturbing other unidentified developmental processes. Nevertheless, the results clearly show that the occurrence of pairing and its persistence are separable phenomena. The distinctive feature of normal meiosis, as we pointed out in our introduction, is not pairing by itself, but the coincidence of pairing and stabilization. More precisely, in normal meiotic cells, conditions are such as to stabilize pairing for a defined interval of time, from zygonema through pachynema; in other types of cells, pairing may persist for the life of the cell, as in some insects, or it may be so transient as to pass unnoticed.

Cytological behavior of explanted premeiotic cells provides no evidence relevant to the hypothesis formulated earlier that the axial element is delayed in its replication. Cytological observations could be explained equally well by assuming a complete synthesis of DNA during the S-phase. If, however, evidence could be adduced in favor of the hypothesis, our interpretation of the relationships among centromere division, pairing, and DNA replication would be very much influenced. We conducted two types of experiments in search of such evidence. In the first, we measured and characterized the DNA synthesis of cells explanted shortly after S-phase or in the G-2 interval. In the second, we tested various inhibitors of DNA synthesis to determine whether such inhibition might prevent explanted cells from undergoing unstable pairing.

If the hypothesis of delayed axial replication is correct, all cells explanted during premeiotic G-2 should show a small amount of DNA synthesis regardless of whether they enter a mitotic or meiotic type of cycle. The test would probably be meaningless if the sole criterion used were the level of DNA synthesis. However, as already shown, the density characteristics of the DNA synthesized during meiotic prophase are distinctly different from those synthesized during the S-phase. In zygonema, the major peak of the newly synthesized DNA is considerably denser than that of the total DNA. Several varieties of lily were tested in this way and all yielded the same kind of results. Cells which entered either a mitotic or an abnormal meiotic cycle on being explanted during the G-2 phase, all showed a small amount of DNA synthesis with density characteristics similar to those found for DNA synthesized during meiotic prophase. The evidence thus clearly favors the hypothesis.

If the abortive pairing in cells explanted during the G-2 phase is a result of premature DNA replication, it should be possible to inhibit such replication so as to permit the consummation of other events essential to the stabilization of pairing. This possibility was tested by exposing cells explanted during the latter part of the G-2 phase to 5-aminouracil, cytosine arabinoside (2), and deoxyadenosine. Most attempts with deoxyadenosine were unsuccessful. At low levels of ADR, pairing was not stabilized, and, at high levels, development was arrested. Attempts to transfer cells exposed to ADR were also unsuccessful, because most died in the course of transfer. For reasons which we do not understand, exposure of the cells to cytosine arabinoside or 5-aminouracil without any subsequent transfer channeled up to 40% of the cells into normal synapsis. Spindle irregularities persisted, but events were normal up to metaphase I. It may be significant that neither cytosine arabinoside nor 5-aminouracil have an appreciable effect on meiotic cells if applied during the prophase interval. These results are promising but not conclusive. They are consistent with the hypothesis of delayed axial replication, but they do not yet provide us with an adequate technique to control the entry of cells into normal meiosis.

CONCLUDING REMARKS

Our principal finding in this series of studies on meiotic regulation is that a small portion of the total nuclear DNA is delayed in its replication until the cells reach the zygotene stage. Our principal interpretation is that the DNA synthesized during zygonema is located in the axial element of the chromosome. We have defined this element as small regions in the DNA filament which, when replicated, result in the formulation of two functional chromatids. We have drawn a major distinction between meiosis and mitosis with respect to the timing of axial replication. The initiation of pairing appears to be coincident with the initiation of axial replication, and evidence indicates that such replication is a necessary condition for pairing to occur. The transient stabilization of pairing during zygonema and pachynema depends upon another set of factors which remain unidentified but which are clearly separable from the factors promoting pairing.

The findings and the interpretation may contribute somewhat to our understanding of meiosis, but they lead to a more difficult question. For, if the events discussed represent distinctive features of the meiotic cell, we should at least be able to identify the time at which a particular cell or its progeny becomes committed to a meiotic, rather than to a mitotic, type of cycle. On this question we have little to report. Our evidence bears only on the time at which a cell becomes <u>irreversibly</u> committed to a particular meiotic event. The evidence permits us to make the following statements: cells in the premeiotic S-phase can revert to a normal mitotic cycle; at the termination of

S-phase, the centromeres are modified in a way which prevents their division even if the cells enter mitosis; following the S-period, the cells are no longer capable of entering a mitotic type of prophase, but are still incapable of stabilizing pairing. If we use the criterion of irreversibility to identify commitment, we must draw the conclusion that cells do not become committed to meiosis in any respect until the completion of the S-phase, and that they do not become fully committed until they reach leptonema. The relevance of this conclusion to an understanding of meiosis is doubtful, for in these very studies we have shown that one distinctive property of a meiotic cell is a delay in replication of a functionally important fraction of the DNA. Yet, at the time that this delay occurs, the cells can still be induced to undergo a normal mitotic cycle. The moral of this study would appear to be that, at the molecular level, the analysis of DNA is an easy target.

REFERENCES

1. Ansley, H.R. 1958. Histones of mitosis and meiosis in _Lox flavicolis_. J. Biophys. Biochem. Cytol. 4: 59-62.
2. Bader, J.P. 1965. Transformation of Rous sarcoma virus: A requirement for DNA synthesis. Science 149: 757-58.
3. Bell, S., and S. Wolff. 1964. Studies on the mechanism of the effect of fluorodeoxyuridine on chromosomes. Proc. Nat. Acad. Sci. U.S. 51: 195-202.
4. Darlington, C.D. 1937. "Recent Advances in Cytology." 2nd ed., Blakiston, Phila. Pa. 671 p.
5. Hotta, Y., M. Ito, and H. Stern. 1966. Synthesis of DNA during meiosis. Proc. Nat. Acad. Sci. U.S. 56: 1184-91.
6. Hotta, Y, and H. Stern. 1963. Inhibition of protein synthesis during meiotic development and its bearing on intracellular regulation. J. Cell Biol. 16: 259-79.
7. Ito, M., and H. Stern. Studies of meiosis in vitro.

I. In vitro culture of meiotic cells. (Submitted for publication.)
8. Ito, M., Y. Hotta, and H. Stern. Studies of meiosis in vitro. II. Effect of inhibiting DNA synthesis during meiotic prophase on chromosome structure and behavior. (Submitted for publication.)
9. Ito, M., Y. Hotta, and H. Stern. Studies of meiosis in vitro. III. Factors in premeiotic interphase which affect the development of cultured meiotic cells. (In preparation.)
10. Lima-de-Faria, A., and K. Borum. 1962. The period of DNA synthesis prior to meiosis in the mouse. J. Cell Biol. 14: 381-88.
11. Monesi, V. 1964. Ribonucleic acid synthesis during mitosis and meiosis in the mouse testis. J. Cell Biol. 22: 521-32.
12. Munch-Petersen, A. 1960. Formation in vitro of deoxyadenosine triphosphate from deoxyadenosine in Ehrlich ascites cells. Biochem. Biophys. Res. Commun. 3: 392-9 .
13. Nichols, W.W., A. Levan, and B.A. Kihlman. 1964. Chromosome breakages associated with viruses and DNA inhibitors. In "Cytogenetics of Cells in Culture," R.J. Harris, ed. Academic Press, N.Y. 255-71.
14. Roth, T.F., and M. Ito. 1966. DNA synthesis during meiotic prophase in relation to pairing and disjunction. J. Cell Biol. (Abstract; in press.)
15. Sheridan, W.F., and H. Stern. 1966. Histones in meiosis. Exp. Cell Res. (In press.)
16. Taylor, J.H. 1959. Autoradiographic studies of nucleic acids and proteins during meiosis in Lilium longiflorum. Am. J. Botany 46: 477-84.
17. Taylor, J.H. 1963. The replication and organization of DNA in chromosomes. In "Molecular Genetics," J.H. Taylor, ed. Academic Press, N.Y., Part I, 65-112.
18. Taylor, J.H., W.F. Haut, and J. Tung. 1962. Effect of fluorodeoxyuridine on DNA replication, chromosome breakage and reunion. Proc. Nat. Acad. Sci. U.S. 48: 190-98.

19. Taylor, J.H., and R.D. McMaster. 1954. Autoradiographic and microspectrophotometric studies of desoxyribosenucleic acid during microgametogenesis in Lilium longiflorum. Chromosoma 6: 489-521.
20. Wimber, D.E., and W. Prensky. 1963. Autoradiography with meiotic chromosomes of the male newt (Triturus viridescens) using H^3-thymidine. Genetics 48: 1731-38.

Section II

Transcription of Genetic Material

*The Species of RNA in the HeLa Cell**

Jonathan R. Warner†

Department of Biochemistry
Albert Einstein College of Medicine
New York

At the outset we should like to point out that, far from being a comprehensive review of the subject of nuclear RNA, this paper consists largely of a subjective summary of the work on RNA in HeLa cells, as carried out in the laboratory of J.E. Darnell. We believe, however, that these observations and conclusions will have considerable general validity.

*The Author's research is supported by Grant #GB 4647 from the National Science Foundation.
†Career Scientist of the Health Research Council of the City of New York.

BASIC CONSIDERATIONS

From the viewpoint of a molecular biologist, the nucleus has two primary functions:

1. To maintain and, when necessary, duplicate the genetic information of the cell (i.e., DNA), and
2. To transcribe from this DNA and to process the appropriate species of RNA in the amounts required for continued cell function and growth.

We are concerned here exclusively with the second of these functions. At present, however, little can be said about cytoplasmic and environmental control of RNA synthesis. In fact, we are just beginning to understand the synthesis of various classes of RNA in maximally growing cells. Nevertheless, from what follows it should be apparent that the definition of various species of RNA in the cell will undoubtedly provide clues for the solution of some problems of the control of nuclear function.

There are two fundamental assumptions that underlie most of our thinking concerning the origin and function of RNA:

1. All RNA is made on a DNA template and, therefore, it is made in the nucleus of the cell (exceptions: RNA viruses; the potential transcription of mitochondrial and plastid DNA).
2. All RNA is related to the process of protein synthesis (including, perhaps, the control of that synthesis).

These assumptions are based on a great deal of experimental evidence accumulated over the years. We shall not attempt to review this material in detail (see reviews by Moldave (1) and Prescott (2)), although we shall present a number of substantiating experiments. While exceptions to either of these assumptions may eventually be found, a heavy burden of proof will rest upon the claimant.

CELL FRACTIONATION

The earliest experiments investigating the role of the various organelles of the cell in RNA production were autoradiographic in nature (3, 4). While invaluable, this method has the serious handicap of being unable to differentiate between the various species of RNA.* The significance of that liability is immediately apparent when one considers that there are at least eight identifiable species of RNA in the HeLa cell. The solution to this problem, more easily said than done, is the biochemical characterization of the RNA from the various cell fractions.

The problems posed by cell fractionation are numerous:

1. The adequacy of the fractionation;
2. The retention of macromolecules within the appropriate fraction;
3. The lack of degradation of the macromolecules;
4. The proof that the fractionation has some physiological validity.

For our work with HeLa cells, we have used cytoplasmic extracts prepared by Dounce homogenization in hypotonic buffer, followed by low-speed centrifugation (5). These preparations are relatively free of nuclear contamination by two criteria: (1) the small amount of DNA present (Table 1), and (2) the complete absence of the 45S ribosomal precursor RNA. The latter is probably the better criterion, since approximately 3% of the cells are in mitosis at any one time, and some of the mitotic DNA probably remains in the cytoplasmic fraction. To prepare nuclei free of cytoplasmic contamination is more difficult, but a technique using a detergent wash, developed by Penman (6), gives very satisfactory results for HeLa cells. The striking result he obtained is that there are very few riboso-

*Abbreviations: rRNA = ribosomal RNA; tRNA = transfer RNA; mRNA = messenger RNA; H.S. RNA = heterogeneously sedimenting RNA.

mal particles in the nucleus, and that the few that are there have just been assembled. Electron micrographs (7) indicate that much of the material removed from the nuclei during detergent treatment consists of extranuclear membranes laden with ribosomes. These

TABLE 1

Distribution of macromolecules in HeLa cell fractions[a]

	% of Total		
	Protein	RNA	DNA
Cytoplasm	81	95	4.5
Nuclear Supernatant	17	1.2	90[b]
Nuclear Pellet	1.4	3.6	5[b]

[a]Data from reference 35.

[b]The estimate of the amount of DNA in the nuclear fractions is very rough, due to the use of DNAase in the fractionation procedure.

results have been confirmed and extended by Vaughan et al. (8), who have shown that (1) _in vivo_, there is passage of newly synthesized particels from the nucleus to the cytoplasm but no substantial passage of particles back into the nucleus, and (2) during fractionation of the cell, there is no substantial loss of newly formed ribosomal particles from the nucleus to the cytoplasm. In a steady-state situation, less than 0.05% of the 16S rRNA is in the nucleus. These results raise again the question of the existence of any protein synthesis in the nucleus.

The nucleus can be further fractionated (9) into a nuclear supernatant fraction, containing most of the DNA, and a nuclear pellet fraction consisting largely of nucleoli. Although the pellet fraction represents only 10% of the nuclear protein, it contains all of the 45S and 32S ribosomal precursor RNA.

CYTOPLASMIC RNA - THE PROTEIN SYNTHETIC APPARATUS

The number of identifiable species of RNA continues to increase. It may be worthwhile, before starting to discuss the synthesis of RNA in the nucleus, to describe the various species of RNA that are found in the cytoplasm of the cell, since it appears that much of the nuclear RNA is, in fact, being synthesized and processed before passing out into the cytoplasm (see Table 2).

TABLE 2

Species of RNA in the HeLa cell

	Origin	Function
Nuclear		
H.S.	de novo	Precursor to messenger? Control?
45S	de novo	Precursor to ribosomal RNA
32S	45S	Precursor to 28S RNA
Cytoplasmic		
28S	32S	Major part of large ribosomal subunit
16S	45S	Major part of small ribosomal subunit
5S	32S	Part of large ribosomal subunit
transfer	?	Amino acid carriers
messenger	H.S.?	Carries information for specification of amino acid sequences of protein

Ribosomal RNA

By far the largest portion of the RNA in the cell is in the two species of ribosomal RNA designated 28S and

16S because of their sedimentation constants. Each of these make up a major portion of the ribosomal subunits, which sediment at 50S and 30S, respectively. A great deal of evidence indicates that the ribosome (ergo the rRNA) plays a relatively passive role in the protein synthetic process (10), and that the actual designation of the amino acid sequence is brought about by messenger RNA (11). The chief characteristics of rRNA are its abundance, the strict homogeneity of size of its two components (see Figure 1), and its base

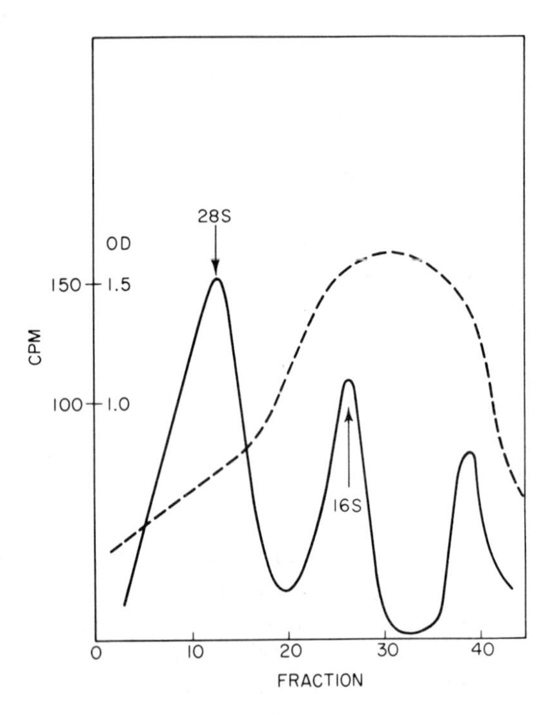

Figure 1. Sedimentation analysis of RNA from polyribosomes. RNA was extracted from the polysomes of cells which had been exposed to ^{3}H uridine for 25 minutes. _____ designates the optical density, which is largely 28S and 16S ribosomal RNA. ---- designates the radioactivity which is largely messenger RNA. (Figure adapted from reference 16.)

composition, which is particularly rich in guanine and, to a lesser extent cytosine, and is quite unlike the base composition of DNA (see Table 3). The way in

TABLE 3

Base composition of various species of HeLa RNA

	G	C	A	U(T)	G&C
H.S.[a] (Nuclear supernatant)	22	22	26	30	44
H.S.[a] (Nuclear pellet > 45S)	25	22	25	28	47
45S[a]	37	28	15	19	65
32S[a]	36	33	15	16	69
28S[b]	36	32	16	16	68
16S[b]	30	27	21	22	57
4S[b]	30	25	21	24	55
Cytoplasmic messenger[c]	21.5	25.5	26	27	47
DNA[d]	22	21	29	28(T)	43

[a]Data from reference 35.
[b]Data from reference 34.
[c]Data from reference 5.
[d]Data from reference 36.

which the ribosome is manufactured in the nucleus has been extensively investigated and is described in detail below.

The rate of turnover of ribosomal RNA has not been measured in HeLa cells. Two investigations (12, 13) of the stability of ribosomal RNA in rat liver give a half-life of 2 to 5 days. This represents a surprisingly rapid turnover for such slowly growing cells.

Messenger RNA

Messenger RNA, whose base sequence specifies the amino acid sequence of a protein, was first postulated by Jacob and Monod (14) to explain the control of bacterial enzyme formation. A fraction of rapidly labeled RNA which appeared to correspond to mRNA was soon isolated from phage-infected bacteria (15). However, several years passed before techniques were developed which allowed the detection of mRNA in mammalian cells (5). Use was made of the facts that a significant amount of ^{3}H rRNA does not appear in the cytoplasm for nearly an hour after ^{3}H uridine is added to the cells, while ^{3}H mRNA rapidly enters the cytoplasm and becomes an integral part of the polyribosomes, which can easily be separated from the bulk of the cytoplasmic material. A sucrose gradient profile of the ^{3}H mRNA found on polysomes after a short pulse of ^{3}H uridine is shown in Figure 1. This mRNA is heterogeneous in size, as expected, since it codes for proteins of different sizes; it has a base composition much like that of the DNA (Table 3).

Although the amount of mRNA present is difficult to measure, there is probably 2 to 5% as much mRNA as rRNA. There have been a number of attempts to measure the half-life of mammalian mRNA, chiefly through the use of actinomycin D to block further RNA synthesis. The value obtained for HeLa cells is approximately 3 hours (5), while reports on rat liver vary from 4 (17) to 40 (18) hours. Much of the difficulty lies in the interpretation of experiments using actinomycin. If a high dose is used, completely stopping RNA synthesis for an extended period, the treatment is lethal and many unknown side effects probably occur; if a lower dose is used, the small amount of continuing synthesis of RNA is likely to be preferentially mRNA (19) and inconclusive results are obtained.

Transfer RNA

The third major RNA species that is involved in protein synthesis is transfer RNA. These molecules carry the amino acids from the activating enzyme to the ribosome. There are 40 to 60 varieties of tRNA, which are about 77 nucleotides in length - about one twentieth the size of the smaller ribosomal RNA molecule. Approximately one sixth of the tRNA is bound to the polysomes and thus actively engaged in amino acid transfer. Although a number of experiments dealing with the origin of tRNA have been reported, the amount of tRNA is so small and the possibility that other RNA can be degraded to the size of tRNA is so great, that the question must be considered undecided. The large number and variety of the "unusual" bases present in tRNA (20) should prove to be a good tracer in establishing its origin. Although no data has been reported on the turnover of mammalian tRNA, it is known that the terminal nucleotides exchange with nucleotide triphosphates in the cell, even in the absence of any RNA synthesis (21). If uncharacterized, such turnover may be mistaken for rapid labeling of cytoplasmic RNA. Although both terminal cytosine and adenosine have been shown to turn over in rabbit reticulocyte tRNA, recent reports indicate that in rat liver only the terminal adenosine turns over (22).

5S RNA

There is one newcomer to the catalog of cytoplasmic RNAs. From both bacterial (23) and mammalian sources (24), a small RNA molecule containing approximately 105 nucleotides has been isolated from the larger ribosomal subunit. The molar ratio of 28S to 5S RNA is approximately 1:1, suggesting that there is one molecule of 5S RNA per 50S ribosomal particle. The function of this RNA species is unknown, but it almost certainly is involved in protein synthesis in some capacity. Its origin is also unknown, although it is clearly distinct from tRNA not only in its base composition, but also in its base sequence, as determined by hybridization with DNA (25).

In summary, then, there are at least five types of RNA in the cytoplasm, each of which is intimately involved in protein synthesis. Since there are two molecules of tRNA involved (26, 27), it is likely that there are a total of six molecules of RNA within a few

Ångstroms of the site of peptide bond formation. It will be difficult, indeed, to establish the molecular relationship of all these components.

NUCLEAR RNA

Heterogeneous Nuclear RNA

Figure 2 represents the radioactive RNA isolated from purified, fractionated nuclei taken from cells that had received a 40 minute label with $^{32}PO_4$. At this labeling time, more than 90% of the cell's radioactive RNA is nuclear. The RNA has been isolated, free of DNA and protein, by the method of Scherrer and Darnell (28). From Figure 2, it is evident that there are two classes of RNA present: a prominent peak at 45S in the nuclear pellet fraction, which represents a precursor to ribosomal RNA, discussed below; and a considerable amount of heterogeneously sedimenting (H.S.) RNA, which is present in both the nuclear pellet and supernatant fractions. The latter is significant not only for its heterogeneity, but also for its great size. The larger molecules sediment at 90S or more, and probably have a molecular weight in excess of 10 million (29). A number of control experiments have been carried out to determine if there are protein or DNA "linkers" (30), but all available evidence indicates that the molecules are single polynucleotide chains. Furthermore, preliminary experiments dealing with its sedimentation properties under various ionic conditions indicate (30) that it has considerably less secondary structure than does 45S RNA, and more closely resembles the viral RNAs. A striking feature of H.S. RNA is its base composition, which strongly resembles that of the cell's DNA (see Figure 2 and Table 3). RNA of similar properties has been isolated from duck erythrocytes (31) from *Xenopus laevis* embryos (32), and from FL cells (33).

Neither the fate nor the function of H.S. RNA has been satisfactorily explained. Attardi et al. (31) argue persuasively that in duck reticulocytes, where the H.S. RNA is more readily evident because of the

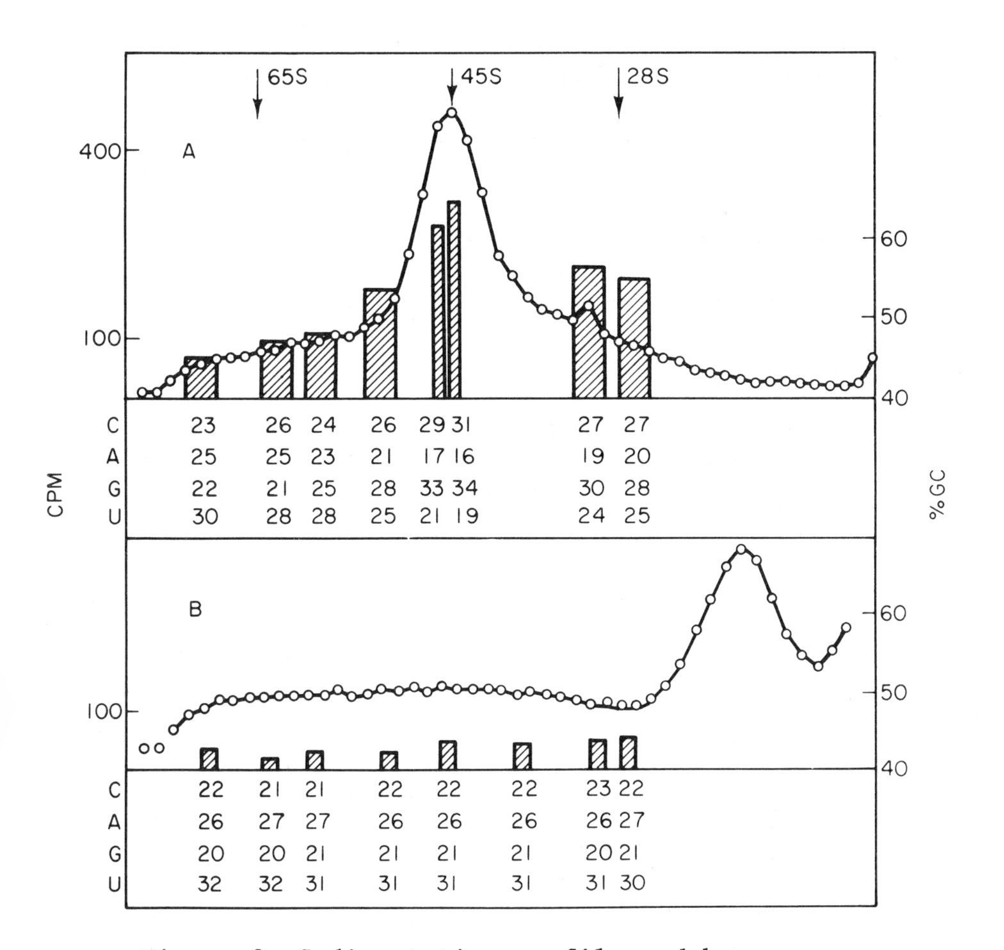

Figure 2. Sedimentation profile and base analysis of rapidly labeled RNA in the "nuclear pellet" (A) and "nuclear supernatant" (B) fractions. RNA was isolated from these fractions after treatment of the intact cells with $^{32}PO_4$ for 40 minutes. Portions of selected gradient fractions were used to determine the base composition of the RNA. (From reference 34).

lack of rRNA synthesis, the kinetics of uridine incorporation show that the bulk of the H.S. RNA is degraded within an hour. This may be a special case, however, since the reticulocyte cell is largely directed toward the synthesis of a single protein. The most interesting hypothesis is that the H.S. RNA is in some way a precursor to cytoplasmic messenger RNA. The two classes of RNA share a number of distinctive features:

1- the rapidity of labeling;
2- the DNA-like base ratio;
3- the apparent lack of an extensive secondary structure;
4- the heterogeneity of size.

Although the H.S. RNA is far larger than the bulk of the cytoplasmic RNA, the maturation of 45S to 28S and 16S rRNA shows that the cell has a method for the specific cleavage of large RNA molecules. There has been an attempt to compare the amount of H.S. RNA made with the amount of 45S RNA made, and, by using the steady-state ratio of mRNA to rRNA and the half-life of mRNA, to estimate the amount of H.S. RNA needed to maintain that ratio. However, the uncertainties in a number of the measurements have precluded a definitive answer (34). The rigorous test of the hypothesis is to determine if the H.S. RNA and the mRNA share base <u>sequences</u> as well as base ratios. Hybridization experiments to determine this point are underway.

It should be pointed out that within the heterogeneous RNA a number of relatively minor species of RNA might be hidden. For instance, if the tRNA were made as a large molecule and cleaved specifically to the appropriate size, the precursor molecules could be anywhere in the gradient. Furthermore, the H.S. RNA partitions between the nuclear pellet and nuclear supernatant fractions in a ratio of about 4:1 (35). The physiological significance of this fractionation is not clear, but the two fractions seem to have slightly different base compositions.

SYNTHESIS OF RIBOSOMES

During the last few years, the synthesis of ribosomes in HeLa cells has been examined in considerable detail. Our present view of the process is presented in Figure 3 and in the following discussion.

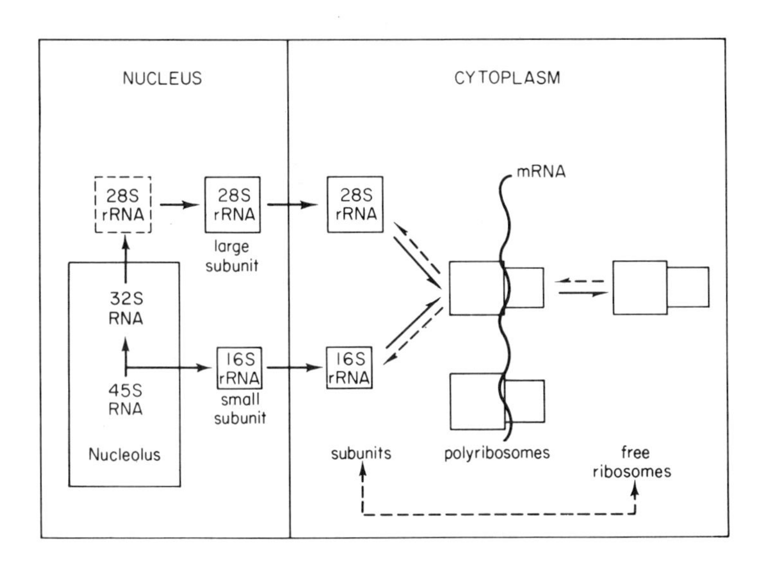

Figure 3. Scheme of the synthesis, maturation, and assembly of ribosomes. (From reference 8).

RNA Precursor

With the experiment shown in Figure 4, Scherrer and Darnell (28) showed the course of incorporation of a radioactive isotope into the RNA of HeLa cells. At early times there is a large amount of heterogeneous material, but a peak appears at 45S. The optical density represents the bulk RNA of the cell. As the incorporation continues, this peak becomes more prominent, and then a second peak appears, in the region of 32S. At length, after more than an hour, radioactive material begins to accumulate in the regions of the optical density peaks, at 28S and 16S. Finally, after

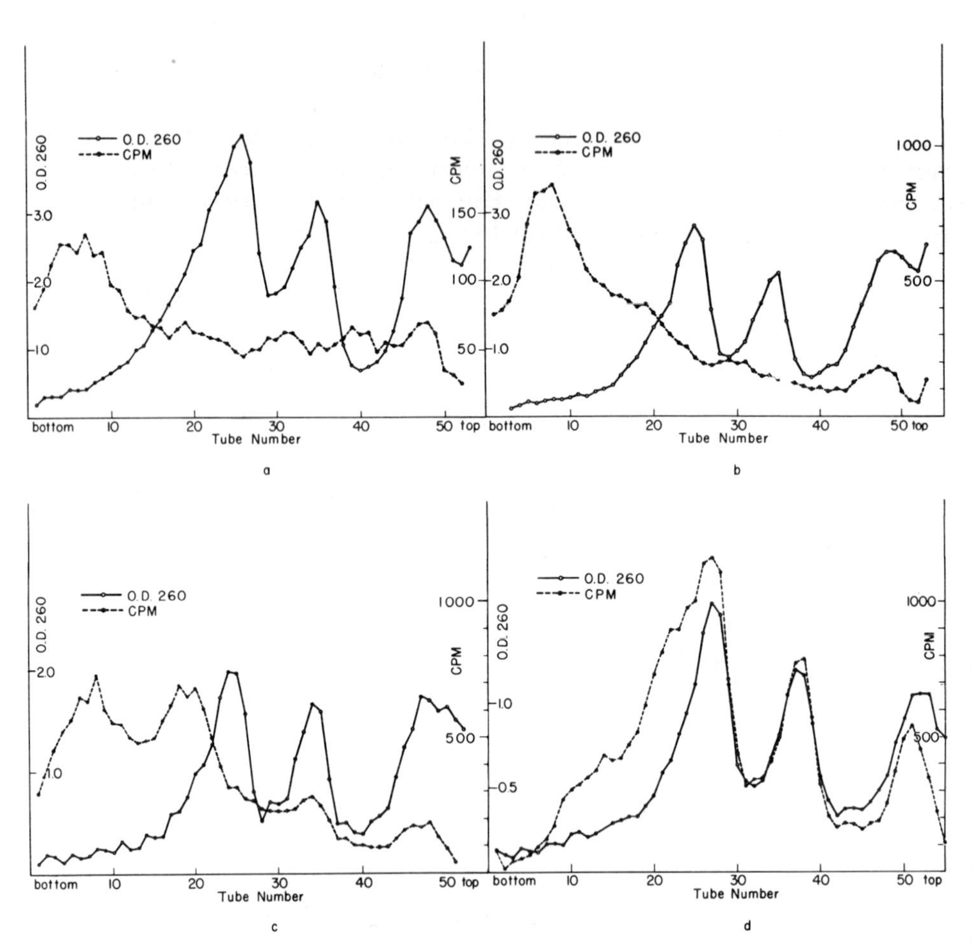
O.D. 260
CPM
3.0
2.0
1.0
150
100
50
1000
500
bottom
10
20
30
40
50
top
Tube Number
a
b
c
d
0.5

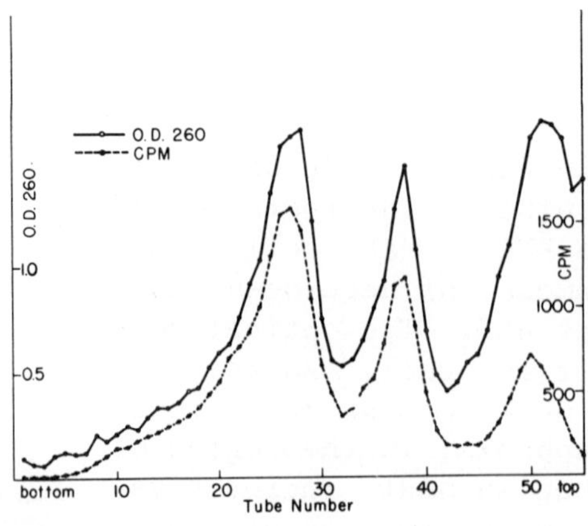
O.D. 260
CPM
1.0
0.5
1500
1000
500
bottom
10
20
30
40
50
top
Tube Number
e

continuous labeling for a generation, the radioactivity follows the optical density profile, and there is little or no sign of 45S and 32S RNA. Furthermore, in Table 3 it can be seen that the base composition of the 45S RNA and 32S RNA resembles closely that of the ribosomal RNA, and is quite different from that of the other species of RNA. Such results immediately suggested a precursor-product relationship, and this has been established by a series of experiments.

This relationship was established directly by the use of actinomycin D (36), which blocks all RNA synthesis (37). Actinomycin was added to cells that had been incorporating ^{14}C uridine for 20 minutes (similar to Figure 3B). It was observed in sucrose gradients that there was a shift of radioactivity from the 45S to the 32S region and, thence, to the 28S and 16S regions (Figure 5). Thus, 28S and 16S RNA are formed _in the absence of RNA synthesis_ if 45S RNA is present. This relationship between 45S RNA and ribosomal RNA has been confirmed in a number of ways: the degree of methylation is similar in 45S, 35S and ribosomal RNA (38); in the presence of low doses of actinomycin, the synthesis of 45S RNA is selectively inhibited, and no new ribosomal RNA is found (19); in anucleolate mutants of _Xenopus laevis_, the genes for ribosomal RNA have been lost (39), and no 45S RNA synthesis can be detected (32). Penman (6) has recently concluded from kinetic analyses that the 16S RNA arises at the same time as the 32S RNA, probably as a result of a scission of 45S RNA:

Figure 4. (Opposite page.) Sucrose gradient analysis of RNA from HeLa cells growing with a 24-hour doubling time. Cells were labeled by exposure to ^{14}C uridine 0.03-0.07 mM, 0.54 μC/μM, according to the following schedule: (a) 10.0 μC, 250 ml cells, for 5 minutes; (b) 5.0 μC. 150 ml cells, for 30 minutes; (c) 2.5 μC, 100 ml cells, for 60 minutes; (d) 1.0 μC, 75 ml cells, for 4 hours; (e) 0.5 μC, 100 ml cells, for 24 hours. + 2.0 μM uridine (total spec. act., 0.17 μC/μM). (Figure from reference 28.)

45S ⟶ 32S and 16S

In view of the fact that the recently discovered 5S RNA is associated with the 28S RNA in the larger ribo-

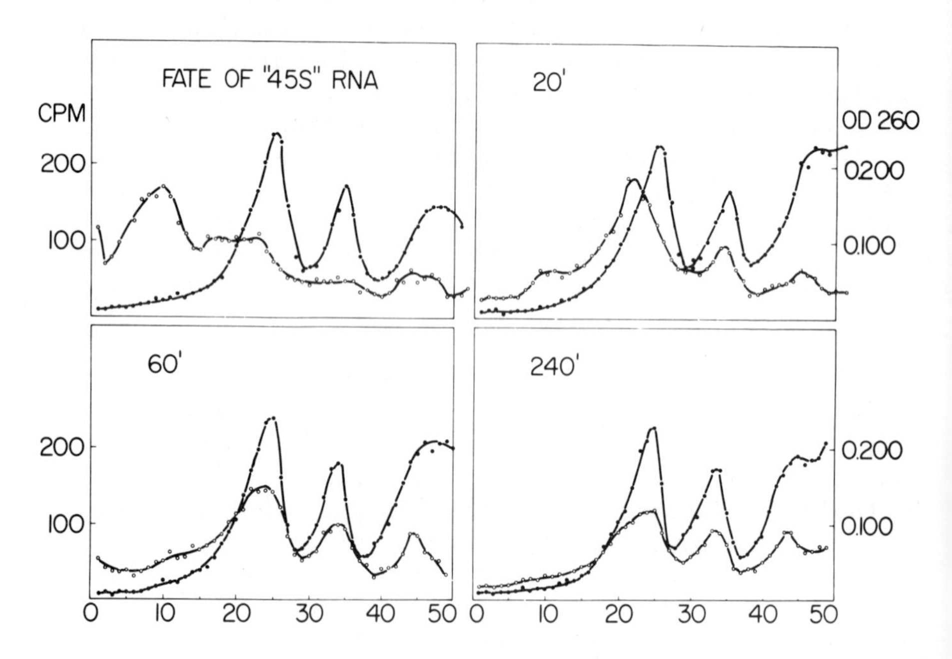

Figure 5. Fate of 45S RNA after actinomycin treatment. Cells were labeled for 30 min with ^{14}C uridine (upper left), at which time actinomycin D was added, and the fate of the RNA observed at subsequent times. (From reference 36.)

somal particle, it is tempting to frame the hypothesis that the second scission takes place as

32S ⟶ 28S and 5S

This possibility is being examined at present. It should be pointed out that the only available measurement of the size of any of these large RNA molecules is the sedimentation constant, from which a molecular weight can be calculated by extrapolation of the data of Hall and Doty (29), which shows that the molecular weight is approximated proportional to the square of the sedimentation coefficient. This extrapolation is very large for the larger molecules. If this calculation is correct, however, the 45S RNA is much larger than the sum of 32S plus 16S, just as 32S is much larger than the sum of 28S plus 5S. Thus, it is not unlikely that some RNA is degraded during these maturation processes.

All the 45S and 32S RNA is associated with the nuclear pellet (nucleolar) fraction prepared according to Penman et al. (9). This finding helps to substantiate a large number of reports which implicate the nucleolus in ribosome formation (19,39,40,41). Preliminary evidence indicates that the nucleolus also contains pools of ribosomal proteins (42).

Ribosomal Subunits

On the other hand, the nuclear supernatant contains small amounts of 28S and 16S RNA (9). Vaughan et al. (8) have carried out extensive kinetic analyses of this fraction and have shown that its 28S and 16S RNA are in the form of complete or nearly complete ribosomal subunits that are in transit from nucleolus to cytoplasm. For example, after a 45 minute label with ^{14}C uridine, the specific activity of the nuclear 50S subunits is more than 20 times greater than that of the cytoplasmic 50S particles.

Finally, ribosomal particles appear in the cytoplasm as the complete 50S and 30S subunits. These become part of mature, functioning polyribosomes, and eventually equilibrate with the pool of single ribosomes.

Perturbations of Ribosome Synthesis

Only recently, with the details of the process of ribosome formation becoming clear, has it been possible to examine perturbations of the process. We simply list a few of the observations, for as yet there is no unified theory to explain the complex processes of synthesis, maturation, and assembly of ribosomal macromolecules.

1. Drugs which inhibit protein synthesis cause an extensive diminution of uridine uptake into both heterogeneous and 45S RNA (44).
2. There are pools of ribosomal proteins and, after protein synthesis has been completely halted by the action of cycloheximide, these pools can be drawn upon for the continued synthesis of ribosomes (45). On the other hand, if puromycin is the inhibitor used, no ribosomes are made (44, 46).
3. After infection by poliovirus, when host cell protein synthesis has been inhibited by 50%, the conversion of newly synthesized 45S RNA to 32S RNA is inhibited; the previously formed 28S rRNA accumulates in nuclear 50S subribosomal particles (47).
4. In developing embryos of *Xenopus laevis*, ribosomal RNA synthesis is totally repressed until the onset of gastrulation (48), while H.S. RNA is synthesized continuously (32).

In summary, the process of synthesis and assembly of the HeLa cell ribosome has many steps, several of which we now understand in outline. Our present efforts are bent toward finding intermediates in the assembly process, i.e., RNA partially covered with specific protein; and toward understanding the transitions between one stage and another, by studying the effects of agents which interrupt or accelerate such transitions.

CONCLUSION

The finding that ribosomal RNA is made as a single, large piece of RNA which is subsequently cleaved into appropriate fragments lends a new dimension to a discussion of RNA metabolism. Potentially, any of the cytoplasmic species of RNA may come from precursor molecules that are many times larger. The search for the origin of tRNA and mRNA must take this possibility into account. Furthermore, there is the intriguing problem of isolating the appropriate nucleases and defining their specificity. It is worth noting that if the 45S RNA is cleaved to 28S, 16S, and 5S rRNA, the cell has a method for automatically ensuring a constant ratio of the ribosomal RNA molecules.

The large number of RNA species has made it impractical to investigate RNA synthesis in general terms. It is not only feasible but necessary to use the whole arsenal of biochemical techniques: sucrose gradient analysis, column chromatography, base ratio analysis, RNA-DNA hybridization, and even genetic analysis in some instances. From such detailed investigations will undoubtedly come new insight into the organization of the cell, into its complex assembly processes and, most important, into the manner in which the cell maintains the essential balance in its production of macromolecules while growing at widely varying rates.

ACKNOWLEDGMENT

The continuous keen insight of J.E. Darnell has made this work possible. Valuable participants at various stages along the way have been Klaus Scherrer, Sheldon Penman, Yechiel Becker, Harriet Latham, Marc Girard, Ruy Soeiro, Chaim Birnboim and Maurice Vaughan.

REFERENCES

1. Moldave, K. Ann. Rev. of Biochem., 34, 419 (1965).
2. Prescott, D. Prog. Nucleic Acid Res., 3, 33 (1964).
3. Zalokar, M. in Control Mechanisms in Cellular Processes, ed. D.M. Bonner, The Ronald Press, N.Y., 87 (1960).
4. Perry, R. J. Biochem. Biophys. Cytol., 11, 1 (1960).
5. Penman, S., Scherrer, K., Becker, Y., and Darnell, J.E. Proc. Nat. Acad. Sci., U.S., 49, 654 (1963).
6. Penman, S. J. Mol. Biol., 17, 117 (1966).
7. Holtzman, E., Smith, I. and Penman, S. J. Mol. Biol., 17, 131 (1966).
8. Vaughan, M., Warner, J. and Darnell, J.E. J. Mol. Biol., (in press).
9. Penman, S., Smith, I. and Holtzman, E. Science,

(in press).
10. Brenner, S., Jacob, F. and Meselson, M. Nature, 190, 576 (1961).
11. Nirenberg, M. and Matthaei, J. Proc. Nat. Acad. Sci., U.S., 47, 1588 (1961).
12. Hadjiolov, A.A. Biochi. Biophys. Acta, 119, 447 (1966).
13. Loeb, J.N., Howell, R.R. and Tomkins, G.M. Science, 149, 1093 (1965).
14. Jacob, F. and Monod, J. J. Mol. Biol., 3, 318 (1961).
15. Hall, B. and Spiegelman, S. Proc. Nat. Acad. Sci., U.S., 47, 137 (1961).
16. Latham, H. and Darnell, J.E. J. Mol. Biol., 14, 1 (1965).
17. Staehelin, T., Wettstein, F.O. and Noll, H. Science, 140, 180 (1963).
18. Revel, M. and Hiatt, H. Proc. Nat. Acad. Sci., U.S., 51, 810 (1964).
19. Perry, R.P. Nat. Cancer Inst. Monograph, 14, 73 (1964).
20. Holley, R.W., Apgar, J., Everett, G.A., Madison, J.T., Marquisee, M., Merrill, S.H., Penswick, J.R., and Zamir, A. Science, 147, 1462 (1965).
21. Holt, C.E., Joel, P.B. and Herbert, E. J. Biol. Chem., 241, 1819 (1966).
22. Landin, R. and Moulé, Y. Biochim. Biophys. Acta, (in press).
23. Rosset, R., Monier, R. and Julien, J. Bull. Soc. Chim. Biol., 46, 87 (1964).
24. Galibert, F., Larsen, C.J., Lelong, J.C. and Boiron, M. Nature, 207, 1039 (1965).
25. Zehavi-Willner, T. and Comb, D.G., J. Mol. Biol., 16, 250 (1966).
26. Warner, J. and Rich, A. Proc. Nat. Acad. Sci., U.S., 51, 1134 (1964).
27. Arlinghaus, R., Shaeffer, J. and Schweet, R. Nat. Acad. Sci., U.S., 51, 1291 (1964).
28. Scherrer, K. and Darnell, J.E. Biochem. Biophys. Res. Comm., 7, 486 (1962).
29. Hall, B. and Doty, P. in Microsomal Particles and Protein Synthesis, ed. R.B. Roberts, Wash. Acad.

Sci., Wash. D.C.

30. Warner, J., Soeiro, R., Birnboim, H. and Darnell, J. J. Mol. Biol., 19, (1966)(in press).
31. Scherrer, K. and Marcaud, L. Bull. Soc. Chim. Biol. 47, 1697 (1965). Attardi, G., Parnas, H., Hwang, M. and Attardi B. J. Mol. Biol., (in press).
32. Brown, D.D. and Gurdon, J.B. J. Mol. Biol. (in press).
33. Yoshikawa-Fukada, M. Biochim. Biophys. Acta, 123, 91 (1966).
34. Soeiro, R., Birnboim, H. and Darnell, J.E. J. Mol. Biol., 19, (1966) (in press).
35. Vaughan, M.H., Soeiro, R., Warner, J. and Darnell, J.E. (in preparation).
36. Scherrer, K., Latham, H. and Darnell, J.E. Proc. Nat. Acad. Sci., U.S., 49, 240 (1963).
37. Reich, E., Franklin, R., Shatkin, J. and Tatum, E. Proc. Nat. Acad. Sci., U.S., 48, 1238 (1962).
38. Greenberg, H. and Penman, S. (in press).
39. Wallace, H. and Birnstiel, M.I. Biochim. Biophys. Acta, 114, 296 (1966).
40. Ritossa, F.M. and Spiegelman, S. Proc. Nat. Acad. Sci., U.S., 53, 737 (1965).
41. McConkey, E. and Hopkins, J. Proc. Nat. Acad. Sci., U.S., 51, 1197 (1964).
42. Warner, J.R. (unpublished observation).
43. Girard, M., Latham, H., Penman, S. and Darnell, J.E. J. Mol. Biol., 11, 187 (1965).
44. Soeiro, R., Vaughan, M. and Darnell, J.E. (in preparation).
45. Warner, J., Girard, M., Latham, H. and Darnell, J.E. J. Mol. Biol., 19, (1966) (in press).
46. Latham, H. and Darnell, J.E. J. Mol. Biol., 14, 13 (1965).
47. Darnell, J.E., Girard, M., Baltimore, D., Summers, D.F. and Maizel, J.V. in Molecular Biology of Viruses, Academic Press, (in press).
48. Brown, D.D. and Littna, E. J. Mol. Biol., 8, 669 (1964).

*Early Control of Gene Expression**

Martin Nemer and Anthony A. Infante

Institute for Cancer Research
Philadelphia

INTRODUCTION

The theme of this paper is that during early embryonic development there is a coordinated use of both preexisting and newly synthesized agents of genetic expression. We have organized this topic into four sections:

1. examination of the nature of the problem of early genetic expression;
2. changes in genic activity as evident in the changes in RNA synthesis during development;
3. coordination of consumption and biosynthesis of ribosomes;

*This investigation was supported by U.S.P.H.S. Research Grant CA-05936 from the National Cancer Institute.

4. coordination in the use of preexisting and newly synthesized messenger RNA.

The discussion is based only on recent research on the sea urchin embryo.

PROBLEM OF EARLY GENETIC EXPRESSION IN THE SEA URCHIN EMBRYO

In the sea urchin, the protein synthetic machinery is switched on at the ribosomal level after activation of the egg, either through fertilization or parthenogenesis (Hultin, 1961). Polyribosomes become detectable (Monroy and Tyler, 1963; Stafford, Sofer, and Inverson, 1964), and the rate of protein synthesis rises sharply during the first few hours. The rate of this synthesis appears to be limited only by m-RNA activity, because ribosomes from unfertilized eggs respond competently to synthetic messenger polyribonucleotides, such as polyuridylic acid (Nemer, 1962; Wilt and Hultin, 1962; Tyler, 1962), and eggs appear to have adequate concentrations of t-RNA and activating enzymes (Nemer and Bard, 1963). This early increase in template RNA activity is not attributable primarily to the synthesis of new RNA, but to an activation of m-RNA stored in the egg. The necessity for an activation of egg m-RNA was deduced from observations that eggs treated with actinomycin (Gross and Cousineau, 1963; Gross, Malkin, and Moyer, 1964) or parthenogenetically activated after enucleation (Denny and Tyler, 1964; Baltus, et al., 1965) synthesized protein at the same rate as normally fertilized eggs. Template RNA in the mature egg should be very stable, a considerable period probably having elapsed from the time of its synthesis. In the mature shed egg, no RNA synthesis is detectable. The unfertilized egg is either dormant or so impermeable to exogenous RNA precursors that only background, bacterial incorporation may be detected (Glisin and Glisin, 1964). The presence of m-RNA in the egg has been indicated by the demonstration of a d-RNA (DNA-like) component (Gross, Malkin, and Hubbard, 1965) and of template activity (Maggio, et al.,

1964), attributable to possibly 4 to 5% of the egg RNA (Slater and Spiegelman, 1966).

The egg m-RNA may be protected by a mask, very likely of protein. A direct activation of egg ribosomes through digestion with trypsin has been achieved (Monroy, Maggio and Rinaldi, 1965). The postulated protein mask may also be a repressor of protein synthesis, but we do not know yet whether the tryptic activation focuses primarily on m-RNA or ribosomal activity.

Embryonic development seems to get under way quite adequately without the intervention of nuclear activity. Even the most readily detectable RNA incorporation in the zygote is cytoplasmic - that of end addition to transfer RNA (Glisin and Glisin, 1964; Gross, Kraemer, and Malkin, 1965). This end addition may be prominent because of the relatively great cytoplasmic mass juxtaposed to a nucleus of low activity, rather than because of the absence of genic activation. If there were no de novo RNA synthesis during early development, as previous studies once indicated, expressed genetic information in the early stages would be that translated on polysomes solely directed by egg m-RNA. Indeed, the bulk of information translated at this time appears to be attributable to the stored egg m-RNA. This conclusion was drawn from a comparison of the newly synthesized proteins of actinomycin-treated and normal embryos (Spiegel, Ozaki, and Tyler, 1965). The embryos synthesized largely the same population of proteins in the presence and absence of RNA synthesis. However, slight differences did suggest the possibility that some new information was being used (Terman and Gross, 1965).

De novo synthesis of RNA has been detected in the early cleavage stages. This RNA was shown to be metabolically labile (Wilt, 1964; Nemer, 1963), heterogeneously sedimenting, and d-RNA, as early as the 4-cell stage (Nemer and Infante, 1965). This RNA synthesis and its implied genic activation occurs even before the first cleavage (Infante and Nemer, in preparation). Our inquiry concerning early genetic expression in the sea urchin embryo has, then, led to a paradox, for we cannot be sure to what use this early RNA synthesis may be put. Furthermore, the new m-RNA is detectable in the cytoplasm. This cytoplasmic m-RNA is associated with two classes of structure: the one sediments with polysomes (Wilt, 1964; Spirin and Nemer, 1965); the other sediments more slowly than ribosomes (Spirin and Nemer, 1965; Nemer and Infante, 1965). The latter structures, called informosomes by Spirin, were originally observed in fish embryos (Belitsina, et al., 1964; Spirin, Belitsina, and Ajtkhozhin, 1964). Although their function is not yet known, these complexes between m-RNA and protein account for all the cytoplasmic m-RNA not associated with polysomes (Infante and Nemer, in preparation).

The use of stored egg m-RNA in the activation of protein synthesis after fertilization has obvious advantages, if the amount of newly synthesized m-RNA is not large enough to get protein synthesis off to its fast start. Similarly, new ribosomes are not synthesized to any large extent through much of early development (Nemer, 1963); instead, egg ribosomes are used extensively. In both cases, development does eventually become dependent upon newly synthesized material. A rough estimate of the functional half-life of egg m-RNA is ca. 20 hr (Gross, Malkin, and Hubbard, 1965). Egg ribosome longevity has not been studied previously. Our results indicate that they are consumed in a manner correlated with the synthesis of new ribosomes, observed to gain momentum between the mesenchyme blastula and gastrula stages (Nemer and Infante, in preparation). An important problem for the embryo, then, is the integration of the use of stored material with the synthesis of new material. This problem, however, is interwoven with that of development, involving the regulation of the use of genetic information toward the creation of diversity in the cellular progeny. The integration of biosynthesis and consumption represents a response to a special metabolic situation; the process of development involves a concerted programming of events. Each process is resolved especially through the synthesis of RNA and protein.

The nature of RNA synthesis and its changes in the course of embryonic development can be taken as a signature of nuclear function. The apportionment of gene expression for the synthesis of the different RNA classes has been shown to change emphatically toward the synthesis of ribosomal RNA after the mesenchyme blastula stage (Nemer, 1963). But, importantly, the types of new messenger RNA may be changing extensively. Recent papers concerning DNA-hybridizable RNA from different embryonic stages show significant developmental changes in the d-RNA population, termed messenger by the authors (Whiteley, McCarthy, and Whiteley, 1966; Glisin, Glisin, and Doty, 1966). The notation "d-RNA" refers operationally to that RNA label, detectably hybridized with DNA, when the specific activities of the ribosomal and transfer RNA have been rendered diminishingly small. In other words, it is non-4S, nonribosomal RNA, because its base composition is different from these and tends to reflect that of DNA. However, only a portion of the total cellular output of d-RNA may be messenger (Attardi, et al., 1966; Warner, et al., 1966).

A DEVELOPMENTAL TRANSITION IN GENOMIC OUTPUT

RNA Classes

RNA synthesis in the developing embryo occurs in varied proportions among four general classes:

1. m-RNA, heterogeneously sedimenting with a mean sedimentation constant of 24S and characterized as d-RNA, because of its high proportion of hybridization with DNA;
2. nuclear RNA (N-RNA), high molecular weight d-RNA, displaying modes of sedimentation at 70S and 90S;
3. ribosomal RNA (r-RNA) precursor, 45S, giving rise to 28S and 18S r-RNA (Perry, 1962; Scherrer, Latham, and Darnell, 1963);
4. transfer RNA (t-RNA), 4S, but in sedimentation profile cannot be distinguished from, and may include, "5S RNA" (Rosset, Monier, and Julien, 1964; Comb and Katz, 1964).

The pulse-labeled RNA from various embryonic stages was characterized by sedimentation analysis and hybridization with DNA to determine the extent of synthesis of each general class.

Developmental Shifts

In the zygote, incorporation of labeled precursors in RNA is largely end addition to transfer RNA (Glisin and Glišin, 1964; Gross, Kraemer, and Malkin, 1965). However, pulse-labeled RNA of the zygote (Figure 1)

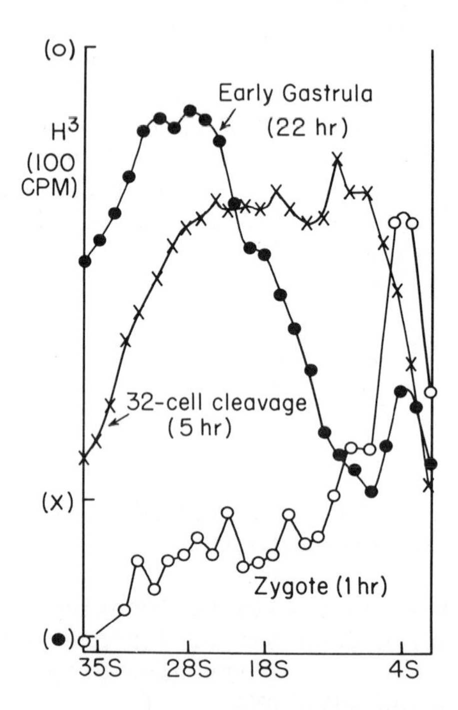

Figure 1. Sedimentation analysis of pulse-labeled RNA. Embryos of L. pictus of the indicated stages were incubated for 5 to 15 min with ^{3}H uridine. The extracted RNA (Scherrer and Darnell, 1962) was centrifuged at 39,000 rpm through sucrose gradients (Nemer, 1963) for 3.5 hr. Sedimentation constants were estimated by the method of Martin and Ames (1961).

contains considerably more of the heterogeneously sedimenting components than 4S RNA. This heterogeneous RNA label reflects de novo synthesis and thus an early activation of gene function. During the course of development through cleavage, the 4S incorporation becomes less prominent and the heterogeneous pulse-labeled RNA becomes more prominent. The distribution in the sucrose gradient of this heterogeneous RNA of late cleavage is similar to that of the zygote. In the early gastrula of Lytechinus pictus, the mean sedimentation constant of the pulse-labeled RNA shifted to

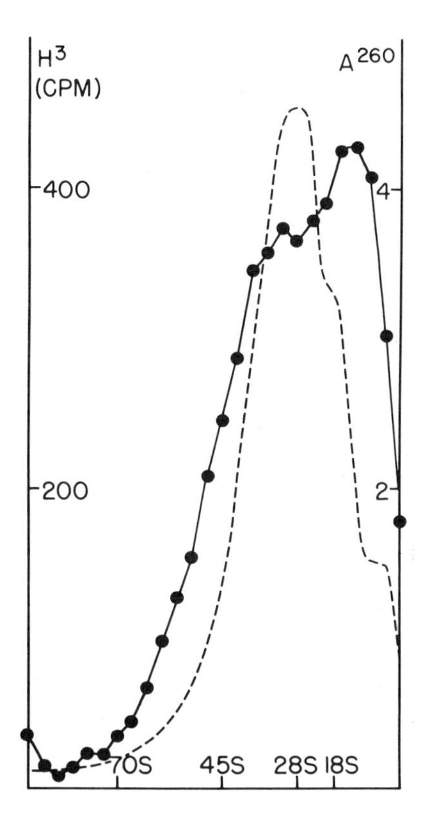

Figure 2. Sedimentation analysis of pulse-labeled RNA of 5-hr cleaving embryos. Same as Fig. 1, except centrifugation was for 2 hr. Closed circles represent ^{3}H uridine incorporation in RNA. Dashed line represents absorbance at 260 mμ (A^{260}).

a very high value, so that a considerable portion of the label was not represented in Figure 1. The change resulted from the appearance of a substantial amount of 45S RNA, ribosomal RNA precursor.

A broader coverage of the spectrum of RNA classes synthesized may be accomplished by using much shorter centrifugations (Figures 2 and 3). Pulse-labeled RNA

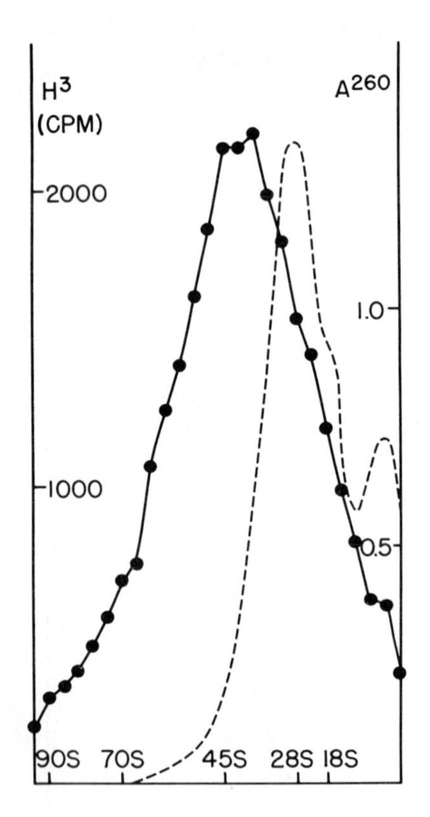

Figure 3. Sedimentation analysis of pulse-labeled RNA of 31-hr gastrula. Same as Fig. 2.

of the 5-hr cleaving embryo was centrifuged in a sucrose gradient at 39,000 rpm for 2 hr (Figure 2). The most prominent contribution to the sedimentation pattern was in the range 10S to 35S, with some material in the 45S region and very little in the 70S and 90S regions. On the other hand, when the same experiment was performed on the 31-hr gastrula (Figure 3), the 45S RNA predominated and the 70S and 90S had proportionately much more RNA label than earlier. If pulse-chase experiments had been done, very little RNA label recognizable as ribosomal would have accumulated during the chase in the early embryo, but a substantial amount would have been found in the late embryo, as in the

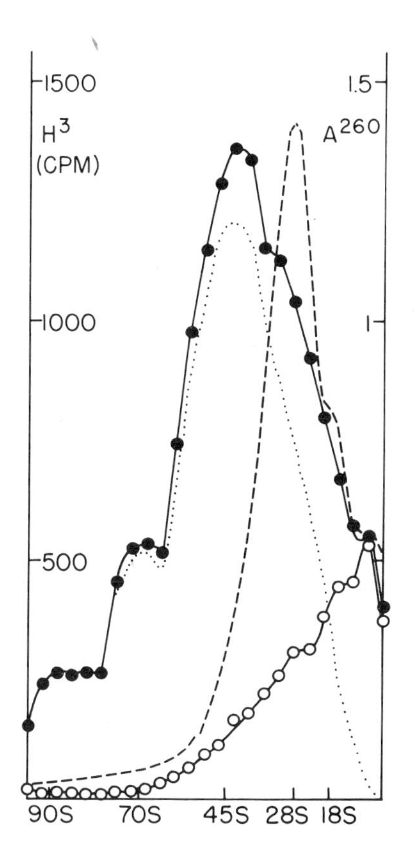

Figure 4. Sedimentation analysis of differentially extracted, pulse-labeled RNA of 48-hr plutei. Same as Fig. 2, except open circles represent uridine incorporation in RNA, extracted with 20°C phenol. The dotted line is the difference between the two curves for RNA incorporation, and thus represents the nuclear pulse-labeled RNA.

purple sea urchin (Nemer, 1963).

A similar examination was made with pulse-labeled RNA of the 48-hr pluteus of _L. pictus_ (Figure 4). At this late developmental stage, the 70S and 90S RNA label showed up as distinct sedimentation modes. Besides the 60°C sodium dodecyl sulphate (SDS)-phenol method of extraction (Scherrer and Darnell, 1962) used to obtain the total pulse-labeled RNA, a simple 20°C phenol extraction was employed on a portion of the embryos. This latter extraction method yielded the cytoplasmic RNA, but left behind the RNA label of the gel interphase, which was enriched with nuclei (Sibatani, et al., 1962; Nemer and Infante, unpublished). Thus, even after only a 5-min pulse, a substantial amount of the two ribosomal RNA components were seen to be labeled together with 4S RNA label in the cytoplasm. The curve for the 20°C phenol extraction has been subtracted from the curve representing total RNA label to give the nuclear pulse-labeled RNA pattern. Here we see again the 70S and 90S are nuclear and comprise a high percent of the pulse-labeled RNA; 45S dominates the pattern. A shoulder on the light side of the 45S RNA peak extends to about 10S. We shall treat these components quantitatively later.

Hybridization of Pulse-Labeled RNA with DNA

The non-4S pulse-labeled RNA from various embryonic stages was subjected to hybrid formation with DNA in the presence of an excess of unlabeled ribosomal RNA (Nygaard and Hall, 1963; McConkey and Hopkins, 1964). The very high percent of hybridization, 40% in the 2-hr cleaving embryo, dropped to 35% in the blastula, 26% in the gastrula, and 20% in the pluteus. From the efficiency of 44% of this method in this system, we calculated the relative amounts of d-RNA and non-d-RNA. We assumed that the non-d-RNA was entirely ribosomal, and thus plotted the ratios of d-RNA to r-RNA as a function of development (Figure 5). These values are indicative of the relative output of the two RNA classes.

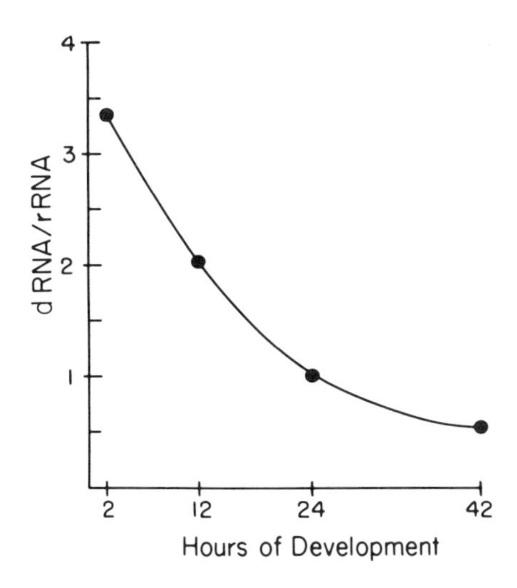

Figure 5. Developmental change in the proportion of d-RNA/r-RNA detected in non-4S, pulse-labeled RNA. Hybridizations (Nygaard and Hall, 1963) were performed in the presence of excess unlabeled r-RNA with sperm DNA (Nemer and Infante, 1965). Efficiency hybridization of previously hybridized RNA label (purified d-RNA) was 44 ± 8%. Ratios of d-RNA to non-d-RNA were calculated from the percent hybridization and this efficiency.

Differential Genomic Output

By plotting the Gaussian distribution of the components of the previous sedimentation diagrams, we can estimate the relative contributions of the different RNA classes to the nuclear pulse-labeled pattern (Figure 6). The proportions of d-RNA and non-d-RNA classes estimated graphically were similar to those obtained independently and directly by hybridization. The mean sedimentation constant of approximately 24S displayed by the so-called "m-RNA" class agrees with the mean value observed with polysomal d-RNA (Nemer and Infante, 1965) and with cytoplasmic nonribosomal, non-4S RNA (Infante and Nemer, in preparation). This

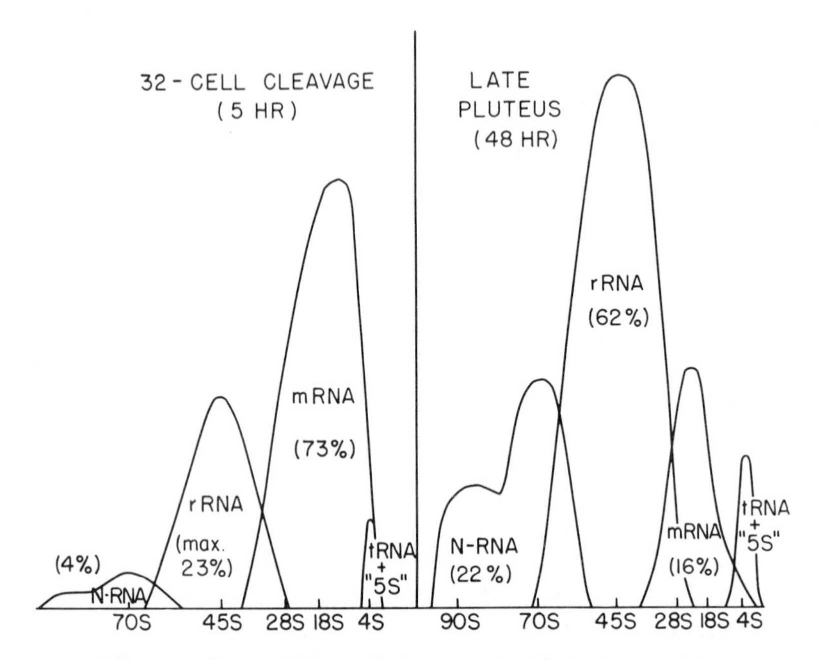

Figure 6. Differential genomic expression in early and late embryos. The quantities and distributions of the RNA classes were graphically estimated from Figures 2 and 4, by the fitting of Gaussian curves. Percentages do not include the 4S material.

d-RNA class is distinguished from the N-RNA class by the very high S values of the latter (Attardi, et al., 1966; Warner, et al., 1966). These diagrams should serve to point up the great difference in the apportionment of the embryonic genome for the synthesis of these RNA classes. In the cleaving embryo, as much as 73% of the output may be m-RNA, but this amount drops to only 16% in the late pluteus. Inversely, the 45S RNA precursor, which accounted for less than 23% of the early pulse-labeled RNA, contributes 62% in the late embryo.

Perhaps the most interesting change, because it is enigmatic, occurs in the relative output of N-RNA. In the cleaving embryo, almost 20 times more m-RNA label was observed than N-RNA label, but in the pluteus, the

N-RNA component was actually greater than the m-RNA component. If the N-RNA were a precursor to m-RNA, as the 45S RNA is to the 28S and 18S RNA, we might expect a fairly constant ratio, the one thus depending on the other. But their relative outputs seem to be under widely different control. Therefore, these observations might be added to the observed kinetics of formation and decay in nondeveloping systems (Attardi, et al., 1966) as evidence that the N-RNA class is probably not a precursor to m-RNA. On the other hand, if the N-RNA is a precursor of m-RNA, the relative conversion of one to the other is considerable during development.

The N-RNA, consisting of 70S and 90S classes with an average molecular weight of, perhaps, 20 million (Attardi, et al., 1966), is distinct and apparently unrelated to the other RNA classes. It appears to be strictly nuclear, and, perhaps, changes its relative degree of participation in nuclear activity during the course of embryonic development. Its synthesis or turnover gains prominence as development proceeds, indicating that it may be a component in the differentiation of the nucleus and in cellular differentiation.

CONSUMPTION AND BIOSYNTHESIS OF RIBOSOMES

The problem of the control of early genetic expression involves an integration of the use of stored material with the biosynthesis of new material. In this context, we might usefully examine the relationship between the developmental fate of egg ribosomes and the synthesis of new ribosomes. Egg ribosomes may be labeled when the egg is in the ovary (Gross, Malkin, and Hubbard, 1965), but the use of such prelabeled eggs to study the decay and half-life of egg ribosomes becomes complicated by both labeled precursor pools and the recycling of labeled nucleotides, in this closed system, from degraded old ribosomal RNA into new ribosomes. Therefore, another device was needed.

A unique marker for egg ribosomes turned up unexpectedly when we found (Nemer, 1963) that the ribosomal RNA of the eggs of the purple sea urchin frequently yielded a 13S component upon extraction at elevated temperatures, the method of Scherrer and Darnell (1962), but usually yielded only the normal 28S and 18S ribosomal RNA upon extraction at 20°C. This 13S RNA product diminished in yield as development proceeded (Figure 7). The riddle seemed to be solved when we

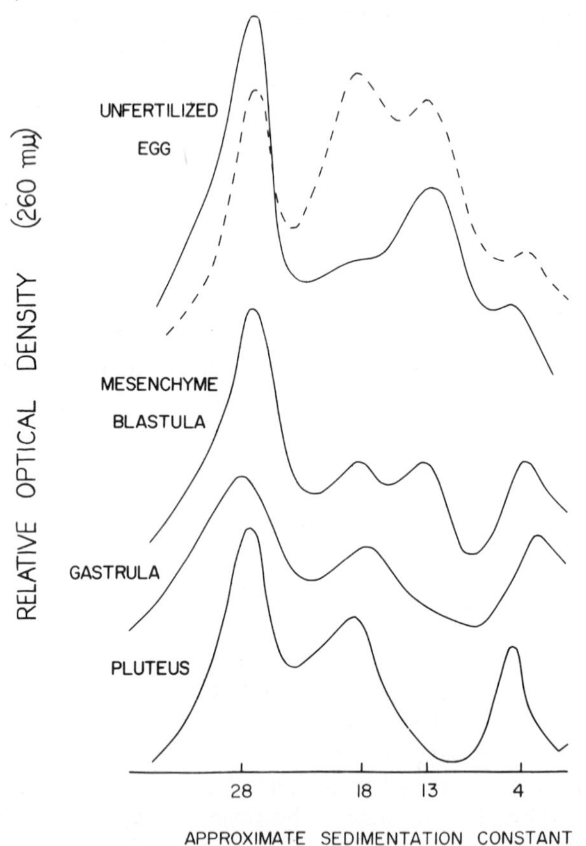

Figure 7. Sedimentation patterns of the bulk RNA of the purple sea urchin eggs and embryos. Extractions were the same as for Figure 1. Centrifugations were 12 hr in the large swinging-bucket rotor at 25,000 rpm. The curves for the unfertilized egg represent the variations observed among batches.

noted that the egg 18S ribosomal RNA, extracted with cold phenol from the purple sea urchin (and only from this species), was transformed into an approximately 13S component when heated to 60°C (Nemer and Infante, in preparation). It appeared, then, that in some batches of eggs of this species, there may have occurred a subtle nuclease attack upon the 18S ribosomal RNA during ovarian storage, resulting in discrete breaks in the chain, which had no effect on the RNA structure. The structure apparently held together through cold extraction, but was melted out at higher temperatures.

Therefore, we plotted the percent of 13S ribosomal RNA for each embryonic stage (Figure 8). Values at

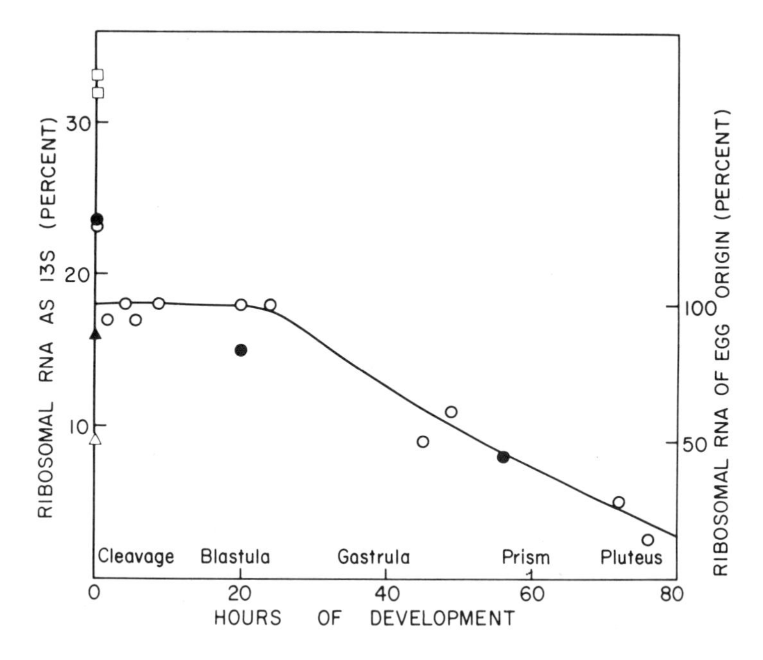

Figure 8. Developmental change in the proportion of the 13S component in ribosomal RNA of the purple sea urchin. Each kind of symbol refers to a different batch of eggs.

zero time show the scatter of observed amounts in various batches of unfertilized eggs. Frequently, there was essentially no 13S RNA; however, batches of eggs containing this ribosomal lesion could be followed through development, with the result that the percent held constant until the mesenchyme blastula stage. Thereafter the percent diminished gradually, indicating a change in the population of ribosomes. An interpretive ordinate has been constructed on the right in Figure 8, to show the percent of ribosomal RNA of egg origin represented in the population of ribosomes.

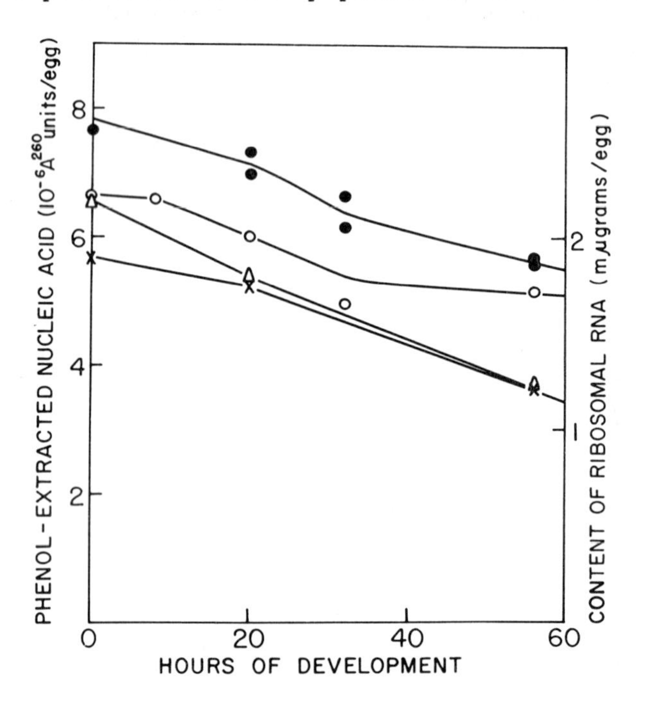

Figure 9. RNA content of the eggs and embryos of the purple sea urchin. Closed circles represent 60°C SDS-phenol extracted nucleic acid (10^{-6} A^{260}unit/egg), and open circles, 20°C phenol extracted nucleic acid. Ribosomal RNA content was the product of the fraction of total phenol-extracted nucleic acid that was ribosomal according to sedimentation diagrams, and the values shown for the different extractions: triangles, 60°C SDS-phenol; crosses, 20°C phenol.

In order to evaluate quantitatively this apparent decay in the proportion of surviving egg ribosomes, we should know how the total content of ribosomes changes in development in this species. The total amount of material absorbing at 260 mμ was noted at each embryonic stage, according to two methods of extraction (20°C

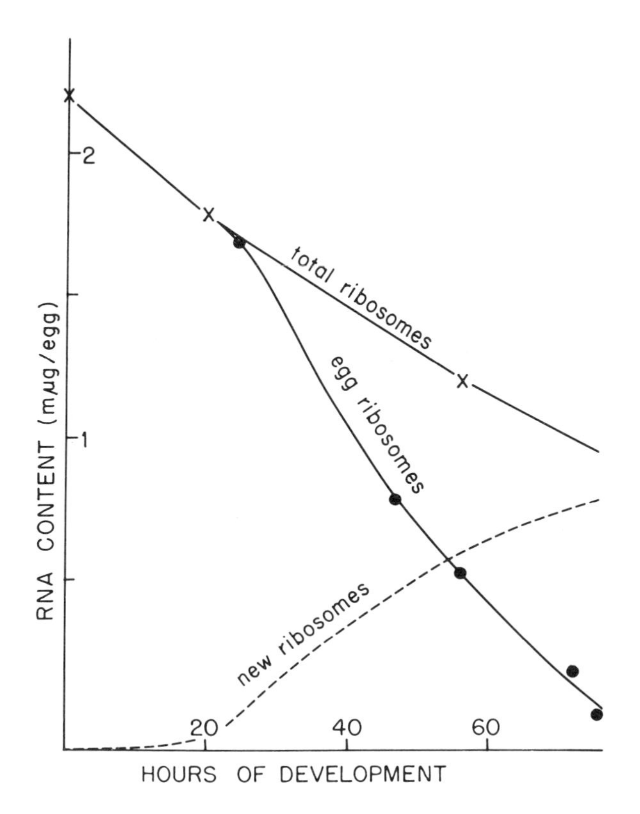

Figure 10. Consumption of egg ribosomes and the synthesis of new ribosomes during development. Crosses represent the total ribosomal RNA content (Figure 9). Closed circles represent the content of egg ribosomal RNA, obtained as the product of the total ribosomal RNA and the proportion of surviving ribosomal RNA of egg origin (Figure 8, right-hand ordinate). The difference between these curves is the curve of new ribosomal synthesis (dashed line).

phenol and 60°C SDS-phenol). From the sedimentation diagrams at each stage, the ribosomal proportion of this material was used to calculate the total ribosomal RNA content per embryo (Figure 9). The original content of 2.2 mμg per egg diminished gradually during development to 1.2 mμg per gastrula at 56 hr.

Now we may replot the change in total ribosomal content (Figure 10) with an estimation of the absolute content of egg ribosomes, derived as the product of the total ribosomal content and the proportion of these that are represented by surviving egg ribosomes. Hence, the content of ribosomes, newly synthesized during development, is the difference between the other two curves. In the sea urchin, then, there is from the beginning a utilization of stored ribosomes, not only functionally in protein synthesis but also as a biosynthetic reservoir. The original decline in content becomes more precipitous after the mesenchyme blastula stage, or approximately when the synthesis of new ribosomes gains momentum (Nemer, 1963). A closer and more accurate analysis of these changes, especially between the mesenchyme blastula and gastrula stages, ought to give us a good idea of the absolute rates of ribosomal RNA synthesis per emrbyo. From fertilization to the mesenchyme blastula stage, egg ribosomes were consumed with a half-life of about 55 hr, but afterwards, the consumption curve indicated a half-life of less than 20 hr.

COORDINATED EXPRESSION OF OLD AND NEW MESSENGER RNA

The Reign and Decline of Egg Messenger RNA

The functional half-life of egg m-RNA was estimated from the decay of the rate of protein synthesis in the presence of actinomycin to be 20 hr (Gross, Malkin, and Hubbard, 1965), but the data lent itself to any estimate from 10 to 20 hr. A value of 12 to 15 hr was obtained for the metabolic half-life of egg d-RNA in the normal embryo (Nemer and Infante, unpublished). The agreement of these values suggests that the functional decay reflects a metabolic decay.

The content of template RNA of the egg was found to be 4 to 5% of the total RNA in *Arbacia punctulata* (Slater and Spiegelman, 1966). If this result were applied to *Strongylocentrotus purpuratus*, its egg would contain approximately 130 picograms of m-RNA. After the 6-hr stage, the rate of protein synthesis began to decline in the presence of actinomycin (Gross, Malkin, and Hubbard, 1965). The activity of egg m-RNA became rate-limiting, and its activity at 6 hr of development represented the minimal m-RNA requirement for sustaining protein synthesis at its quantitatively normal level. Therefore, the egg's reservoir of 130 picograms of m-RNA may have dropped to 90 picograms in the first 6 hr, according to its estimated half-life. The egg may have stored about 1.5 times its required amount of messenger. It is this abundant supply of m-RNA that may account for the rapid formation of polysomes after fertilization.

The Genesis of Polyribosomes

The proportion of total ribosomes present in polysomal structures increases after fertilization and through development (Monroy and Tyler, 1963). We have examined and quantitated this change through a series of sedimentation analyses of the postmitochondrial supernatant fluid, prepared from different embryonic stages (Figure 11). In the unfertilized egg, no more than 6% of the ribosomes are detectable as polysomes. During the period of 3 hr following fertilization, the content of polysomes rises sharply to include approximately 50% of the cytoplasmic ribosomal population; this level remains constant through development to the gastrula stage.

Differential Polysomal Activity

An examination of polysomes extracted from the embryo after short incubations with ^{3}H uridine (30 to 60 min) and 2-min pulse incubations with ^{14}C leucine, revealed a variety of differential activities (Figure 12). The polysomes themselves were distributed in two

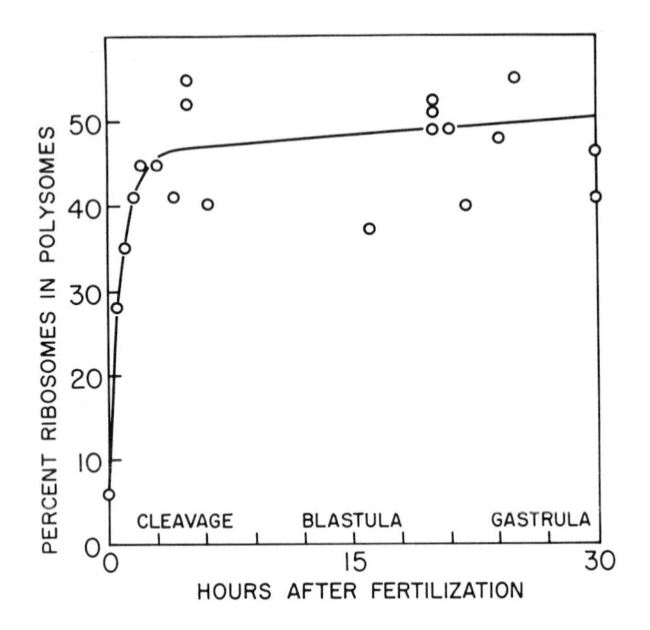

Figure 11. Polysomal content during development. The proportion of the total ribosomes detectable in polysomes was obtained from 260 sedimentation patterns of post-mitochondrial supernatant ("S15") fluids prepared at various stages of the purple sea urchin embryo.

sedimentation modes of approximately 200S and 300S, respectively. Most of the nascent protein (^{14}C leucine) was associated with the 300S structures. These polysomes had twice the specific activity (^{14}C polypeptide/A^{260} unit) of the 200S polysomes, also found to be true in vitro. Furthermore, this relationship held at all embryonic stages examined.

On the other hand, RNA label was found predominantly in the 200S polysomes of the cleaving embryo. In the gastrula, substantial RNA label was associated with both polysomal classes. The same relationship held for each of two species studied, L. pictus in these diagrams, and S. purpuratus, of which the 6 hr cleavage stage is shown in Figure 13. Electron micrographs revealed an average of 7 ribosomes per polysome in the 200S mode and 23 ribosomes per polysome in the 300S mode

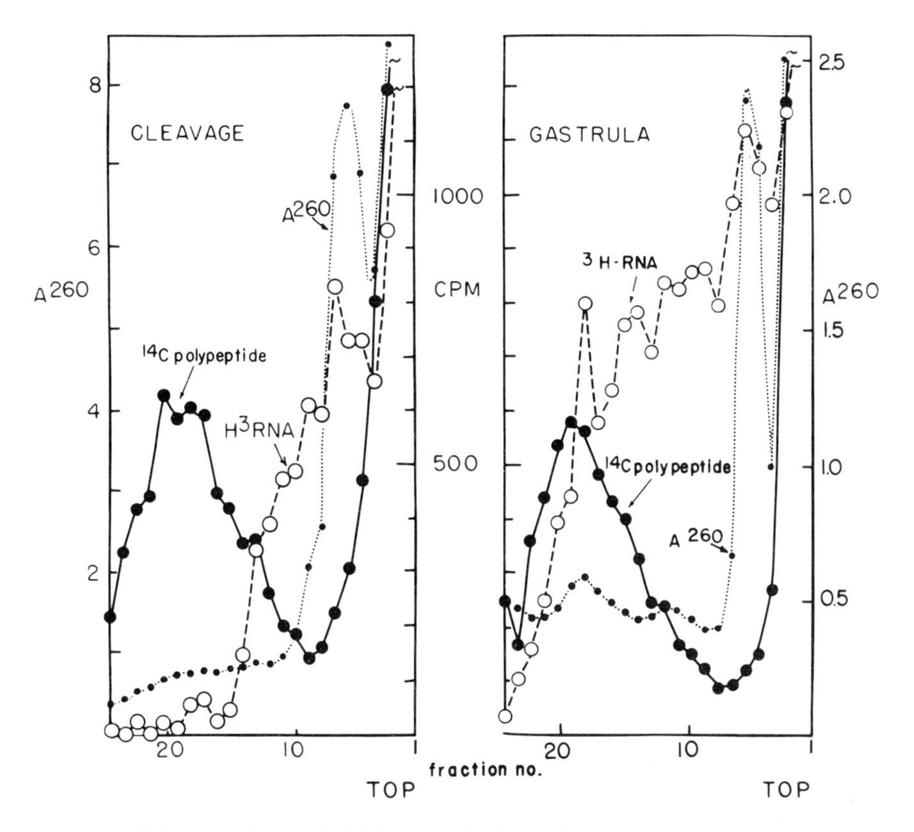

Figure 12. Differential polysomal activities in development. Two-hour cleaving embryos or 24-hr gastrulae of L. pictus were incubated with ^{3}H uridine for 30 min, and then with ^{14}C leucine for 2 min. The prepared "S15" fluids were centrifuged in 15 to 30% sucrose gradients at 25,000 rpm for 140 min.

An Early Transition in the Use of New Messenger RNA

Incorporation of RNA label in each polysomal class was followed with separate and similar incubations in ^{3}H uridine throughout early cleavage. Although proportionately much less RNA label was found in the 300S polysomes (and this tended to be a negligible amount in the earliest period after fertilization), the pro-

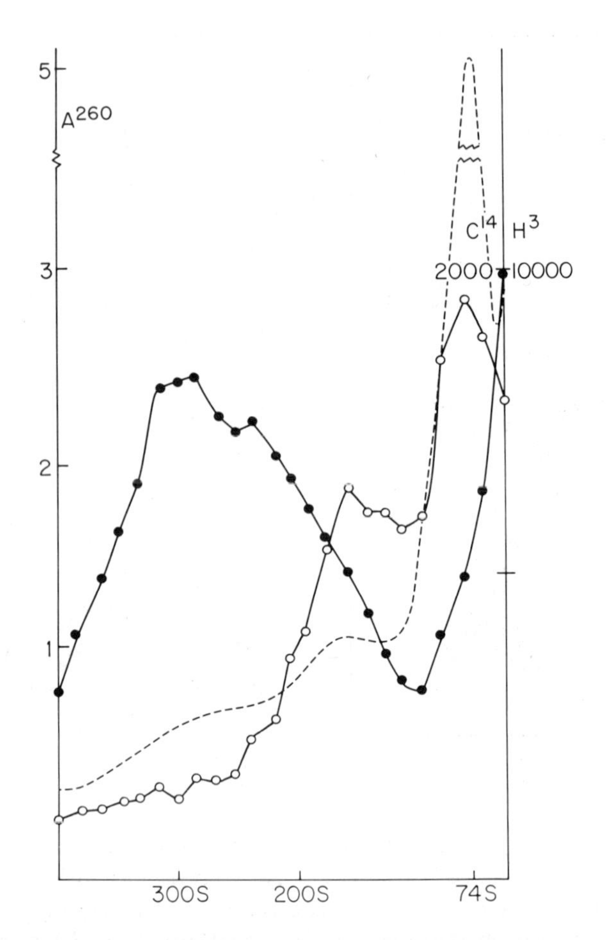

Figure 13. Differential polysomal activities of the 6-hr cleaving embryo. Same as Fig. 12, except the purple sea urchin was used. The dashed line is A^{260}. Closed circles are ^{14}C leucine incorporation; open circles are ^{3}H uridine incorporation.

portion rose steadily as the cleavage stages progressed (Figure 14). Expressed either as total RNA label in each polysomal class or as specific activity here, an increasingly greater proportion of newly synthesized RNA, probably m-RNA (Nemer and Infante, 1965), appeared capable of being either loaded with ribosomes or fully active during this early development.

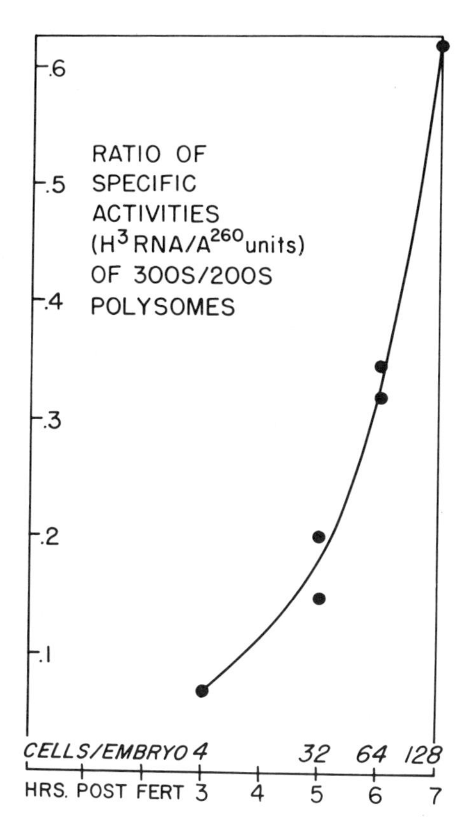

Figure 14. Early developmental transition in the ratio of specific activities of RNA label in polysomal classes. The specific activities of the two polysomal classes were measured in gradients such as that of Figure 13, and of various early cleavage stages.

We cannot yet guess the significance of these two classes of polysomes. They seem diagnostic of a differential messenger RNA activity. The fully active members of the m-RNA population are thus fully loaded with ribosomes. The less active members are incompletely loaded. The agents of this regulation may underlie the peculiar shift during the cleavage stages in the proportion of new RNA associated with fully active polysomes. It is during this transition that the use of newly synthesized m-RNA becomes mandatory. The coordination of the expenditure of egg m-RNA and the utilization of new m-RNA may involve a regulation basic to the expression of genetic information at the translational level.

SUMMARY

Early development coordinates the use of preexisting and newly synthesized agents of genetic expression. After fertilization, polyribosomes (polysomes) form rapidly, preempting 50% of the ribosomes within the first 3 hr of development. The proportion of polysomes and ribosomes remains constant at a level of 1:1, at least until the gastrula stage. New m-RNA (heterogeneous) is synthesized before the first cleavage; however, essentially all the polysomes are directed by preexisting egg m-RNA. The polysomes consist of two classes:

1. slow, in both their rate of protein synthesis and sedimentation (200S);
2. rapid, in both their rate of protein synthesis and sedimentation (300S).

Newly synthesized RNA is distributed predominantly in the former in the early cleaving embryo, but a greater proportion of new RNA finds its way into the rapid polysomes as development proceeds through cleavage. In the gastrula, a considerable portion of the new RNA (DNA-like) is associated with the rapid polysomes. A regulation of the use of new m-RNA appears likely, especially in the very early embryo, in which it must be coordinated with a decline in the activity of preexisting egg m-RNA.

Early development to blastulation is dominated by m-RNA synthesis, with much smaller proportions of the other RNA classes being synthesized. These classes can be observed in pulse-labeled RNA as the ribosomal RNA precursor and two sedimentation modes of 70S and 90S RNA, given the term nuclear RNA (N-RNA) because this material appears to be restricted to the nucleus. As the embryo develops past the mesenchyme blastula stage, the content of original egg ribosomes begins to decay at an enhanced rate and new ribosomal synthesis becomes increasingly more important quantitatively. Concomitantly, the proportion of 45S ribosomal RNA precursor observable in pulse-labeled RNA increases during this period of development, and the degree of hybridization of non-4S pulse-labeled RNA declines.

In the late gastrula to pluteus, ribosomal RNA synthesis quantitatively overshadows the synthesis of other RNA classes, and the bulk of ribosomes are no longer of egg origin, but newly synthesized. Another RNA class to gain prominence in the later embryo is the N-RNA. Whereas in the cleaving embryo it represented about 5% of the m-RNA observed in a sedimentation profile of pulse-labeled RNA, in the pluteus it appeared actually in higher proportion than the m-RNA class. It is suggested that N-RNA, the synthesis or turnover of which gains quantitative importance as development proceeds, may be a component in the differentiation of the nucleus and in cellular differentiation.

REFERENCES

Attardi, G., H. Parnas, M. Hwang, and B. Attardi. 1966. J. Mol. Biol. (In press.)

Baltus, E., J. Quertier, A. Ficq, and J. Brachet. 1965. Biochim. Biophys. Acta 95: 408.

Belitsina, N.V., M.A. Ajtkhozhin, L.P. Gavrilova, and A.S. Spirin. 1964. Biokhimiya 29: 363.

Comb, D.G., and S. Katz. 1964. J. Mol. Biol. 8: 790.

Denny, P.C., and A. Tyler. 1964. Biochem. Biophys. Res. Commun. 14: 245.

Glisin, V.R., and M.V. Glisin. 1964. Proc. Natl. Acad. Sci. U.S. 52: 1548.

Glisin, V.R., M.V. Glisin, and P. Doty. 1966. Proc. Natl. Acad. Sci. U.S. 56: 285.

Gross, P.R., and G.H. Cousineau. 1963. Biochem. Biophys. Res. Commun. 10: 321.

Gross, P.R., K. Kraemer, and L.I. Malkin. 1965. Bio-

chem. Biophys. Res. Commun. 18: 569.
Gross, P.R., L.I. Malkin, and M. Hubbard. 1965. J. Mol. Biol. 13: 463.
Gross, P.R., L.I. Malkin, and W.A. Moyer. 1964. Proc. Natl. Acad. Sci. U.S. 51: 407.
Hultin, T. 1961. Exp. Cell Res. 25: 405.
Maggio, R., M.L. Vittorelli, A.M. Rinaldi, and A. Monroy. 1964. Biochem. Biophys. Res. Commun. 15: 436.
Malkin, H.M. 1954. J. Cellular Comp. Physiol. 44: 105.
Malkin, L.I., P.R. Gross, and P. Romanoff. 1964. Develop. Biol. 10: 378.
Martin, R.G., and B.N. Ames. 1961. J. Biol. Chem. 236: 1372.
McConkey, E.H., and J.W. Hopkins. 1964. Proc. Natl. Acad. Sci. U.S. 51: 1197.
Monroy, A., and A. Tyler. 1963. Arch. Biochem. Biophys. 103: 431.
Monroy, A., R. Maggio, and A.M. Rinaldi. 1965. Proc. Natl. Acad. Sci. U.S. 54: 107.
Nemer, M. 1962. Biochem. Biophys. Res. Commun. 8: 511.
Nemer, M. 1963. Proc. Natl. Acad. Sci. U.S. 50: 230.
Nemer, M., and S.G. Bard. 1963. Science 140: 664.
Nemer, M., and A.A. Infante. 1965. Science 150: 217.
Nygaard, A.P., and B.D. Hall. 1963. Biochem. Biophys. Res. Commun. 12: 98.
Perry, R.P. 1962. Proc. Natl. Acad. Sci. U.S. 48: 2179.
Rosset, R., R. Monier, and J. Julien. 1964. Bull. Soc. Chim. Biol. 46: 87.
Scherrer, K., and J.E. Darnell. 1962. Biochem. Biophys. Res. Commun. 7: 86.
Scherrer, K., H. Latham, and J.E. Darnell. 1963. Proc. Natl. Acad. Sci. U.S. 49: 240.
Sibatani, A., S.R. de Kloet, V.G. Allfrey, and A.E. Mirsky. 1962. Proc. Natl. Acad. Sci. U.S. 48: 471.
Slater, D.W., and S. Spiegelman. 1966. Proc. Natl. Acad. Sci. U.S. 56: 164.
Spiegel, M., H. Ozaki, and A. Tyler. 1965. Biochem. Biophys. Res. Commun. 21: 135.
Spirin, A.S., and M. Nemer. 1965. Science 150: 214.
Spirin, A.S., N.V. Belitsina, and M.A. Ajtkhozhin. 1964. Zh. Obshch. Biol. 25: 321.
Stafford, D.W., W.H. Sofer, and R.M. Iverson. 1964.

Proc. Natl. Acad. Sci. U.S. 52: 313.
Terman, S.A., and P.R. Gross. 1965. Biochem. Biophys. Res. Commun. 21: 595.
Tyler, A. 1962. Proc. Conf. Immuno-Reproduction Population Council, N.Y. 13.
Warner, J., R. Roeiro, C. Birnboim, M. Girard, and J. E. Darnell. 1966. J. Mol. Biol. (In press.)
Whiteley, A.H., B.J. McCarthy, and H.R. Whiteley. 1966. Proc. Natl. Acad. Sci. U.S. 55: 519.
Wilt, F. 1964. Develop. Biol. 9: 299.
Wilt, F., and T. Hultin. 1962. Biochem. Biophys. Res. Commun. 9: 313.

*Synthesis, Transport, Use and Stabilization of m-RNA in the Developing Feather**

Eugene Bell and Charlotte Merrill

Department of Biology
Massachusetts Institute of Technology
Cambridge

INTRODUCTION

Most m-RNA used in the cytoplasm originates in the nucleus. The mode of m-RNA transport from nucleus to cytoplasm has recently received some attention (Joklik and Becker, 1965; Belitsina, et al., 1964; Spirin and Nemer, 1965) and is, in part, the subject of this paper. In particular, we have studied the movement of newly synthesized RNA through various pools of cytoplasmic particulates in cells of the developing chick feather. We shall present data which show that newly made m-RNA becomes associated with 40S or 60S ribosomal subunits before it enters a pool of particles which sediment between 85S and 90S. The unit of this pool may consist of a 40S or 60S particle in association with a molecule of m-RNA and a 72S ribosome. Large

*Supported by N.S.F. Grant GB-614.

messages pass into the 85S to 90S pool more rapidly than small, and newly made RNA generally bypasses the pool of single ribosomes. Subsequently, the newly made m-RNA becomes associated with polysomes active in protein synthesis.

Transport of m-RNA in the cytoplasm can occur in the absence of protein synthesis and probably with previously synthesized subunits as vehicles. It is possible to reduce, but not eliminate, the available pool of subunits by culturing feathers in vitro for 18 hr in the absence of protein synthesis.

We shall also discuss the use and stabilization of m-RNA. Stable m-RNA is found in cytoplasmic extracts of feathers only after 13 days of incubation, but as early as 10 to 11 days, synthesis of protein on m-RNA of long half-life can be demonstrated in whole-feather extracts.

To resolve the apparent dilemma, we have studied the kinetics of decay of protein synthesis in operationally defined fractions from feathers treated with actinomycin D to suppress RNA synthesis. At 12 days, in a fraction which consists largely of keratinizing feather sheath cells, the bulk of protein synthesis occurs on m-RNA of long half-life, while in cytoplasmic extracts from the remainder of the feather, synthesis occurs on m-RNA of short half-life.

Synthesis of protein mediated by stable m-RNA before 13 days is restricted, then, to the most differentiated cells, and it can be correlated with the development of birefringence. Birefringence, and probably keratinization, depend upon protein synthesis, but for a period of at least 24 hr they can proceed independently of RNA synthesis.

THE FEATHER AT 12 DAYS AND LATER

At 12 days of incubation, the embryonic chick feather resembles a cylinder nearly 1 cm in length and 1 mm in cross section. It consists of many layers of living epidermal cells which in cross section surround a slim mesodermal core filled loosely with mesenchymal cells and containing two capillary vessels that feed and drain the shaft (Davies, 1889). The outermost layers of epidermal cells make up the sheath, which is cast off at hatching when the down dries. By the time the chick is ready to hatch, the mesodermal core has retracted and the cells of the down feather are keratinized and dead.

At 12 days, the feather has not yet entered the period of maximal elongation and growth (Bell and Humphreys, 1967a); however, it has already begun to differentiate. The sheath and future barbs near the tip are birefringent (Bell and Thathachari, 1963). The layers of epidermal cells beneath the sheath are thrown into folds, and, near the feather tip, cells have begun to organize into barbs and barbules.

We have shown that polysomes from cytoplasmic extracts decay with a relatively short half-life when RNA synthesis is inhibited in 12- 13-day feathers (Humphreys, Penman, and Bell, 1964), but after 14 days of development, in the absence of RNA synthesis, some polysomes are stabilized to function in protein synthesis for long periods. The thirteenth to fourteenth day of development is a period of critical transition. The adult X-ray diffraction pattern for β-keratin is observed (Bell and Thathachari, 1963); growth is maximal and occurs primarily in the base, as it has from 10 days on (Bell and Humphreys, 1967a); and barbs and barbules are differentiating disto-proximally with greater rapidity than the feather is elongating. We shall study closely that period just prior to the burst of metabolic activity occurring between days 13 and 15.

KINETICS OF RNA TRANSPORT

Plucked 12-day feathers were pulse-labeled in virto for 10, 25, or 40 min with ^{3}H uridine (50 to 100 μc/ml), and cytoplasmic extracts were displayed in 15 to 30% linear sucrose gradients and spun for 5 hr at 24,000 rpm in an SW 25 rotor (Spinco). Figures 1 through 3 show the distribution of acid-precipitable radioactivity in relation to OD 260 sedimenting particulates. Single ribosomes sediment at 72S. In some profiles of optical density, 60S and 40S peaks can be distinguished.

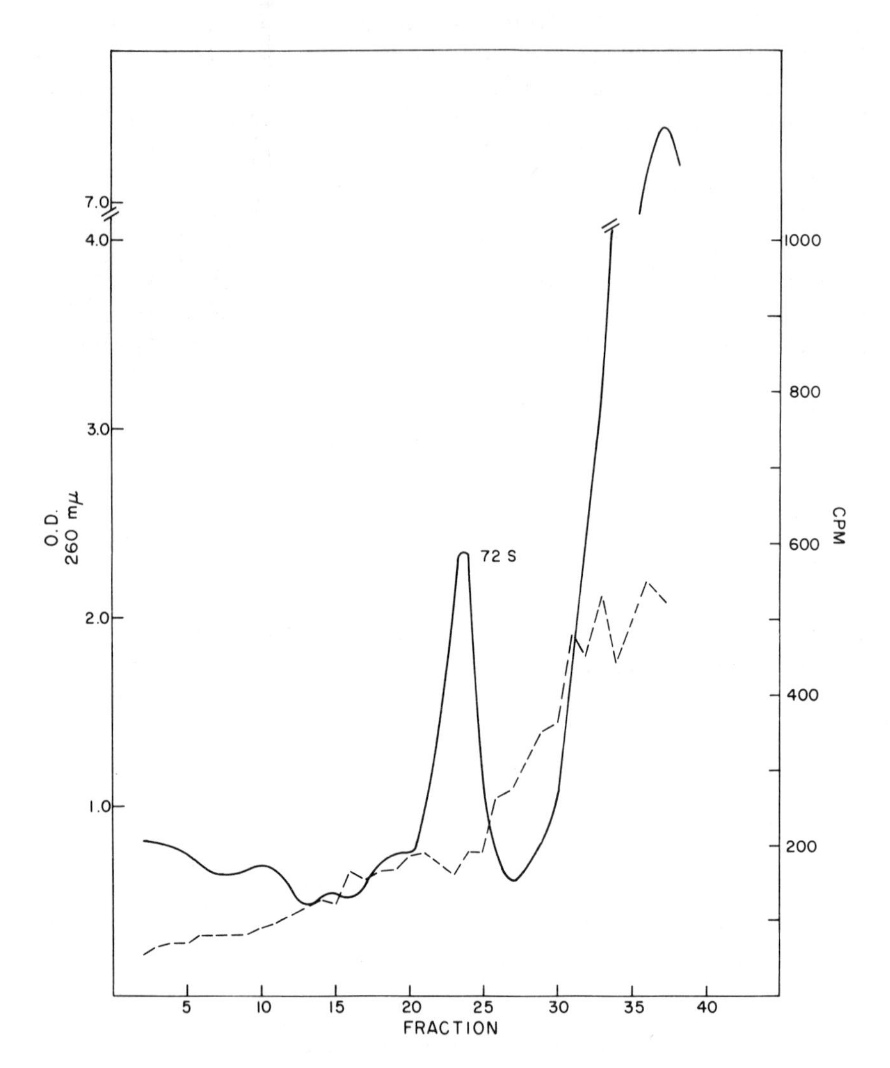

Figure 1. Twelve-day feathers were labeled for 10 min with 100 μc/ml ^{3}H uridine. A cytoplasmic extract was displayed in a 15 to 30% linear sucrose gradient spun for 5 hr at 24,000 rpm in a model L Spinco ultracentrifuge. Acid-insoluble radioactivity sediments in shoulders at 60S and 40S and ascends to the top of the gradient. Dashed line represents radioactivity, and unbroken line, OD at 260 mμ.

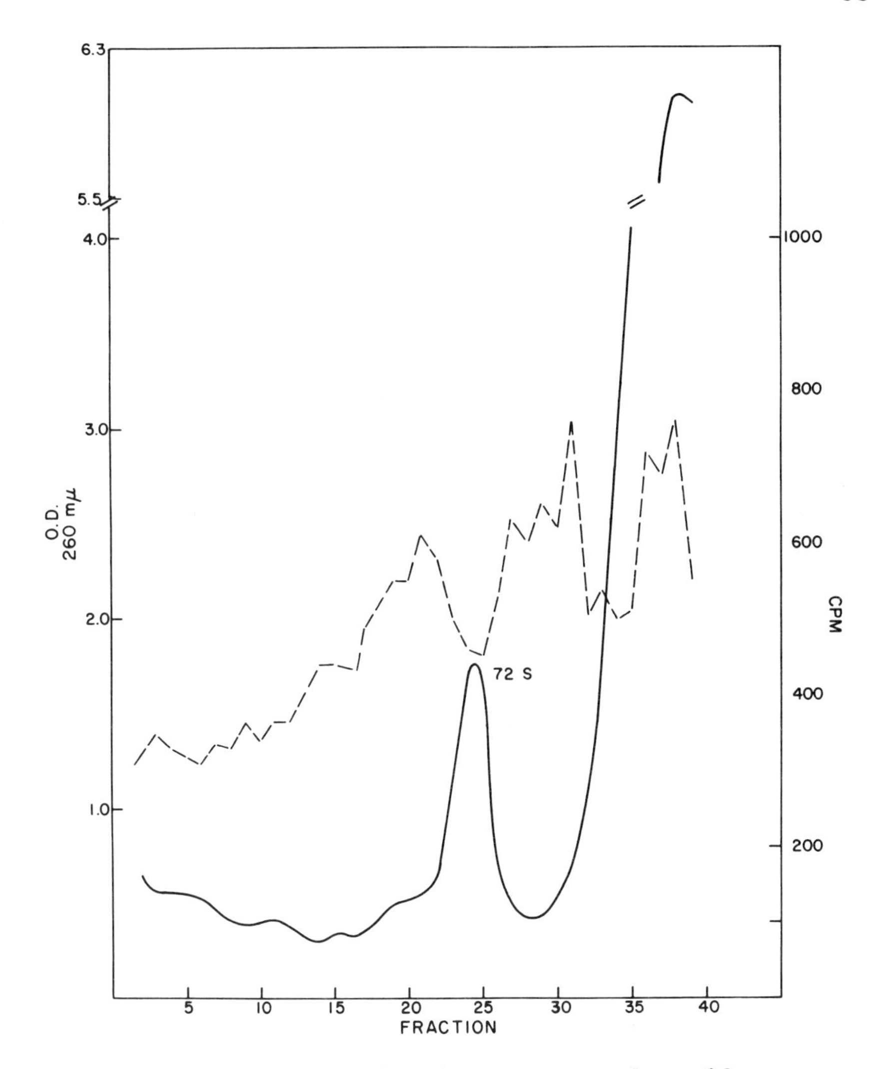

Figure 2. Cytoplasmic extracts from 12-day feathers were labeled for 25 min with 100 μc/ml ^{3}H uridine. In addition to peaks of radioactivity which sediment with particles lighter than ribosomes, acid-insoluble counts are observed in a peak at 85S to 90S and descend to the heavy end of the gradient.

Polysomes consisting of two ribosomes sediment at 120S, three at 130S, and four at 142S.

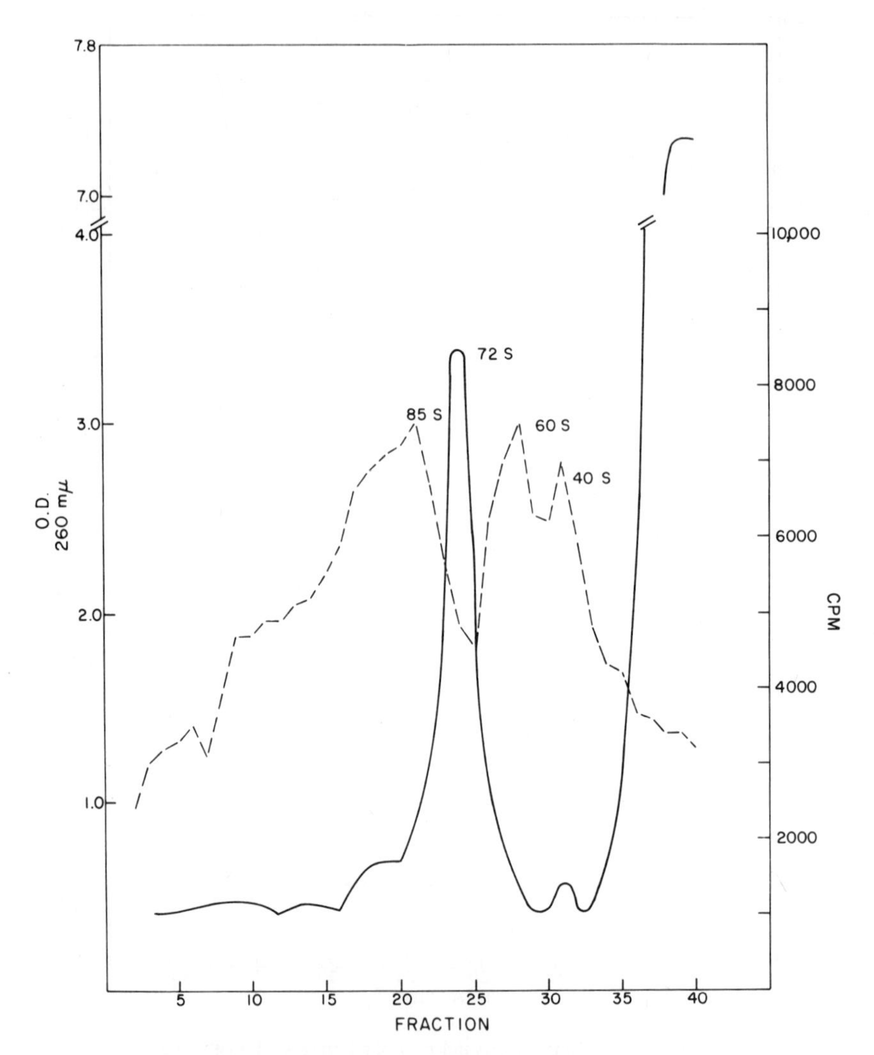

Figure 3. Thirteen-day feathers were labeled for 40 min with ^{3}H uridine. The peak of radioactivity at 85S is as high as those at 40S and 60S.

After 10 min of labeling with ^{3}H uridine, acid-precipitable radioactivity is localized primarily at the top of the gradient and descends through the region of 40S and 60S particles. By 25 min, counts are mainly in the 40S to 60S zone and in a peak which sediments at 85S to 90S, which has no counterpart of optical density. By 40 min, as much or more acid-precipitable radioactivity is associated with the 85S to 90S peak as with the 40S and 60S peaks. At 25 min, sometimes with the exception of 4-ribosome aggregates, polysomes

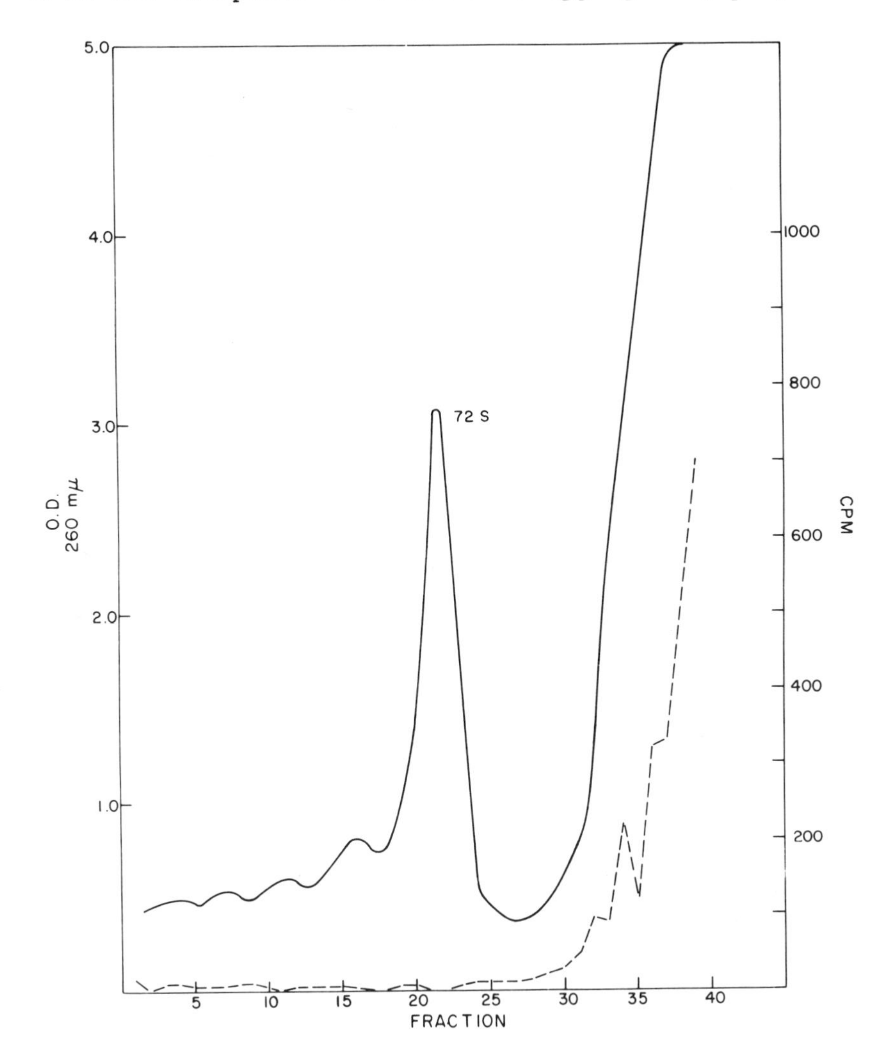

Figure 4. A cytoplasmic extract from 12-day feathers labeled for 40 min with ^3H uridine was treated with 1N NaOH for 8 hr at 25°C. Virtually no acid-precipitable radioactivity is observed in the gradient.

are uniformly labeled regardless of size. The specific activity of single ribosomes is low.

After a 3-hr actinomycin D chase, counts in a cytoplasmic extract of feathers labeled with ^{3}H uridine

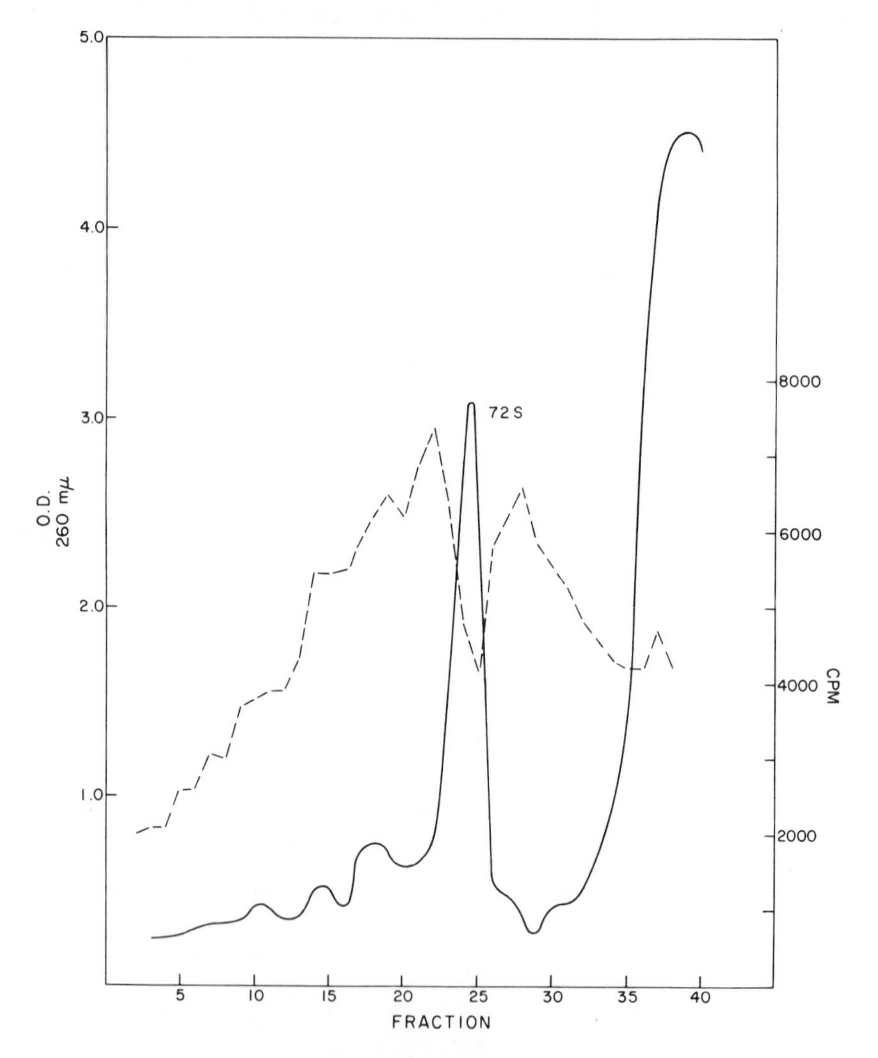

Figure 5. Deoxyribonuclease-treated extract after labeling feathers for 40 min with 100 μc/ml ^{3}H uridine. No significant change is observed when these results are compared with the control gradient shown in Figure 6.

for 40 min are still associated with 40S and 60S particles, and polysomes are labeled as after the 40-min pulse. An 85S to 90S component is still detectable.

After an 18-hr actinomycin D chase following 40 min of labeling with ^{3}H uridine, the peak of acid-precipitable radioactivity which sedimented at 85S to 90S has disappeared entirely, and few counts appear in the region of 40S and 60S particles. Neither chase was entirely effective but both show the movement of radio-

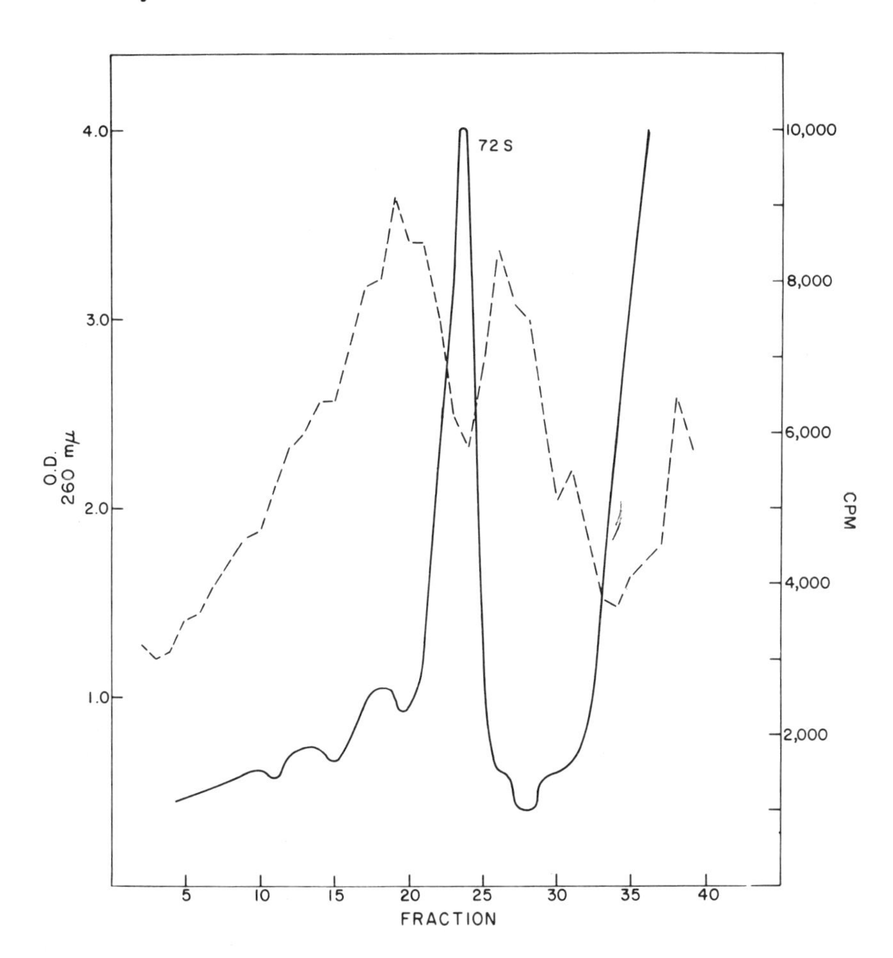

Figure 6. Control gradient for gradient described in Figure 5. Experimental details are similar to those described in the legend of Figure 3.

activity through 40S, 60S, and 85S to 90S pools.

Appropriate control experiments were performed to determine that after 40 min of labeling radioactivity is associated with RNA. After base hydrolysis (Figure 4), no radioactivity appears in the gradient. Digestion with 0.1 μg/ml ribonuclease for 30 min in the cold reduces the radioactivity between the bottom of the gradient, or region of sedimentation of heaviest particles, and the region of particles which sediment at 40S by over 75%. This observation would suggest that the bulk of RNA made during 40 min of labeling is m-RNA, because very much higher concentrations of ribonuclease are required for dissociation of ribosomes and the digestion of protein-bound ribosomal RNA to result.

Treatment of cytoplasmic extracts with 50 μg/ml deoxyribonuclease for 1 hr in the cold produces no change in the OD 260 profile or in the distribution of radioactivity (Figure 5). A control gradient is shown in Figure 6.

CHARACTERIZATION OF THE NEWLY MADE RNA

Additional evidence that the bulk of RNA made during 40 minutes of labeling with ^{3}H uridine is non-ribosomal comes from experiments in which RNA freed of protein is displayed in a 5 to 20% linear SDS (sodium dodecyl sulfate) sucrose gradient. After sedimenting cytoplasmic components in 15 to 30% sucrose gradients spun for 5 hr at 24,000 rpm, various cuts of the gradients were made. Particles were pelleted in an SW 25 or SW 39 rotor, resuspended in SDS buffer at 25°C, and layered on a 5 to 20% SDS sucrose gradient at 25°C.

After spinning for about 10 to 12 hr, the gradients were run through a continuous, flow-through, recording spectrophotometer (Gilford); fractions were collected and acid-precipitable radioactivity was plated and counted. A cut of the lightest material taken from the region between the 40S particles and the top of the gradient yielded RNA sedimenting between 4S and about 10S primarily, but skewed to a 4S peak (Figure 7).

Material taken from the 40S region of a gradient in which a cytoplasmic extract was displayed yielded two

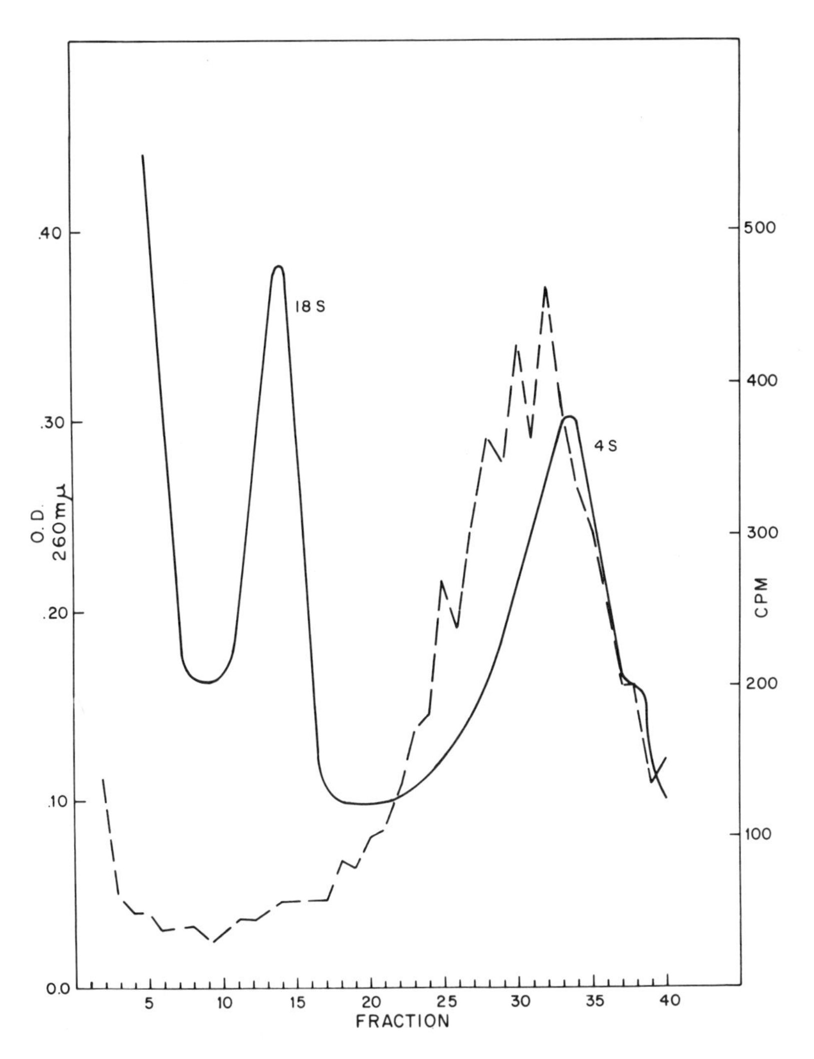

Figure 7. SDS sucrose gradient sedimentation analysis of RNA taken from a region between 40S and the top of a 15 to 30% sucrose gradient in which a cytoplasmic extract was displayed. Feathers were labeled for 40 min with 100 μc/ml ^{3}H uridine.

peaks of RNA, one sedimenting between 18S and 7S and the other at 4S (Figure 8). Both 18S and 28S unlabeled

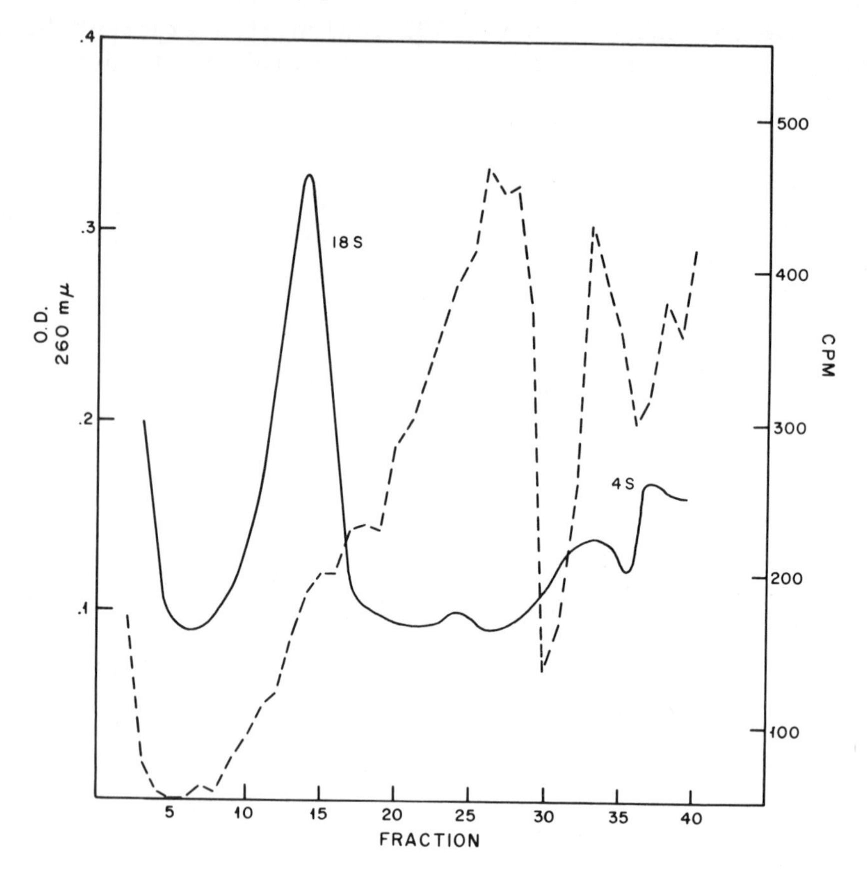

Figure 8. Gradient of RNA taken from region of 40S. See text and Figure legends 1 through 3 for experimental details.

ribosomal RNA peaks were present. Material sedimenting less rapidly than single ribosomes had newly made RNA of smaller size associated with it (Figure 9) than did material sedimenting more rapidly than single ribosomes (Figure 10).

Similarly, when feathers are labeled for 3 hr with ^{3}H uridine rather than for 40 min, the peak of polydisperse RNA from particles smaller than single ribosomes is composed of smaller RNA (Figure 11); it also sediments further to the right than RNA from particles

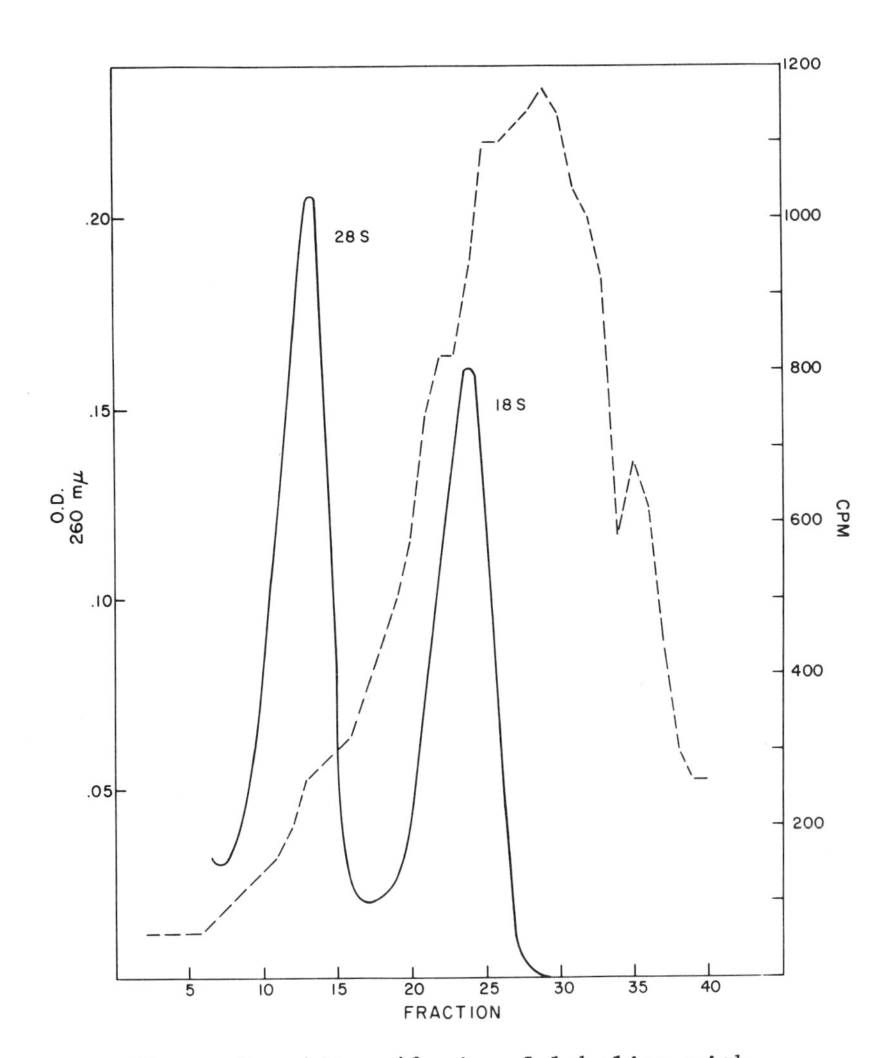

Figure 9. After 40 min of labeling with 100 μc/ml ^{3}H uridine, feathers were homogenized and a cytoplasmic extract displayed in a 15 to 30% sucrose gradient. RNA in fractions containing particulates smaller than ribosomes was extracted and displayed in a 5 to 20% SDS gradient. Radioactivity shown by the broken line is that in newly made RNA.

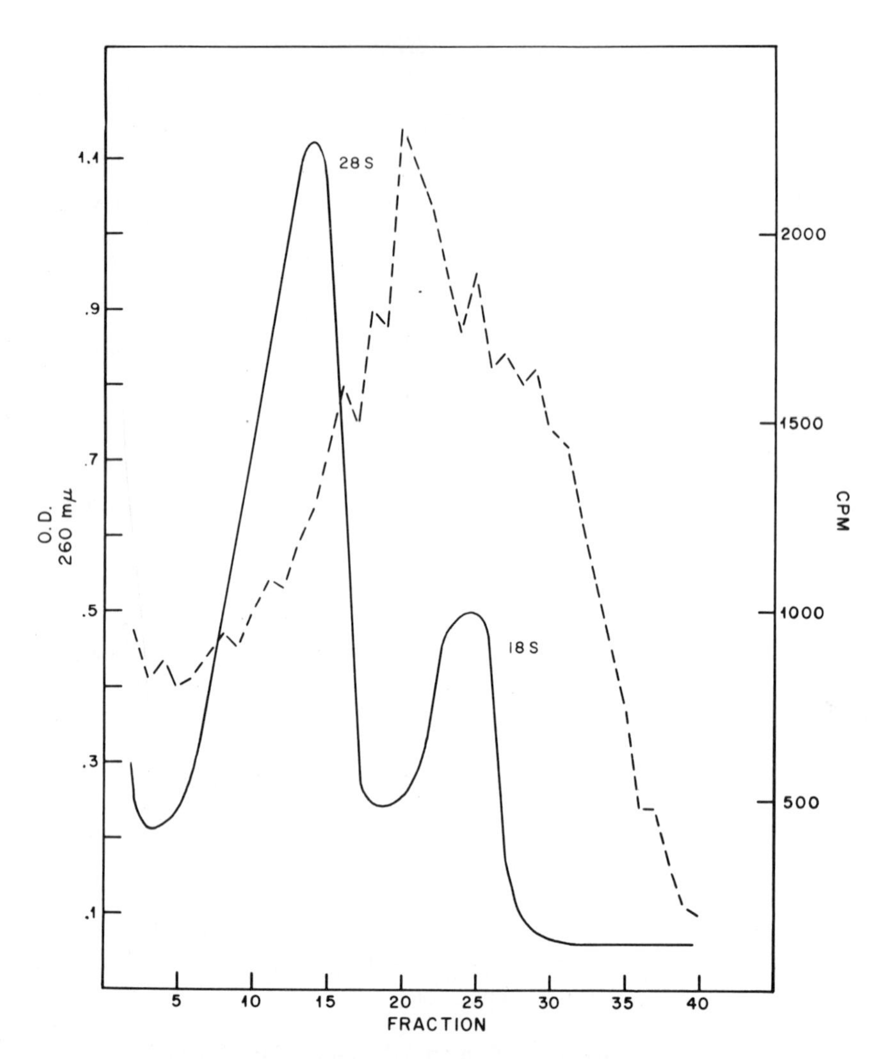

Figure 10. Same experiment as described in Figure 9. Newly made RNA from particles sedimenting more rapidly than single ribosomes.

larger than 72S ribosomes (Figure 12). By this time, some newly made ribosomal RNA has entered particulate pools in the cytoplasm along with polydisperse RNA. The specific activity of 18S ribosomal RNA is greater than that of 28S, which indicates that it is either

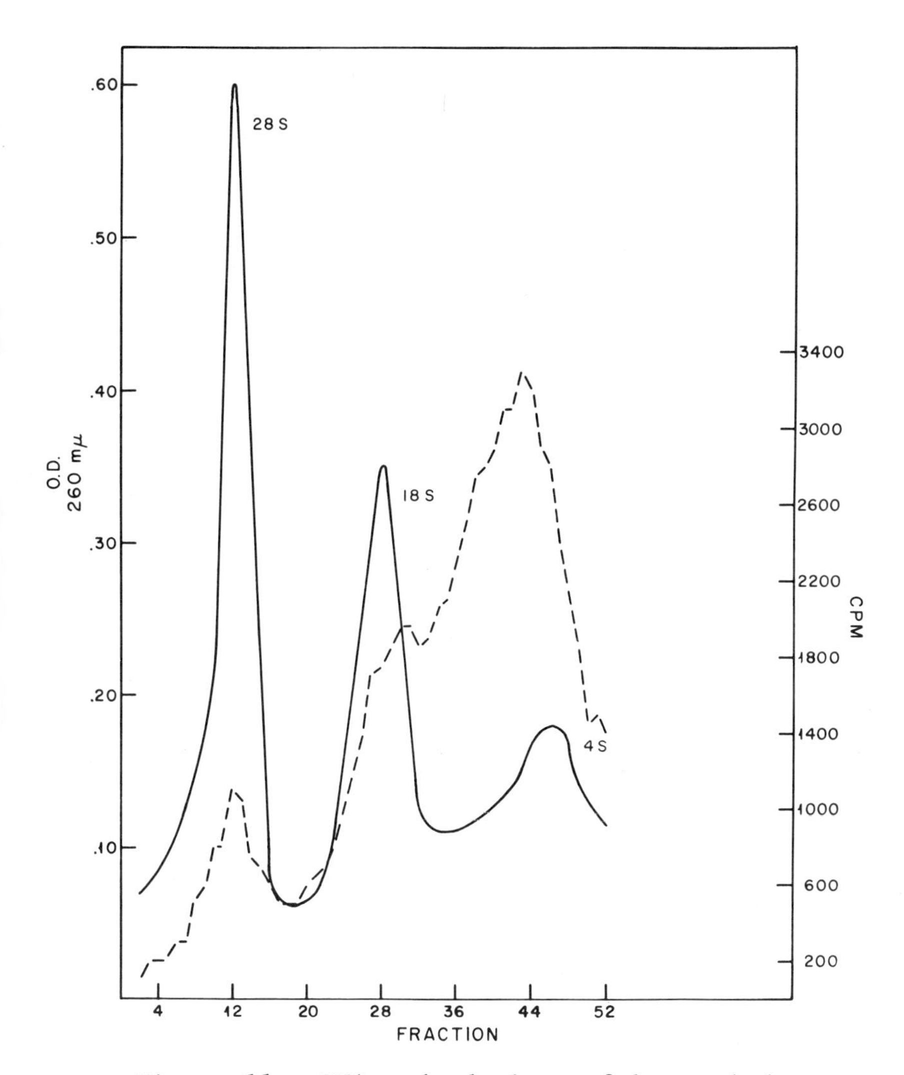

Figure 11. RNA made during a 3-hr period of labeling with ^3H uridine taken from material sedimenting more slowly than single ribosomes.

made at a faster rate or transported more rapidly into the cytoplasm. After 3 hr of labeling, the peak of radioactivity at 60S is many times higher than the shoulder at 40S (Figure 13). The 90S peak is still present and the specific activity of single ribosomes is low.

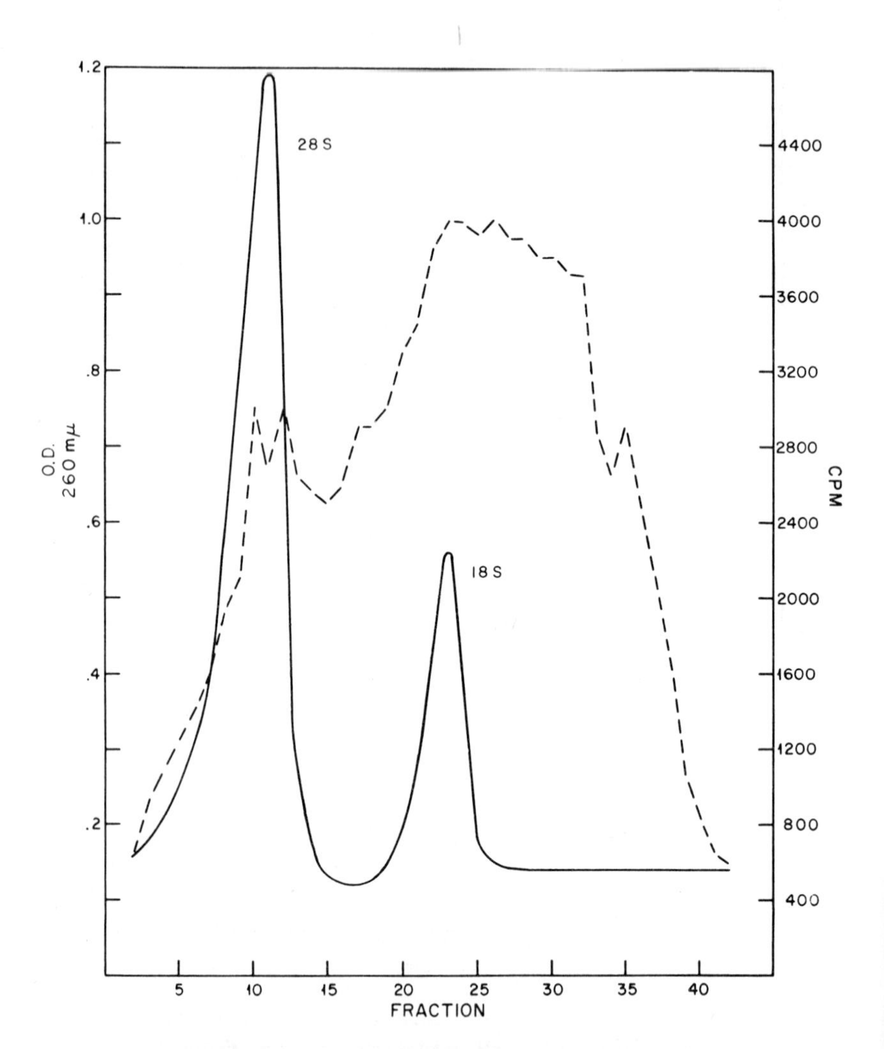

Figure 12. Same experiment as that described in legend of Figure 11. RNA from particles sedimenting more rapidly than 72S ribosomes.

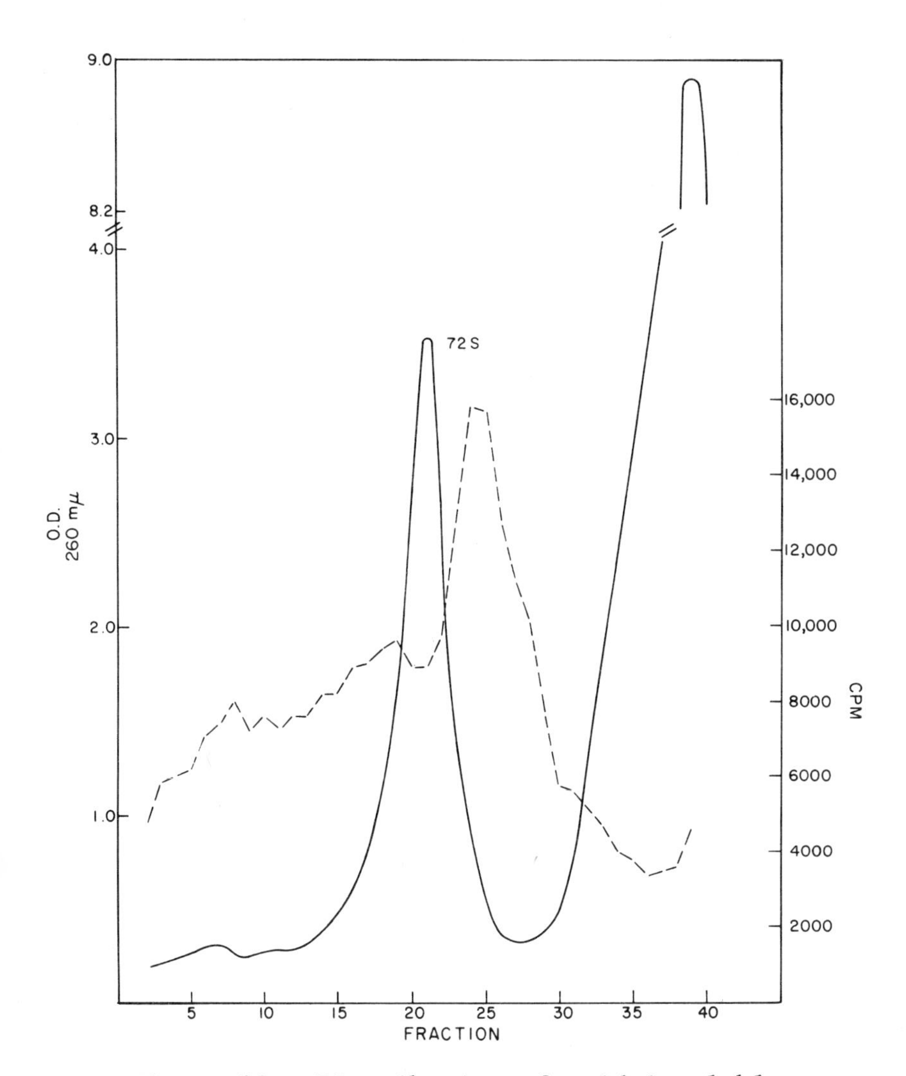

Figure 13. Distribution of acid-insoluble radioactivity in a cytoplasmic extract after labeling feathers for 3 hr with ^{3}H uridine. This experiment provided the RNA displayed in gradients shown in Figures 11 and 12.

SYNTHESIS AND TRANSPORT OF RNA IN THE ABSENCE OF PROTEIN SYNTHESIS

Protein synthesis in the whole 12-day feather is reduced to between 5 and 10% of control levels when

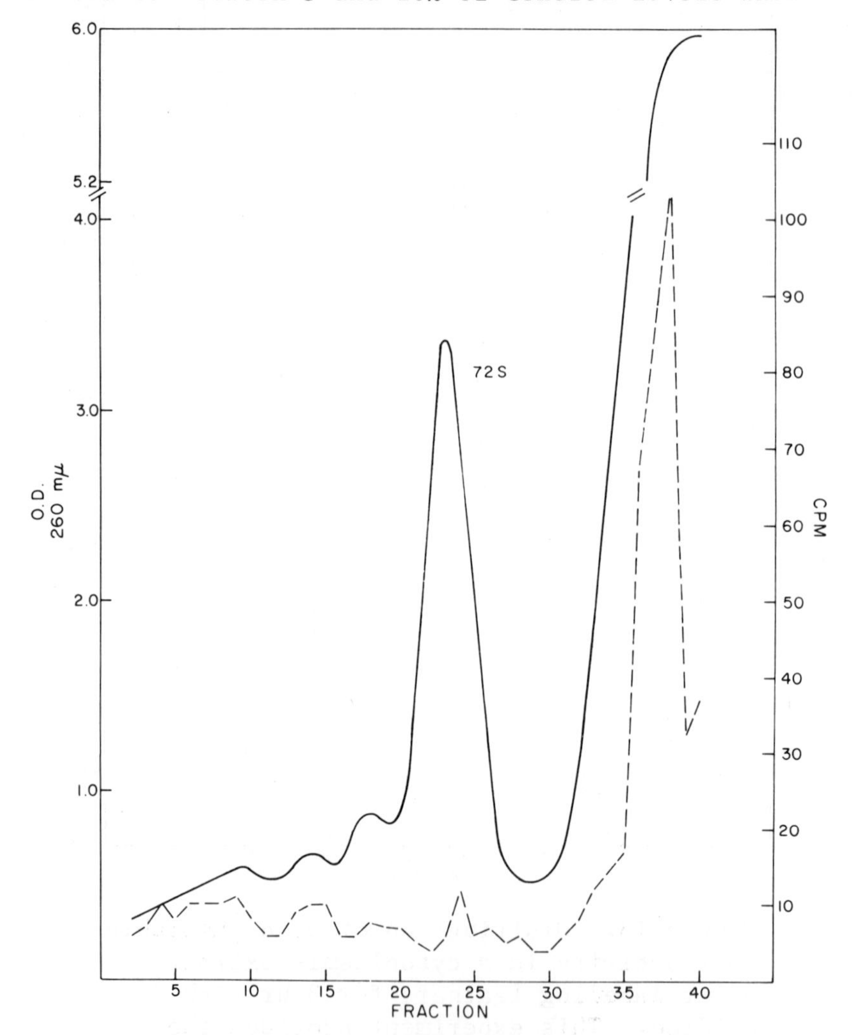

Figure 14. Same experiment as that described in Figure 15, but feathers were pretreated for 2 hr with actidione and remained in it during labeling. Nascent chains are absent and virtually no finished protein has accumulated.

feathers are treated for 2 hr with 100 μg/ml actidione (cycloheximide). New protein associated with cytoplasmic extracts after exposure of feathers to actidione (Figure 14) is also about 5 to 10% of control level (Figure 15).

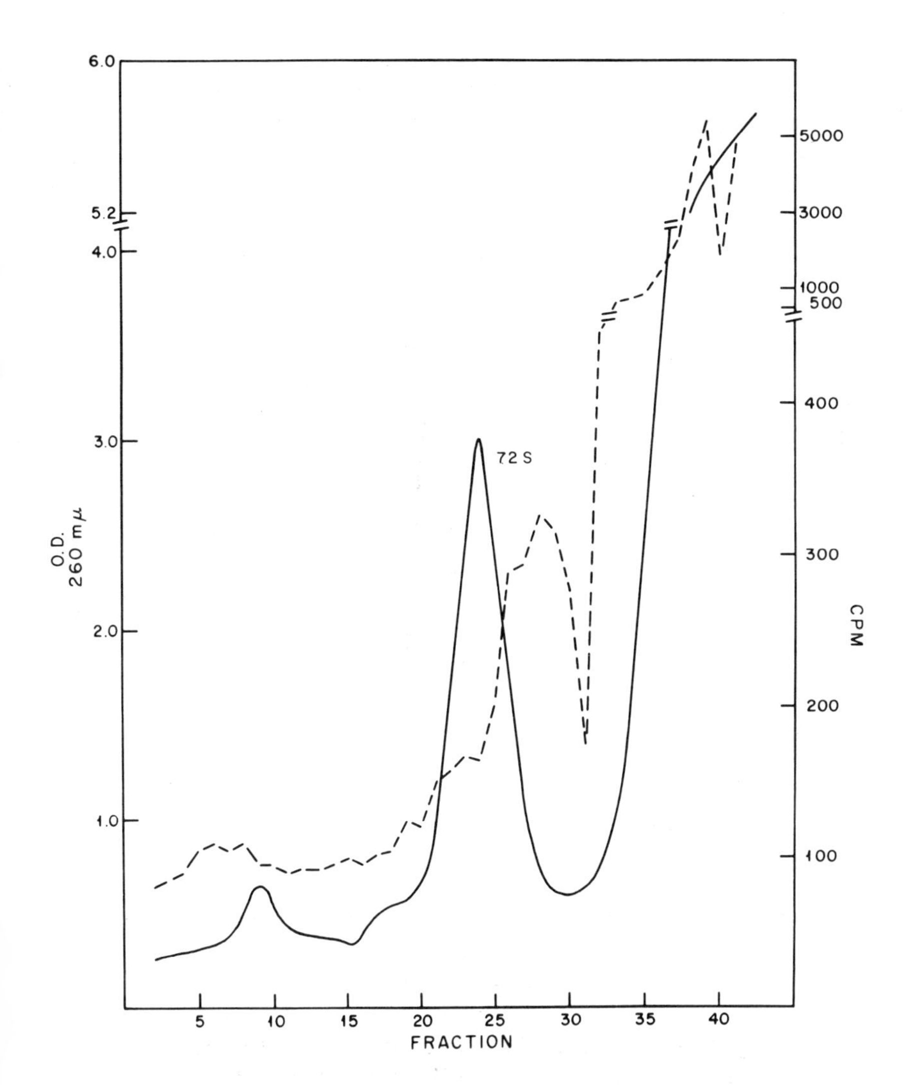

Figure 15. A cytoplasmic extract from 12-day feathers after labeling for 40 min with 10 μc/ml ^{14}C reconstituted yeast protein hydrolysate (Schwarz).

In the absence of protein synthesis there is virtually no change in the movement of newly made RNA through the pools of cytoplasmic particulates already

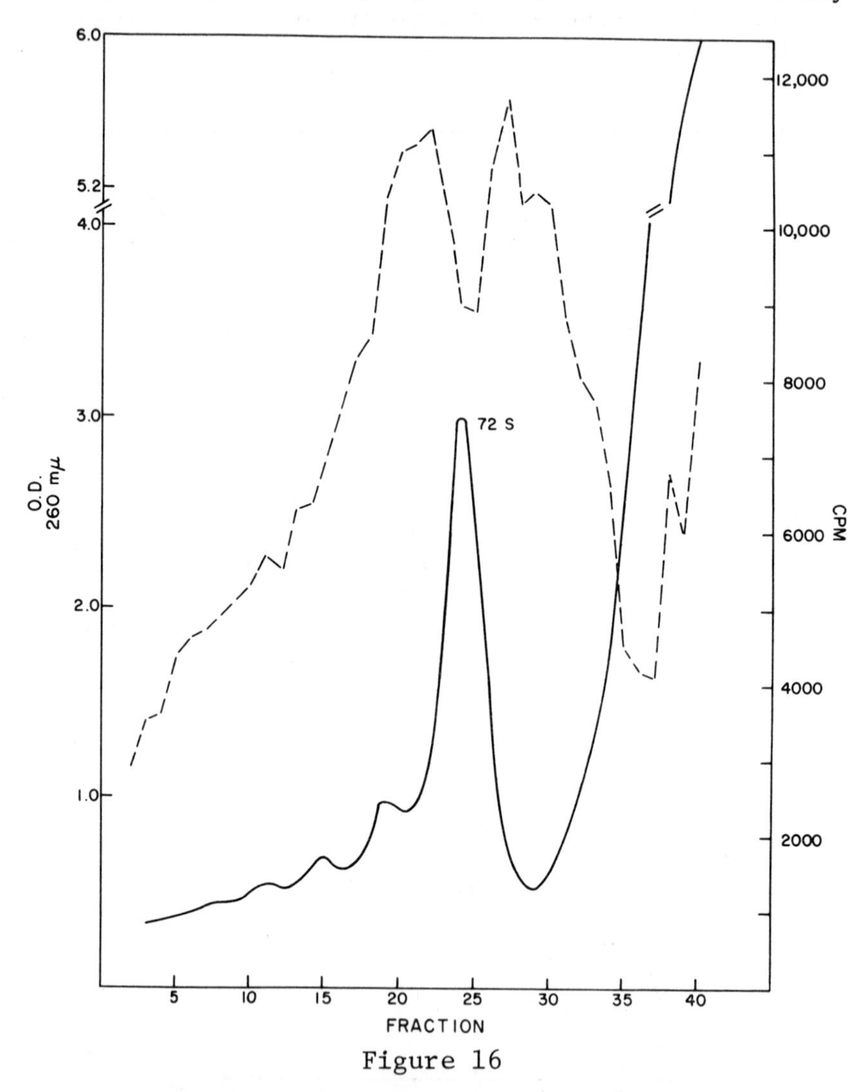

Figure 16

Figures 16, 17, 18, 19, and 20. Experiments are those described in legends of Figures 3, 9, 10, 11, and 12 respectively, with the exception that feathers were treated with actidione for 2 hr before and during the 40 min period of labeling with ^{3}H uridine (100 μc/ml).

discussed. Nor is there a change in the character of the RNA made. Figure 16 shows the distribution of radioactivity in a cytoplasmic extract after feathers are labeled for 40 min with ^{3}H uridine, having been treated for 2 hr prior to, and during labeling with 100 μg/ml actidione. Figure 3 shows the control profile. RNA was extracted from cytoplasmic fractions displayed after treating feathers with actidione and labeling with ^{3}H uridine. RNA to the right of the 72S ribosomes (Figure 17) and that which sediments with particles heavier than ribosomes (Figure 18) is qualitatively similar to RNA extracted from comparable fractions of control extracts. Control gradients were

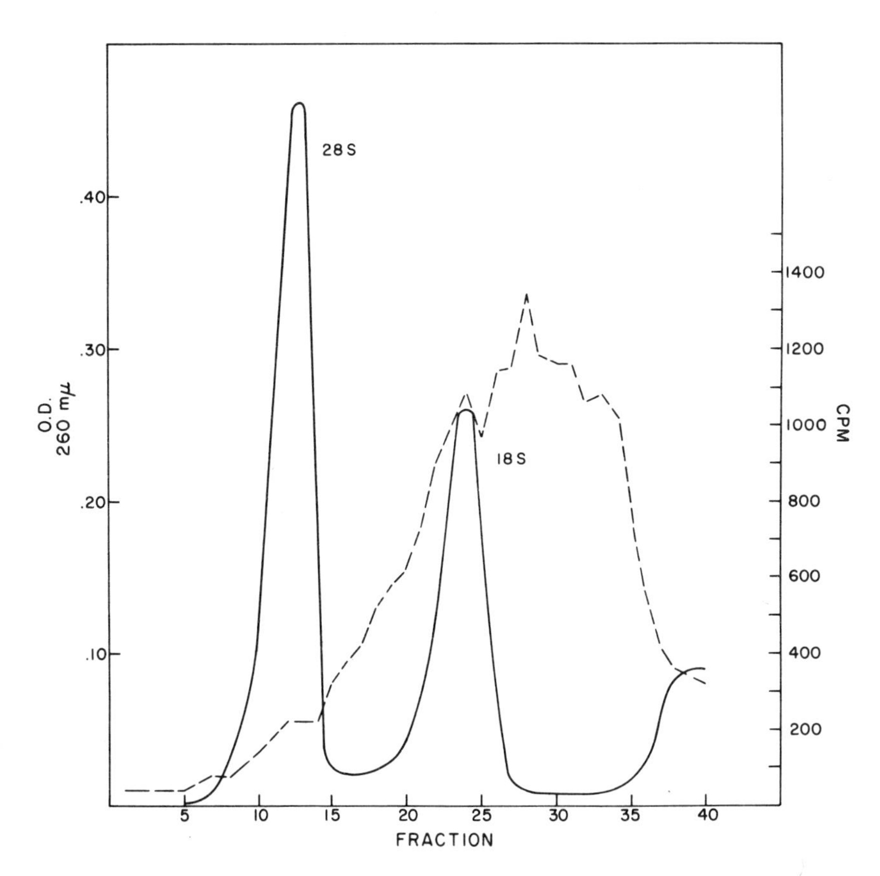

Figure 17

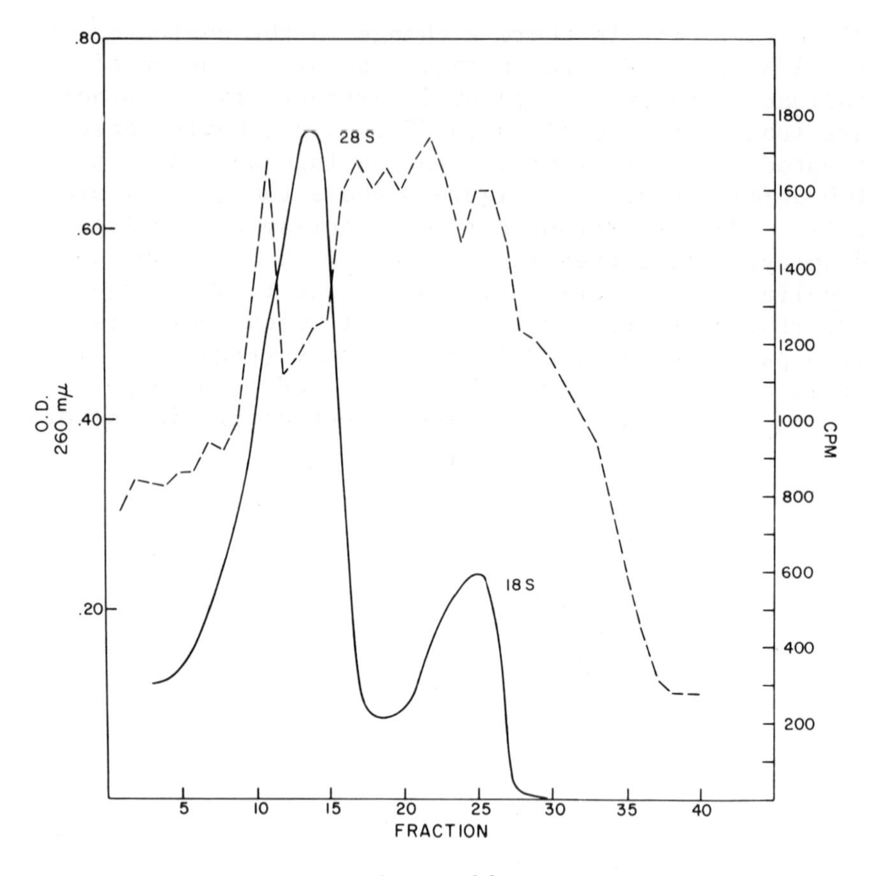

Figure 18

done concurrently and have already been discussed (Figures 9 and 10). Figures 19 and 20 are comparable to control Figures 11 and 12, which show the character of RNA made after 3 hr of labeling with ^{3}H uridine.

DISTRIBUTION OF NEWLY MADE PROTEIN IN CYTOPLASM EXTRACTS OF THE 12-DAY FEATHER AFTER 40 MIN OF LABELING WITH PRECURSORS

In addition to acid-precipitable radioactivity distributed throughout the polysomes and at the top of the gradient, newly made protein is evident in the region

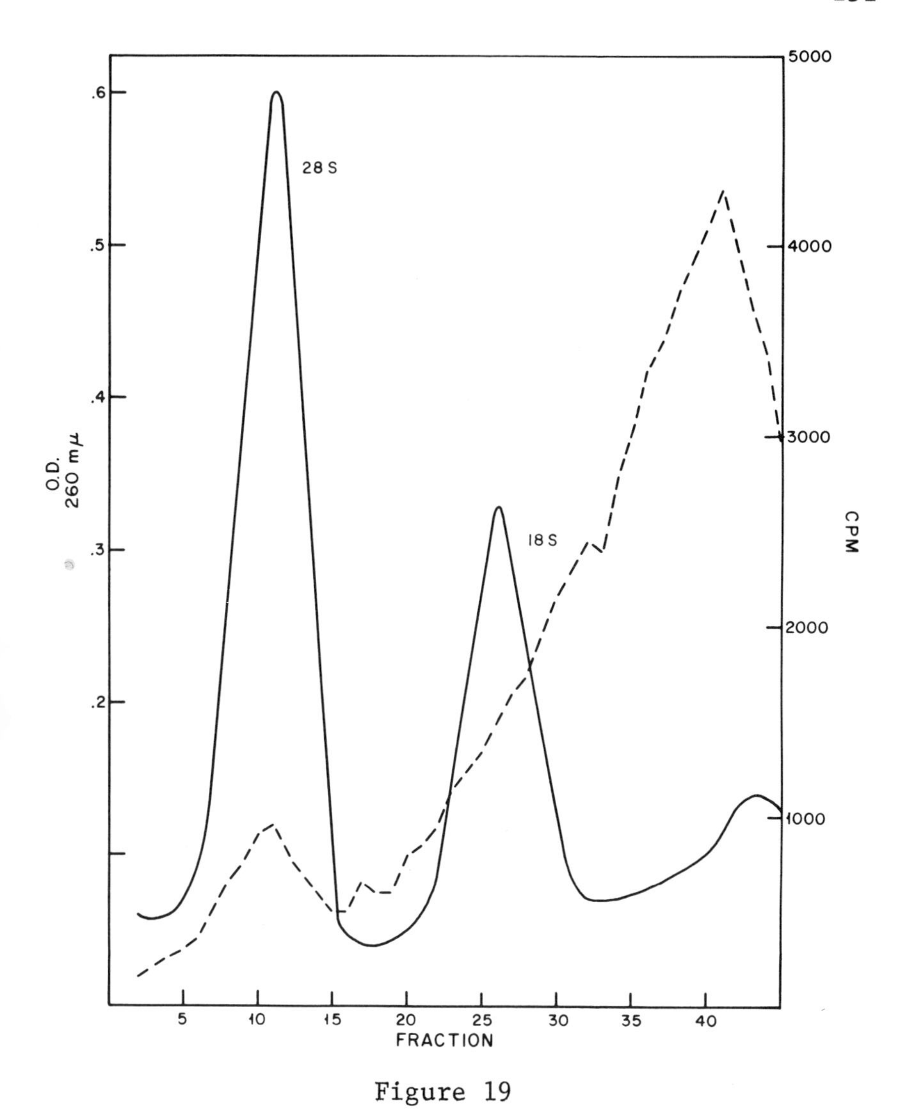

Figure 19

where 40S to 60S (Figure 14) particles sediment. It descends to a shoulder sedimenting between 80S to 90S, which corresponds to the peak of counts observed in gradients of feather extracts after labeling with uridine for 40 min. Thus far we have no information on whether the new protein sedimenting between 40S and 60S and between 80S and 90S is ribosomal or whether it is of some other genre. When feathers are treated

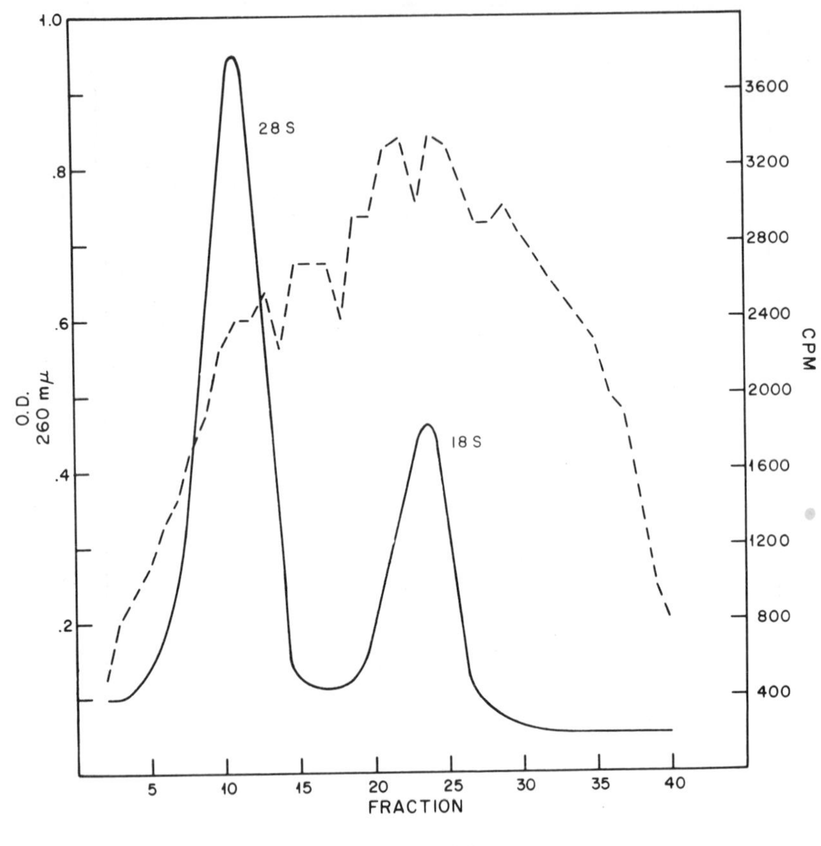

Figure 20

with actidione to inhibit protein synthesis, the transport of RNA is clearly unaffected; therefore, newly made protein is apparently not a requirement for it.

TRANSPORT OF m-RNA

The polydisperse character of RNA made during 40 min of labeling of feathers, that newly made RNA primarily does not sediment at 18S or 28S, and that the newly made RNA is digestible by a very low concentration of ribonuclease when in association with polysomes, suggest that it is m-RNA.

After it leaves the nucleus, it is found associated in the cytoplasm with 40S or 60S particles the RNA of which declares them ribosomal subunits. It is also found in association with a fraction that sediments between 85S and 90S immediately after it leaves the nucleus, or, possibly, immediately after it passes through the pool of lighter-than-ribosome particles. Newly made RNA in association with 85S to 90S particles or with polysomes is larger than newly made RNA found with 40S or 60S ribosomal subunits.

Possibly large messages either pass through the cytoplasmic pools of 40S and 60S particles more quickly than small messages or bypass the presumed subunit pools and become associated with a single ribosome plus a 40S or a 60S particle. The existence of a pool of heavier-than-ribosome particles which consist of m-RNA, a 40S or 60S piece, and a single ribosome has not been previously observed. We can propose that m-RNA, before it leaves the nucleus or as it enters the cytoplasm, picks up a 40S or a 60S ribosomal subunit and either becomes associated immediately with a ribosome to make an 85S or a 90S particle, if it is a large message, or remains in a subunit pool for a longer period, if it is a small message.

The pool of subunits available for m-RNA transport can be presumed to be large, because, in the absence of protein synthesis, neither the mode of transport nor the gross species of m-RNA change. If feathers are kept in actidione for 17 hr and then labeled for 40 min with ^{3}H uridine, acid-precipitable radioactivity recoverable in the cytoplasm is reduced by an order of magnitude (Figure 21) compared with controls (Figure 22) in which protein synthesis is not suppressed. The distribution of newly made RNA in the gradient is qualitatively similar, however, indicating that a pool of subunits was still available for message transport.

En route to utilization as templates for protein synthesis in polysomes, m-RNA seems to bypass the pool of single ribosomes as Joklik and Becker (1965) have reported in studies on HeLa cells. Whether it is functional as part of an 85S to 90S particle until the particle is saturated with a partner for the 40S or 60S subunit to make a second 72S ribosome is not clear.

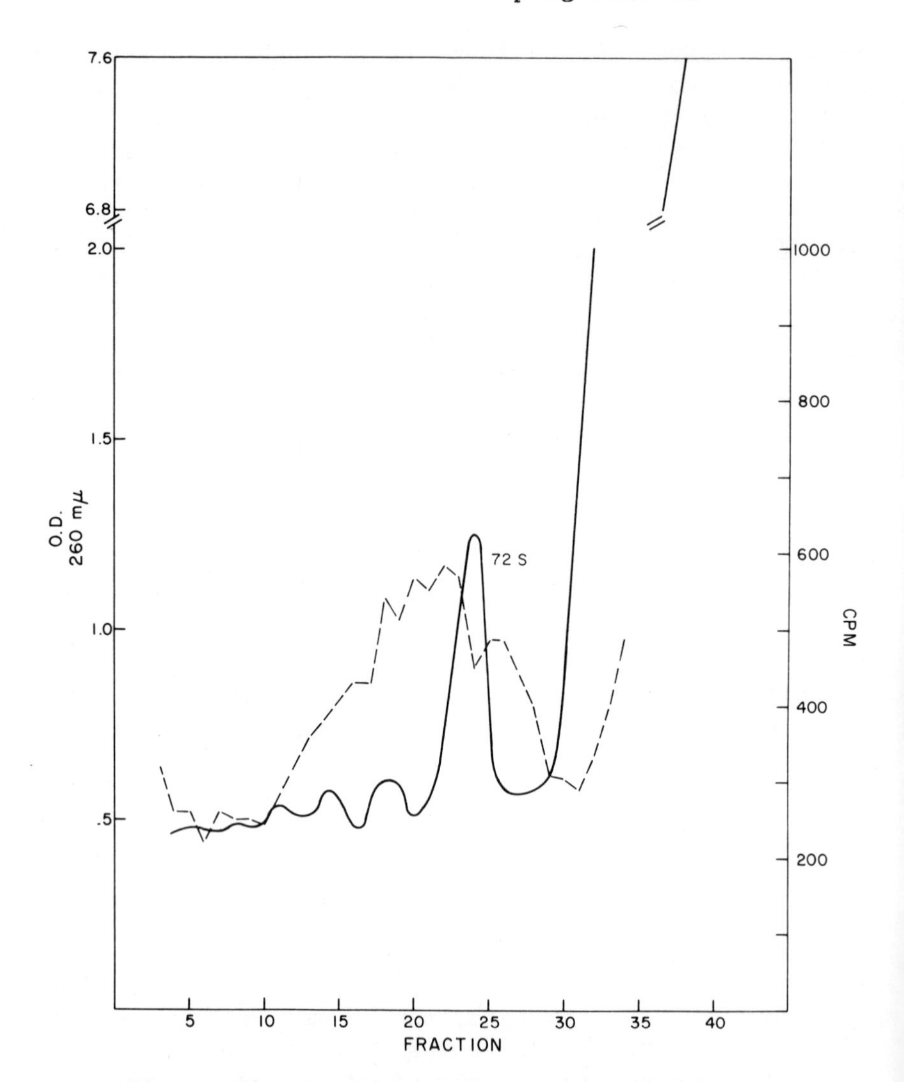

Figure 21. Feathers were cultured for 17 hr in Waymouth medium with 100 μg/ml actidione to suppress protein synthesis. They were then labeled for 40 min with ^3H uridine. Acid-precipitable radioactivity in a cytoplasmic extract is reduced by an order of magnitude compared with the control (Figure 22), but the distribution of radioactivity is similar.

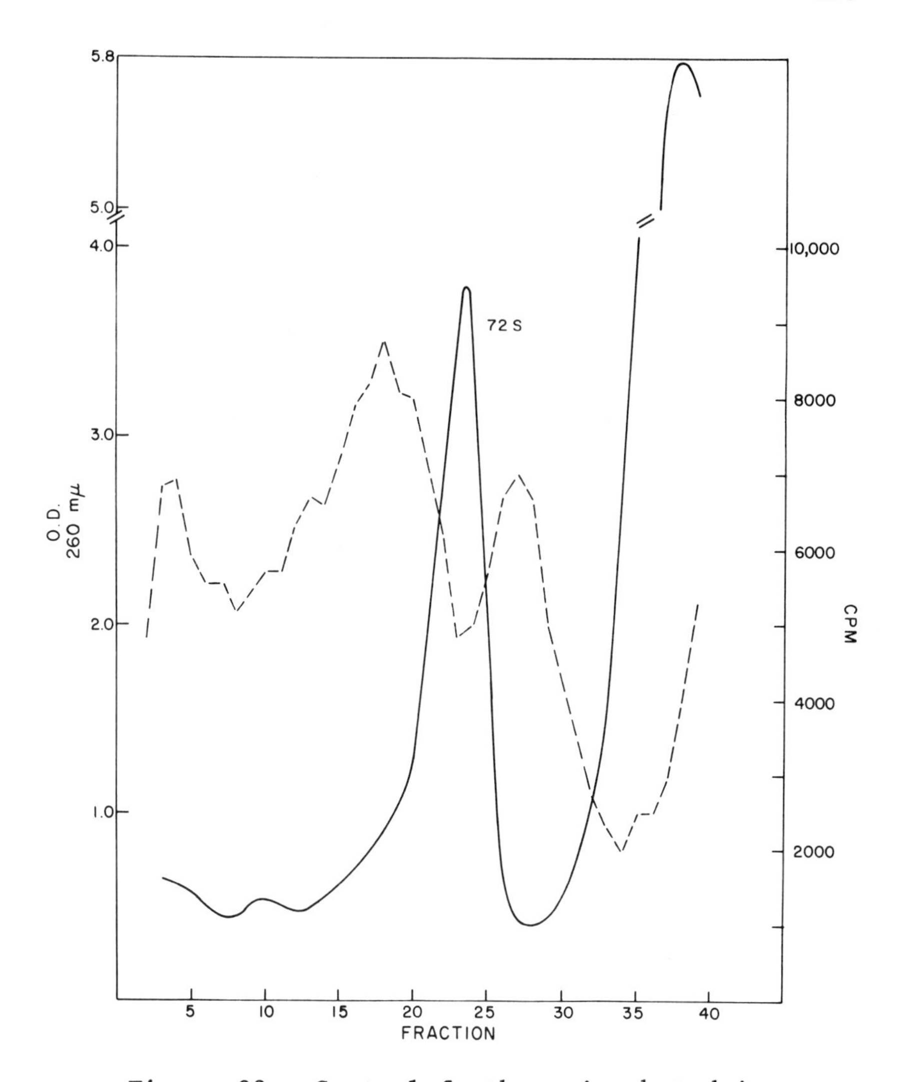

Figure 22. Control feathers incubated in Waymouth medium for 12 hr without actidione. See legend for Figure 21 for experimental details.

Improved resolution in gradients and other experiments will be necessary to determine whether two or more ribosomes and a subunit can occupy and translate a message. If the 85S to 90S particle is inactive in protein synthesis until saturated, it might constitute a device for m-RNA storage; so also might either ribosomal subunit.

It is possible that messages move on a large protein moiety and not on a ribosomal subunit at all, becoming functional as soon as a single ribosome attaches to it. Displacement of the protein carrier would result. The experiments reported do not exclude this method of m-RNA transport, but displacement of the protein moiety should yield a pool of 72S ribosomes plus labeled message; such a pool is not evident even after 3 hr of labeling with ^{3}H uridine. Proposed carriers of this kind have been called informosomes (Belitsina, et al., 1964). If they exist in feather cells, their coincidence of sedimentation with 40S and 60S ribosomal subunits is remarkable.

USE AND STABILIZATION OF m-RNA IN THE 12-DAY FEATHER

We have stated previously that not until 14 to 15 days of incubation do cytoplasmic extracts of the feather yield stable polysomes active in protein synthesis (Humphreys, Penman, and Bell, 1964), yet as early as 10 to 11 days of incubation, synthesis of protein on m-RNA of long half-life occurs in the whole feather (Bell and Humphreys, 1967b).

By homogenizing feathers in a Dounce glass-ball homogenizer and separating the homogenate into a low-speed pellet and a supernatant, we have examined the decay of protein synthesis in these operationally defined fractions after suppressing RNA synthesis with actinomycin D We have shown elsewhere that in the concentrations used, actinomycin D reduces RNA synthesis to less than 2% of that in control feathers (Humphreys. Penman, and Bell, 1964). Figure 23 shows that for 24 hr, protein synthesis in feather parts which sedimented with a low-speed pellet is virtually unaffected relative to controls.

On the other hand, m-RNA, as seen through decay of protein synthesis in the supernatant, appears to be short-lived. Microscopic examination of the pellet fraction revealed the presence of many unbroken flat

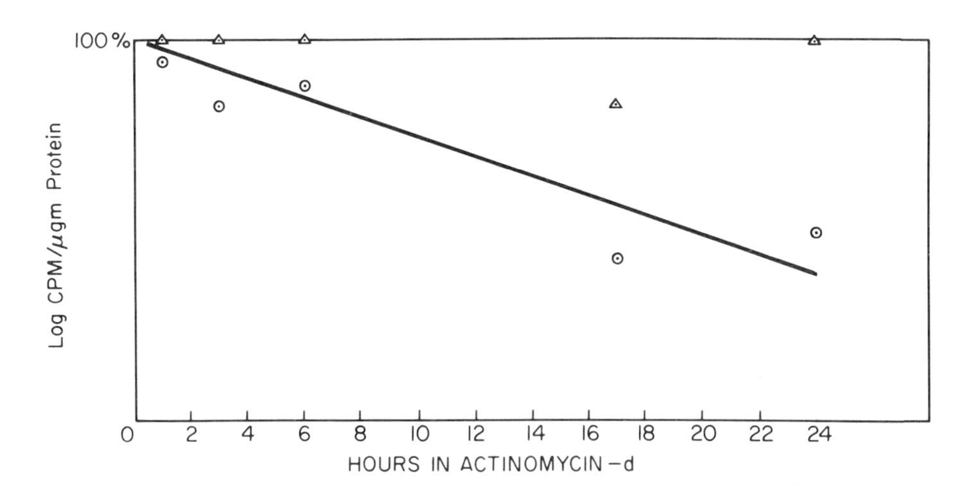

Figure 23. Feathers were incubated in 60 μg/ml actinomycin D for different periods, and the decay of protein synthesis in low-speed pellet and supernatant fractions from a homogenate is plotted. Specific activity of the supernatant fraction decays with a half-life of about 8 to 10 hr, while that of the pellet fraction shows no change over the 24 hr experimental period.

cells resembling feather sheath cells. Homogenization and low-speed centrifugation result in a fortuitous separation of parts that had already diverged morphologically and biochemically. Sheath cells, the most differentiated cells in the 12-day feather, contain m-RNA of long half-life and, in intact form, sediment with the pellet. Less differentiated cells from the remainder of the feather break up when homogenized and yield their contents to a cytoplasmic extract, which is characterized by the presence of short-lived m-RNA.

Further evidence for the geographical segregation of stable m-RNA in the 12-day feather has been provided by autoradiographs of feathers treated with 60 μg/ml actinomycin D and pulse labeled for 1 hr with ^{14}C reconstituted yeast protein hydrolysate (Schwarz). In Figure 24 are shown sections of actinomycin D-treated

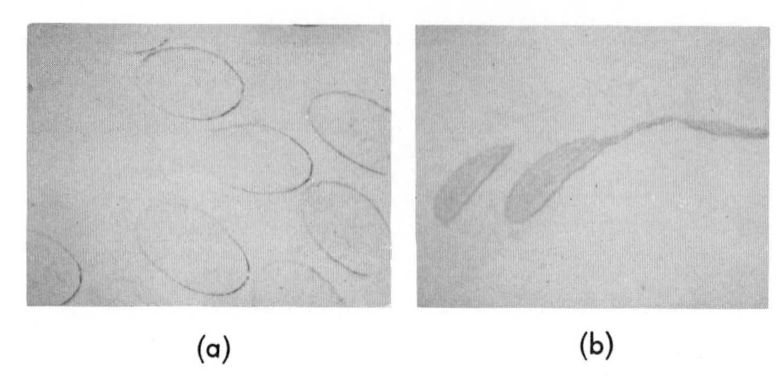

(a) (b)

Figure 24. (a) Eleven-day feathers were incubated with 60 μg/ml actinomycin D for 24 hr and then pulse labeled for 2 hr with ^{14}C amino acids (Schwarz RPH). Autoradiographs of sections of treated feathers show synthesis of protein in sheath cells primarily. (b) In control sections, synthesis occurs uniformly throughout the feather.

and control feathers. Control feathers are nearly uniformly labeled; those treated with actinomycin D have incorporated acid-insoluble radioactivity, mainly in sheath cells.

There is now a close correlation between the utilization of m-RNA of long half-life and the development of birefringence in the feather. At 12 days, the feather sheath is birefringent from tip to base, evidently keratinizing. When 11-day feathers are treated with actinomycin D birefringence continues to develop normally for at least 24 hr indicating the presence of enough stable m-RNA to mediate, undiminished, synthesis of protein which contributes to the development of birefringence.

When protein synthesis is suppressed with 100 μg/ml actidione, further development of birefringence halts, indicating that its progress depends upon a continuous supply of newly made protein.

ACKNOWLEDGMENT

The technical assistance of Miss LaVerne Blanchard is gratefully acknowledged.

REFERENCES

Belitsina, N.V., M.A. Ajtkhozhin, L.P. Gavrilova, and A.S. Spirin. 1964. Messenger RNA of differentiating animal cells. Biokhimiya 29: 363.

Bell, E., and T. Humphreys. 1967a. Growth, regional differentiation and macromolecular synthesis in the developing down feather I. Develop. Biol. (Manuscript submitted.)

Bell, E., and T. Humphreys. 1967b. Growth, regional differentiation and macromolecular synthesis in the developing down feather II. Stabilization of m-RNA. Develop. Biol. (Manuscript submitted.)

Bell, E., and Y.T. Thathachari. 1963. Development of feather keratin during embryogenesis of the chick. J. Cell Biol. 16: 215.

Davies, H.R. 1889. Die Entwicklung der Feder und ihre Beziehungen zu andern Integumentgebilden. Morph. Jahrb. 15: 560.

Humphreys, T., S. Penman, and E. Bell. 1964. The appearance of stable polysomes during the development of chick down feathers. Biochem. Biophys. Res. Commun. 17: 618.

Joklik, W.K., and Y. Becker. 1965. Studies on the genesis of polyribosomes II. The association of nascent messenger RNA with the 40S subribosomal particle. J. Mol. Biol. 13: 511.

Spirin, A.S., and M. Nemer. 1965. Messenger RNA in early sea-urchin embryos: Cytoplasmic particles. Science 150: 214.

*Control of Chromosome Puffing**

Ulrich Clever

Department of Biological Sciences
Purdue University
Lafayette

The nucleus is the principle seat of genetic information in the cells of higher organisms, and it is for this reason that the problem of nuclear behavior and its control has become of central interest in biology. A priori, variations in nuclear activity may reflect variations in the activity of the genome as a whole, or, alternatively, they may reflect changes in a pattern of differential gene activity. The decision between these alternatives requires assay systems which allow the study of nuclear activity at the level of either individual genes or corresponding chromosomal units. Because of their unusually large size, dipteran giant chromosomes and lampbrush chromosomes of developing amphibian oocytes offer this system.

In these chromosomes, small segments become struc-

*Supported by Grant GB-2639 from the National Science Foundation.

turally modified; the chromosome fibers appear to become uncoiled and form "puffs" or "loops." Chromosomal regions forming a puff or loop are usually not larger than a single chromomere (band), and some authors have used this fact to consider chromomeres the "operational units" of chromosomes (1, 2). The DNA content of single chromomeres (bands) in giant chromomeres varies considerably. In Drosophila, the smallest bands contain about 5×10^3, and the larger single bands have up to 5×10^4 nucleotide pairs per chromatid. These values are large compared to those estimated for the cistrons of microorganisms but are comparable to larger functional units such as the histidine operon of p22 phage with 1.3×10^4 nucleotide pairs (3). What corresponds to a band in genetic terms is not understood (1, 4). Nevertheless, the hypothesis is now generally accepted that puffs represent active gene loci, and that puffing reflects differential activity of the genome (1, 5, 6, 7).

Puffed chromosome regions are distinguished from nonpuffed chromosome regions by their content of RNA and of acid proteins, which may be demonstrated easily by appropriate staining with toluidine blue and light green, respectively (8, 9). Autoradiographic data suggest that the RNA accumulated is synthesized in the puffs themselves (8, 10 - 12). No evidence exists that the protein is synthesized in the puffs. Neither existing nor newly induced puffs became preferentially labeled with tritiated amino acids in short-term experiments. After longer incubations, a diffuse label is evident all over the chromosomes (10, 13). Furthermore, the accumulation of puff proteins is not prevented by inhibitors of protein synthesis (14). After injection of tritiated uridine, the number of silver grains above various puffs is roughly proportional to their size, even after very short incubation periods (8). Thus, puff sizes may be used as a rough measure of the synthetic capacity of a puff; however, puff size actually only indicates the amount of RNA and of protein present at a given moment, and thus reflects the balance between synthesis (or accumulation) and removal.

It is well known that puffs exist which are specifically formed only in one tissue or even only in particular cells of one tissue (6, 15 - 17). Even when the patterns of potentially puff-forming loci overlap, as they actually do for some 80 or 90% (19, 20), the actual pattern of puffs formed at a given moment may be different in the various tissues of an individual larva (5). Similarly, the puffing patterns change with development (5, 16, 18, 21 - 24). Changes in puffing patterns have also been produced by experimental treatments of larvae or of isolated tissues, mostly salivary glands (25 - 31). The conclusion derived from these studies was that chromosomal activity as indicated by puffing is controlled by cytoplasmic metabolism and by factors reaching the nucleus via the cytoplasm. What are these "genotropic" factors? What might be their mode of action? Much effort has been devoted to this problem, but the available information is perplexing rather than elucidating.

In general, we may say that all factors which influence cellular activity also affect puffing: hungry larvae, dormant larvae, or larvae kept at low temperatures usually have fewer and smaller puffs than well-fed and actively growing larvae kept at normal temperatures. Alterations of these situations change puffing correspondingly. It is difficult, however, to discern from such observations the specific intracellular factors which might be involved in the control of the various puffs. In the past few years, many attempts have been made to get this information; however, so far the molting hormone ecdysone still is the only substance known to be normally involved in puffing control.

Postembryonic development of insects is under hormonal control, essentially ecdysone, which induces molting, and juvenile hormone, which determines the nature of a given molt. The expectation that the changes of puffing patterns which accompany molting processes, especially the pupal molt (metamorphosis), are also finally controlled by these hormones was confirmed by several studies (9, 32 - 37). The majority of these puffing changes are certainly an indirect result of hormone action, and we do not have any information about factors involved in the actual control of these loci. A few loci, however, respond to the hormone very rapidly. Their size changes in proportion with the ecdysone concentration, and thus their control seems to be related more closely to ecdysone.

In Chironomus tentans, beginning of puff formation at locus I-18-C is the first indication of beginning metamorphosis in the salivary glands. This puff is small at first and gradually increases, becoming maximal only towards the end of the pupal molt. Some time later, on the average of perhaps 1 or 2 days after this puff, another puff forms at locus IV-2-B. It reaches maximal size in the middle of the molt and finally disappears. Both puffs respond to injected ecdysone within less than 1 hr (9, 18). Injections of various amounts of ecdysone revealed that I-18-C responds to lower concentrations (about 10^{-7} μg/mg) than IV-2-B (about 10^{-6} μg/mg). We therefore concluded that puffing at these two loci during the pupal molt is controlled in some way by the gradually increasing hormone concentration (38).

In the experiment, the induced two puffs disappear as soon as the injected hormone is eliminated, which may occur after a few hours when only very small amounts of ecdysone were injected, or after 1 or 2 days when higher dosages were used (9, 38). If a second injection of hormone is given, both puffs reappear, which would indicate not only that ecdysone is a requirement for activity of these two loci, but also that their activity necessarily follows its presence. However, as previously mentioned, in the end phase of the pupal molt only I-18-C is of maximal size, while IV-2-B disappears. The results that ecdysone did not reinduce IV-2-B in old prepupae, and that haemolymph from such prepupae induced I-18-C and IV-2-B in younger larvae, provided strong evidence for the assumption that the ecdysone-titer is still high at the end of the pupal molt. If this is so, we have to conclude that in larvae of this stage another factor is at work which inactivates IV-2-B despite the presence of its inducer, ecdysone (14). This factor itself must form as a consequence of some ecdysone action. Thus, it would appear that an inducing factor and a repressing factor control the activity of this locus, and that both are formed, although sequentially, by ecdysone stimulation. Conceivably, the repressor is formed in a kind of feed-back to some action of the induced puff itself.

Instead of yielding information on ecdysone function, these results make an understanding even more complicated. Whatever the cellular level might be at which ecdysone or its anatagonist might operate in the cell, it seems clear that a rather complex control machinery is at work to assure proper control of puffing at definite developmental stages.

Experimentally, puffing patterns may be changed by a variety of treatments and agents. A most promising result has been obtained with cultured Drosophila salivary glands. Here, a specific puff was induced when L-tryptophan had been added to the culture medium (39). Unfortunately, this observation has not been pursued further.

Effects of temperature changes have been observed in Chironomus (5, 18), and have been studied in more detail in Drosophila buskii by Ritossa (27, 28) and in Drosophila hydei by Berendes and his associates (30, 41, 42). In Ritossa's experiments, the same loci responded to temperature shocks and to chemical agents such as DNP, sodium salicylate, sodium azide, and dicumarol. He concluded that puffing at these loci is related to oxygen metabolism. Van Breugel (43) recently obtained similar results with Drosophila hydei. Berendes used these ideas to explain various aspects of puffing changes observed in different tissues and during development. However, even if we accept these interpretations, the evidence available is negligible regarding the actual factors involved.

Puffing patterns also change when glands are explanted and incubated in salt solutions or in other tissue culture media (22, 30, 31, 44 - 46). Kroeger and Lezzi (47) emphasized the importance ionic concentrations might have as factors controlling puffing in development. Kroeger found that in Chironomus thummi some of the prepupal puffs were among those which responded when explanted glands were incubated in a variety of media (26, 45). In particular, he observed that one of the ecdysone-sensitive puffs appeared when glands were incubated in KCl solutions of high concentrations, and that NaCl solutions changed puffing to a pattern which he defined as "rejuvenated" (44). Kroeger concluded that the puffing changes characteristic for metamorphosis are controlled by changes of the $K^+:Na^+$ ratio in the nucleus; ecdysone, he suggested, might act by controlling this ratio via alterations of cell membrane permeability (44, 47).

This idea gained some support from Kroeger's discovery that the potential differences across the cell membrane changed with development and were affected by ecdysone (46). However, Ito and Loewenstein (48) did not find significant changes in the cell membrane potential of these cells with development, or after application, of ecdysone. We were not able to confirm Kroeger's results for the ecdysone-sensitive puffs with KCl or NaCl solutions in _Chironomus tentans_ (31), and Berendes, van Breugel, and Holt (30) observed unspecific effects of concentrated KCl solutions in _Drosophila hydei_.

It is expected a priori that experimental treatments such as those employed in these studies provoke a variety of changes in cellular metabolisms, and even in cell structure (31, 51). We would also expect these changes to be reflected at the chromosome level by changing puffing patterns. Whether some of the treatments affect puffing more directly, as Kroeger postulates, cannot be determined now; the relationship of these effects to physiological control mechanisms is not yet understood.

So far we have limited our discussion to some factors influencing puffing, without considering puff metabolic activity, which may have been affected. As we already mentioned, puffs are considered to represent active gene loci, and RNA synthesis is their characteristic synthetic activity. We can reasonably assume that at least part of puff RNA is informational, or messenger, RNA. Edström and Beerman (40) provided supporting data for this hypothesis. That this RNA would have to be transported to the cytoplasm to direct protein synthesis is supported by autoradiographic data (8, 52). We may expect, therefore, that the control of puff formation is intimately related to RNA synthesis and transport and to protein synthesis. To uncover information about these possible relationships, we began to study the effects on puffing and puff induction of various inhibitors of RNA and of protein synthesis.

We began our experiments by asking, how do inhibitors of RNA or protein synthesis affect the action of puff inducers, such as ecdysone? We used actinomycin to inhibit RNA synthesis, and discovered that incubation of larvae in 0.2 μg/ml actinomycin for 6 hr inhibits uridine incorporation drastically. After transfer of such larvae into a fresh culture medium, uridine incorporation gradually resumes, starting about 15 to 20 hr later. If we injected ecdysone during the inhibition period, puffs I-18-C and IV-2-B did not appear. If we transferred these larvae into an actinomycin-free culture medium, both puffs appeared at the time RNA synthesis resumed, provided the inducing hormone was still present at this time (49, 50).

Obviously, actinomycin had inhibited puff formation for the same period of time as RNA synthesis. Two explanations of this result would seem possible.

1. Actinomycin is well known as a specific inhibitor of DNA-dependent RNA synthesis that binds to the guanine residues of DNA (53, 54). It might have inhibited RNA synthesis by this mechanism in our experiment and the puffs did not form because of this inhibition. Puff formation then would have to be considered an effect of the induced RNA synthesis.
2. Alternatively, we might assume that actinomycin prevented in some unknown way, the unfolding of chromosome fibers characteristic for puffing, and that this might be a prerequisite for RNA synthesis.

The idea that puff formation is a prerequisite rather than a result of RNA synthesis was suggested by Pelling (8) to explain that only a relatively small fraction of larvae injected with uridine in his experiments showed any label in the autoradiographs, although puffs were present in all.

Other interpretations of these results, however, are certainly possible. The question might be decided by inhibiting RNA synthesis at another level and examining puffing under these conditions. Beermann (55) performed this experiment in Chironomus tentans, using mainly the large Balbiani rings as assay system. He observed a rapid shrinkage of all puffs and Balbiani rings and an inhibition of uridine incorporation when salivary glands were incubated in vivo or in vitro with actinomycin at concentrations ranging from 0.1 to 2.0 μg/ml. However, he observed a similar shrinkage of puffs and Balbiani rings when RNA synthesis was inhibited with overdoses of adenosine, supposedly not acting at the level of RNA polymerase but rather at some prior step of polynucleotide polymerization. These results would suggest that puffing is an effect of RNA synthesis.

Inhibition of RNA synthesis, however, does not automatically lead to a regression of puffs. Beermann's experiments reported so far had been performed at 20°C. Inhibition of uridine incorporation, but not shrinkage, did occur when the experiments were performed at 4°C, or when 10^{-4} M of dinitrophenol was added to the actinomycin. According to these results, a second factor is apparently involved in puff shrinkage which is inhibited by low temperature and requires ATP. Beermann assumes that the second factor is somehow related to packing and removal of the synthesized RNA, thus affecting the rate of accumulation.

In our experiments, as in Beermann's, the Balbiani rings were largely regressed in larvae treated with actinomycin. Resumption of uridine incorporation was accompanied by a gradual re-formation of the Balbiani rings. In contrast to Beermann, however, we still found many smaller puffs in larvae which had been kept in actinomycin for as long as 50 hr at 18°C. Puffs, in contrast to Balbiani rings, can hardly be recognized in autoradiographs. In our first experiments, we used both glands of individual larvae to study either the puffing pattern in light green orcein preparations or the uridine incorporation in autoradiographs. We used actinomycin at a concentration of 0.2 μg/ml, and although incorporation of uridine was drastically reduced, a few larvae usually still showed some label. Thus, some synthetic activity of the persisting puffs could not be excluded.

In a new series of experiments, we examined one gland of each larvae cytologically and the other autoradiographically; we also used a slightly higher concentration of actinomycin than before (0.3 μg/ml). Furthermore, we used larvae with some stage specific puffs (old prepupae) so that we were independent of puffing changes that might occur during the experiments.

We examined glands of 27 control larvae, all of which were heavily labeled with ^{3}H uridine. In contrast, none of the 29 larvae kept in actinomycin for 15 to 20 hr showed any label (Figure 1, a, a'). The Balbiani rings showed the usual shrinkage in these larvae; however, the pattern of prepupal puffing was the same in both groups (Figure 1, b, b'; c, c'). Obviously, these puffs were not caused to regress despite the inhibition of RNA synthesis. Apparently, then, the inhibition of RNA synthesis is not necessarily followed by a regression of those puffs present when the inhibition begins. The reason for the different behavior of puffs and Balbiani rings is not understood.

In the experiments reported so far, RNA synthesis in puffs ceased only because of some action of actinomycin, and we expected puff regression only for this reason. The cellular situation leading to puff formation at the loci under study, however, possibly still existed when the larvae were fixed. It was conceivable, therefore, that factors controlling puffing at these loci maintain this situation regardless of whether RNA synthesis is taking place. In the case of puffs I-18-C and IV-2-B, the concentration of the inducing factor, ecdysone, may be changed at will.

If small amounts of ecdysone are injected, the induced puffs disappear after several hours, probably because of a rapid elimination of the injected hormone (9, 38). In the experiments we shall now report, we injected 0.002 μg of ecdysone (Figure 2). We knew that in larvae fixed 2 hr after this injection, puffs I-18-C and IV-2-B were present in medium to large size.

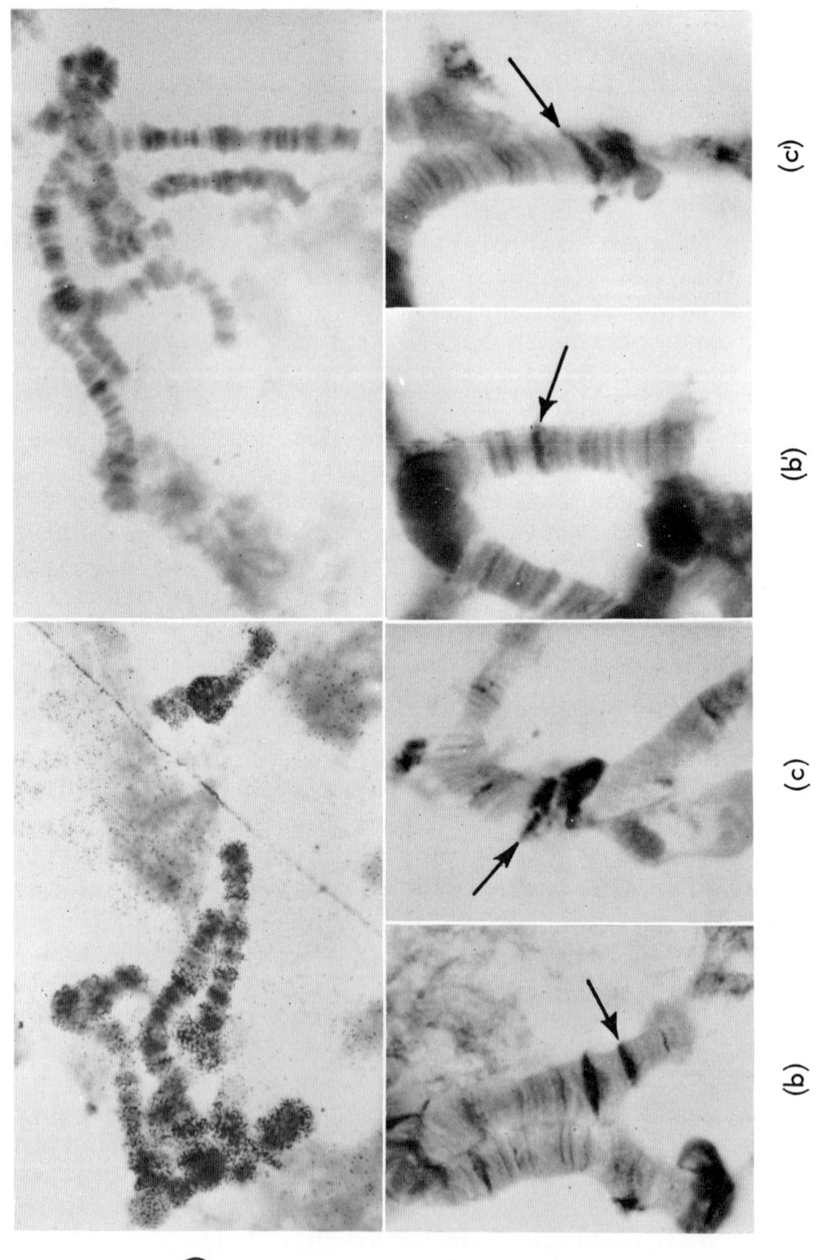
(a)
(a')
(b)
(c)
(b')
(c')

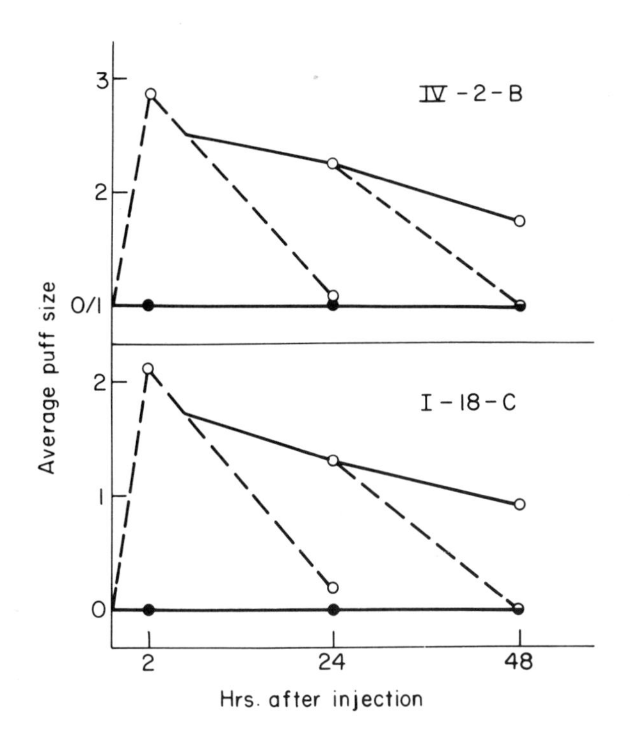

Figure 2. Effect of actinomycin on puff sizes of I-18-C and IV-2-B at intervals after injection of 0.002 μg ecdysone. Solid lines indicate periods during which uridine incorporation was inhibited; dotted lines indicate periods of uninhibited RNA synthesis. At least 10 larvae were used per experiment. Puff sizes are given in arbitrary units as previously defined (9, 38).

Figure 1. (Opposite page.) Effect of actinomycin on uridine incorporation and puffing. (a, b, c) Sister glands from a control prepupa. (a', b', c') Sister glands from a prepupa which had been in actinomycin (0.3 μg/ml) for 17 hr before fixation. (a, a') Autoradiograms after incubation in 10 μc/ml ^{3}H uridine for 45 min. (b, c; b', c') Stained with azure B. (b, b') Puff I-18-C. (c, c') Puff III-9-B.

In larvae fixed after 24 or 48 hr, both puffs had disappeared. If, however, RNA synthesis was inhibited some hours after the injection of ecdysone and the larvae kept in actinomycin, both puffs were still present in most larvae fixed after 24 or 48 hr. Whether the puff size had gradually decreased, as our present data would indicate, has to be reexamined. Uridine was not incorporated by these larvae. In one group of actinomycin-treated larvae, RNA synthesis was allowed to resume at about 24 hr after injection by replacing the actinomycin solution with fresh culture medium. When these larvae were fixed, both puffs had disappeared.

To explain these results, we may assume that actinomycin either inhibited the elimination of ecdysone, which then might have maintained puffing at I-18-C and IV-2-B, or inhibited more directly the regression of these puffs which should have followed the hormone elimination. The regression of both puffs soon after resumption of RNA synthesis favors the second alternative. Furthermore, as already mentioned, ecdysone does not induce these puffs in the presence of actinomycin.

The accumulation of two groups of compounds distinguishes normal puffs from inactive bands: acid proteins and RNA. In our routine staining procedure, we stain the proteins with light green at pH 5. In the actinomycin-treated chromosomes, the puffs appeared green as in the controls. We stained some slides with the metachromatic dye azure B, which colors DNA blue and RNA purple. In both, controls and actinomycin-treated larvae, the puffs stained with similar intensity with azure B, thus probably indicating similar concentrations of RNA (Figure 1, b, c; b', c'). In the actinomycin-treated larvae, this RNA had been synthesized up to 50 hr before fixation. Apparently then, RNA synthesis is necessary not only for puff formation, but also for puff regression and removal of the accumulated material.

Our studies with inhibitors of protein synthesis again were designed primarily to provide some information concerning the role of protein synthesis in ecdysone action on puffing. If *Chironomus* larvae are put into a solution containing 10 μg/ml cycloheximide for 4 hr, protein synthesis is almost completely inhibited (50). Salivary glands from such larvae incorporate ^3H uridine as strongly as untreated control glands. The pattern of incorporation also is the same in both cases: preferentially labeled are nucleoli, Balbiani rings, and puffs (Figure 4).

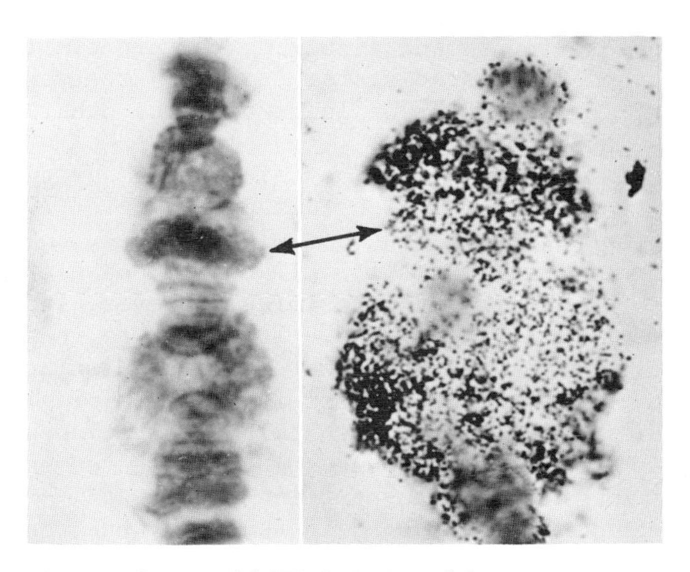

Figure 3. Puff IV-2-B in old prepupae treated with cycloheximide (10 μg/ml) for 17 hr. Autoradiogram after incubation of the gland in 10 μc/ml ^3H uridine for 45 min before fixation.

Ecdysone was injected into larvae pretreated with cycloheximide for 4 hr; the larvae were fixed 2 hr later and examined cytologically. Puffs I-18-C and IV-2-B had appeared in these larvae as in the controls (50). Even when the larvae had been kept in cycloheximide for 15 or 24 hr, ecdysone still induced these characteristic puffs. Autoradiographs revealed that uridine was incorporated into the induced puffs. Similar results were obtained when protein synthesis was inhibited with puromycin instead of cycloheximide (51). Whatever the mechanism of ecdysone action on puffing might be, the steps between its primary action and the activation of some specific puffs do not appear to include synthesis of new protein. The control of puff formation and of RNA synthesis in puffs, then, apparently operates at the transcriptional, rather than the translational, level.

We did not observe any changes of the puffing pattern in larvae treated with cycloheximide for 4 or 6 hr. These larvae showed a puffing pattern similar to that of their untreated sister larvae. Treatment with cycloheximide for 15 hr or longer, on the other hand, affected puffing markedly.

We first observed a "puff-induction" by cycloheximide when we studied the disappearance of IV-2-B in old prepupae (14). In most old prepupae, this puff is either missing or small. All old prepupae treated for 15 to 20 hr with cycloheximide, however, showed the puff maximally developed. It seemed to incorporate uridine as heavily as other puffs of similar size, although, because of the proximity of a Balbiani ring, it was difficult to establish this observation with certainty (Figure 3). Younger larvae treated in the same way did not show any puffing change at IV-2-B.

The experiments designed to test ecdysone concentration in old prepupae had suggested that there must be some stage specific factor which inhibits activity of IV-2-B despite the presence of ecdysone. Evidently this inhibition depends on intact protein synthesis. The assumption of an unstable protein, functioning in some way as a repressor of activity at IV-2-B, would offer an explanation. This interpretation is based on two additional assumptions:

1. that the reappearance of IV-2-B stimulated by cycloheximide reflects an increase in the rate of RNA synthesis, and
2. that this effect of cycloheximide results from its inhibition of protein synthesis.

Effects of cycloheximide on puffing were studied more extensively with intermolt larvae, usually 10- to 12-day-old last instar larvae. When such larvae were kept in cycloheximide solution (10 μg/ml) for 15 to 20 hr, puffs formed which were not present or were present but small in the untreated sister larvae controls. We have not yet mapped the complete pattern of responding loci. As far as we can tell, only those loci responded which are known to be able to form puffs in salivary glands of normal larvae; however, only a relatively small fraction of these loci responded. As we mentioned, IV-2-B did not respond in intermolt larvae. On the other hand, the other ecdysone-sensitive puff, I-18-C, was among those which responded regularly. So far we had examined 71 larvae treated with cycloheximide for 15 to 25 hr. Puff I-18-C was present in all 71, mostly in maximal size. From 64 control larvae, only 7 showed the puff, and most of these only in small size.

In this instance and in similar cases, a puff seemed to have appeared de novo; in other cases, the responding puffs probably had been present before the treatment in smaller size. In section I-2-A, e.g., a small puff is usually present. In practically all larvae treated with cycloheximide for 15 hr or more this puff was very large. Other existing puffs did not respond. For example, in sections I-9-A and I-15-A, puffs are present in most larvae. We found their average size to be the same in treated and untreated larvae. Also, the appearance of the Balbiani rings in treated larvae did not differ from that in untreated controls.

Staining with light green and with azure B revealed that acid protein and RNA had accumulated in cycloheximide-induced puffs as they had in normal ones. After incubation with uridine, they were labeled in autoradiographs. If actinomycin (0.3 μg/ml) was added to the cycloheximide solution in these experiments, no stimulation of puffing occurred. The same was true for the stimulation of IV-2-B in old prepupae. Thus, the cycloheximide-stimulated puff formation, as does a normal one, evidently depends on RNA synthesis.

As normal puffing, therefore, cycloheximide-induced puffing is characterized by a modification of chromosome structure, the accumulation of protein and of RNA, and the incorporation of uridine. A priori, the accumulation in both cases might result from either an increased rate of synthesis or a decrease in the rate of removal. Pelling's data (8) strongly suggest that at least in general the accumulation of RNA reflects a much higher rate of synthesis in puffs than in normal bands, and that this rate is still higher in large puffs than in small ones. Actually, Pelling's results did not provide any evidence that nonpuffed bands incorporate uridine at all. Some of the loci that responded to cycloheximide by puff formation - e.g., IV-2-B in old prepupae and I-18-C, I-8-A, and others in intermolt larvae - seemed to be in an unpuffed condition in most of the respective control larvae. At least in these cases the cycloheximide treatment apparently had actually induced puffing by locally stimulating RNA synthesis. The inhibitory effect of actinomycin supports this interpretation. Nevertheless, we must still keep in mind the alternative possibility that these loci had been active without puff formation and that the rate of removal was affected. In this case, however, we would have to reconsider the entire current concept of puffing.

Other experiments suggested that cycloheximide affected the removal rate of accumulated material rather than its rate of synthesis. If intermolt larvae were injected with small amounts of ecdysone, small puffs were induced at I-18-C and IV-2-B. If the same injection was given to larvae pretreated with cycloheximide for 4 hr, the induced puffs were considerably larger. Inasmuch as IV-2-B in larvae of this age did not respond to cycloheximide even after 20 or 40 hr of treatment, and since both loci had not responded in controls treated only with cycloheximide, the activation seems to have been induced by ecdysone alone, which would leave an effect on transport for cycloheximide. The effect of cycloheximide on some existing puffs also might be interpreted in this way. Since puffing at some of these loci occurs with greatly varying frequency, this hypothesis would easily explain the observed variability in the response of these puffs Finally, the cycloheximide stimulated puffs were frequently, although not always, considerably larger than the homologous normal ones; the excessive puff material sometimes had formed droplets which lay inside the puffs or seemed to be attached to the puff surface.

This observation also might indicate a decreased rate of removal. An accumulation of m-RNA or of high-turnover RNA after cycloheximide treatment has been found in other systems (63, 64).

Thus, it would appear at the moment that the answer to the question of whether synthesis or removal of some puff material may be affected by cycloheximide might be, both. Certainly, more information is needed to decide the problem. One solution may lie in an understanding of the primary effects of cycloheximide in the cell, which in turn affect puffing.

According to recent evidence, cycloheximide inhibits protein synthesis at the ribosomal level (56, 57) by interfering with enzymes involved in the assemblage of charged amino acids (58, 59). Effects on synthesis and/or stability of messenger, and especially of ribosomal, RNA have also been reported (60 - 64). We have already mentioned that protein synthesis was drastically inhibited in our system. This effect was obvious even in larvae treated for only 1 hr. Uridine incorporation, on the other hand, was apparently still normal in larvae which had been in cycloheximide for 4 or 6 hr. In glands treated for 15 hr or longer, however, the rate of uridine incorporation seemed to be lower than in the controls, although our results (with almost 150 glands examined) do not as yet give a clear picture. The glands of some larvae still incorporated uridine as strongly as the controls and into the same chromosomal sites - i.e., puffs, Balbiani rings and nucleoli - (Figure 4). In most glands, however, the rate of incorporation was much lower than in the controls, especially that into nucleolar RNA. It was particularly weak in some series of experiments in which we had not added cycloheximide to the radioactive incubation medium of the glands. Addition of the drug improved incorporation somewhat, but, in most experiments, still not to the level of the controls.

Evidently, then, prolonged treatment with cycloheximide had some effect on RNA synthesis, but this effect was far less pronounced and seemed to begin later than the inhibition of protein synthesis. Our results would be consistent with the idea that only inhibition of protein synthesis is a primary action of cycloheximide,

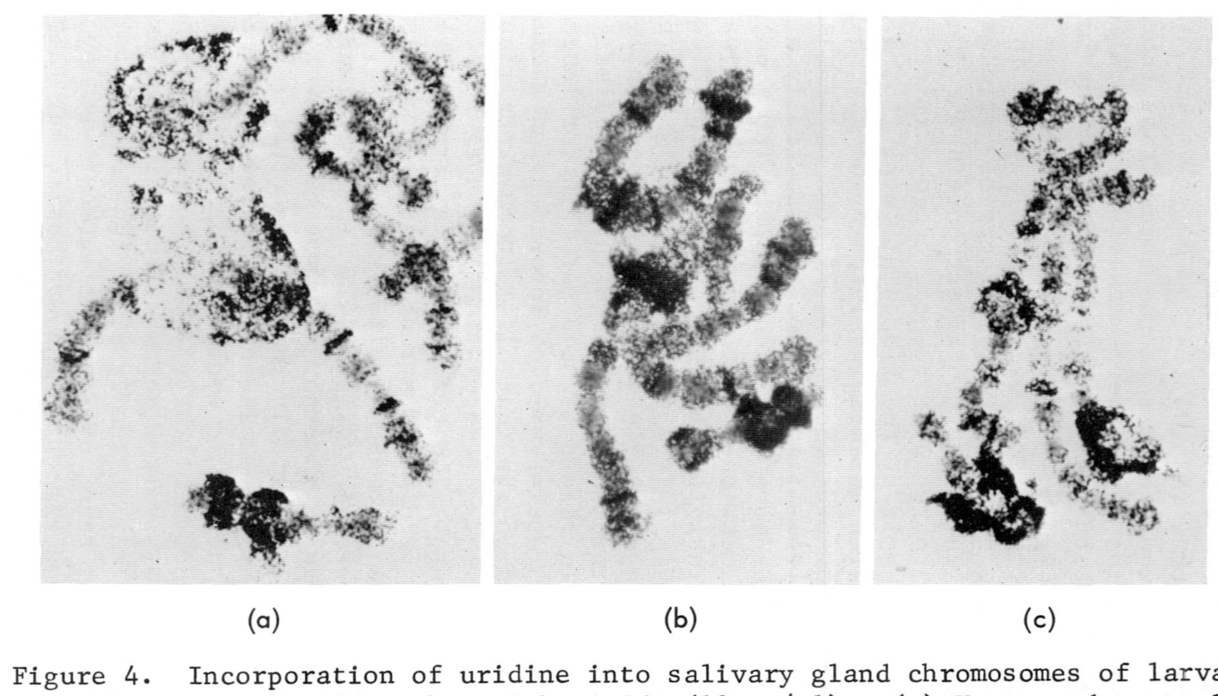

Figure 4. Incorporation of uridine into salivary gland chromosomes of larvae which had been treated with cycloheximide (10 μg/ml). (a) Untreated control. (b) Treated for 6 hr. (c) Treated for 18 hr. The glands were incubated in 10 μc/ml ^{3}H uridine for 30 min before fixation.

and that it is by this action that other cellular systems, especially RNA metabolism, are affected (62). The effects on puffing might conceivably result from changes in either protein or RNA metabolism.

However, since cycloheximide did not affect all chromosomal loci indiscriminately, we should first consider the possibility that the drug itself specifically interfered with the control systems of the sensitive loci, possibily because of a chemical similarity to some factor involved. If it is the inhibiton of protein synthesis per se that provokes the biological effects of cycloheximide, we should expect similar effects with protein inhibitors which are chemically unrelated and have different modes of action. Unfortunately, many of these substances cannot be used in *Chironomus*, because they apparently do not penetrate the larval cuticle and are not effective for a sufficiently long period of time when injected. For example, puromycin did not inhibit protein synthesis when added to the culture medium in concentrations up to 200 μg/ml. When injected (concentration in the larvae ca. 100 μg/ml), it inhibits protein synthesis, but only for a few hours. Nevertheless, inhibition was followed by an increase in puff size at several loci ca. 16 hr after injection. Our results with other antibiotics appear in Table 1.

Pactamycin was the only antibiotic that inhibited amino acid incorporation to a similar degree as did cycloheximide; it also affected puffing in the same way and, as far as we can tell, at the same sites. Incorporation of arginine and lysine was inhibited by Gougerotin at concentrations of 400 μg/ml, but considerably more incorporation occurred than with either cycloheximide or Pactamycin. With the possible exception of Gougerotin, which must be tested further, our data would indicate a correspondence in the effects on protein synthesis and on puffing.

Apparently, then, both the inhibition of RNA synthesis and the inhibition of protein synthesis may affect puffing by influencing two processes: the rate of RNA synthesis and the rate of removal of the accumulated material. What could be the mechanisms involved?

Puff formation seems to succeed RNA synthesis rather

TABLE 1

Effects of various antibiotics on puffing and protein synthesis in Chironomus salivary glands*

Antibiotic	Maximal concentration tested	Effects on: puffing	Effects on: incorporation
Cycloheximide	10 μg/ml	+	+
Streptovitacin A (59, 67) (4-OH-cycloheximide)	20 μg/ml	-	-
Puromycin (68)	200 μg/ml	-	-
Gougerotin (65)	400 μg/ml	-	(+)
Pactamycin (59, 67)	10 μg/ml	+	+
Sparsomycin (67)	10 μg/ml	-	-
Lincomycin (66)	10 μg/ml	-	-

*The larvae were kept in solutions of these drugs for 15 to 20 hr before fixation. Tritiated amino acids (leucine, valine, arginine, and lysine) were injected 2 hr before fixation. Incorporation was examined autoradiographically. The plus sign indicates that the puffing pattern had changed, or that incorporation was inhibited.

than to precede it. We may expect, therefore, that factors controlling puffing do so by influencing the rate of RNA synthesis, which would explain why actinomycin inhibits puff formation. The molecular mechanisms which control chromosomal RNA synthesis are not understood. In a formal way, the application of models developed for microorganisms (69) would seem possible. Lewis (70) and Welshons (71) have compared the genetic subdivisions of the Drosophila chromosome with the organization of the bacterial chromosome according to the Jacob-Monod model, in which factors such as ecdysone have been proposed to act like effectors (13). But so far, we have no convincing evidence that regulator genes and regulator circuits with similar functions are at work in higher organisms as they are in bacteria. The complex chromosome structure might rather indicate that more complicated or additional control systems have developed in evolution. For example, the DNA-histone binding may have to be changed to allow chromosomal RNA synthesis, and control mechanisms may operate at this level.

The stimulation of puff formation by inhibition of protein synthesis seems to reflect a local increase in the rate of RNA synthesis. Undoubtedly, many explanations are possible. One attractive possibility would be the assumption of unstable protein molecules involved in the control, or, more specifically, in the repression of puff activity. This assumption would easily explain the relative unspecificity of the cycloheximide effect. The life span of these proteins would have to be ca. 10 to 20 hr. Nonresponding loci might be controlled by more stable proteins, or this type of control might operate only at definite developmental stages at each locus, as the stage specific responsiveness of IV-2-B suggests. Unstable proteins with control functions have been proposed to exist in bacteria (72, 73), and proteins as regulators have been repeatedly considered for higher organisms (74, 75). The idea of unstable proteinic represssors present in chromosomes would be consistent with the labeling pattern obtained with radioactive amino acids.

We shall add a few words here about the possible relation of puff proteins to puffing control. The bulk of protein present in the puffs stains intensively with light green at pH 5, and we shall discuss one possible function of these proteins. The local amount of histone apparently does not change with puff formation (76). Treatment of chromosomes with injected trypsin, which preferentially attacks basic proteins, increased the size of existing puffs and the local rate of RNA synthesis in _Chironomus thummi_ (77). Pogo, Allfrey, and Mirsky (78) recently reported that acetylation of histones preceded phytohemagglutinin-stimulated RNA synthesis in human lymphocytes.

If this were characteristic for all chromosomal RNA

induction, we would expect that puffs become labeled if tritiated acetate is present at the moment of induction. As a test, we injected ecdysone (0.25 μg) and Na-acetate-^{3}H (6 μc in 1 μl; spec. act. 4.9 c/mM) into last instar _Chironomus_ larvae. The larvae were fixed 2 hr after injection, i.e., when puffs I-18-C and IV-2-B were maximally developed. In weakly labeled glands, silver grains were almost exclusively distributed above the cytoplasm. In the more heavily labeled glands, there was also some diffuse label above the chromosomes. However, neither the induced puffs I-18-C and IV-2-B, nor any other chromosomal regions (such as nucleoli or Balbiani rings), showed any preferential labeling.

Both the inhibition of protein synthesis and that of RNA synthesis seemed to interfere with RNA (and protein) removal from the puffs. If it is m-RNA which is being formed in the puffs, it seems questionable whether such molecules could leave the nucleus by themselves. It has been suggested recently that m-RNA must combine with protein to form "informosomes" (79) or with 40S ribosomal subunits (80, 81) to leave the nucleus. Ribonucleoprotein particles for which a carrier function has been proposed, have been observed in puffs and Balbiani rings (76, 82 - 84), and the concentrations of puff RNA and puff proteins seem to change correspondingly. If we assume that these particles have to pick up m-RNA or that they have to form in the puffs, both hypotheses would explain an accumulation of RNA in the chromosomes after protein synthesis has ceased. The assumption that ribosomal subunits function as carriers of m-RNA could furthermore explain why inhibition of RNA synthesis by actinomycin blocks RNA removal from puffs.

The speculative nature of some of these last considerations need not be emphasized, and new experimental results are obviously needed before more definite conclusions can be drawn. Apparently more than one process is controlled at the puff level. RNA and protein molecules and their synthesis seem to play a crucial role in the control mechanisms, and the experimental techniques may now be available for deciding what role this is.

ACKNOWLEDGMENTS

Carole G. Romball, Susan Bormann and Maike U. Hinrichs collaborated and assisted in various parts of these studies. Ecdysone was supplied by Dr. Peter Karlson. Sparsomycin, Pactamycin, Streptovitacin A, and Lincomycin were gifts from Dr. C.G. Smith of the Upjohn Company, Kalamazoo, Michigan. Gougerotin was a gift from Dr. A. Miyake, Takeda Chemical Industries, Osaka, Japan, and from Dr. J.M. Clark, Biochemistry Division, University of Illinois, Urbana, Illinois.

REFERENCES

1. Beermann, W. 1965. Naturwiss. 52: 365.
2. Pelling, C. 1966. Proc. Roy. Soc. London Ser. B. 164: 279.
3. Rudkin, G.T. 1965. Genetics 52: 665.
4. Edström, J.-E. 1964. In "Role of Chromosomes in Development," J. Locke, ed. Academic Press, N.Y.
5. Beermann, W. 1952. Chromosoma 5: 139.
6. Breuer, M., and C. Pavan. 1953. Caryologia, Suppl. 6: 778.
7. Gall, J.G. 1963. In "Chromosomes and Cytodifferentiation," J. Locke, ed. Academic Press, N.Y.
8. Pelling, C. 1964. Chromosoma 15: 71.
9. Clever, U. 1961. Chromosoma 12: 607.
10. Pelling, C. 1959. Nature 184: 655.
11. Rudkin, G.T., and P.S. Woods. 1959. Proc. Natl. Acad. Sci. U.S. 45: 997.
12. Sirlin, J.L. 1960. Exp. Cell Res. 19: 177.
13. Clever, U. 1964. In "The Nucleohistones," J. Bonner and P. Ts'o, eds. Holden-Day, San Francisco.
14. Clever, U. 1966. Develop. Biol. (In press.)
15. Beermann, W. 1952. Z. Naturforsch. 7b: 237.
16. Mechelke, F. 1953. Chromosoma 5: 511.
17. Beermann, W. 1961. Chromosoma 12: 1.
18. Clever, U. 1962. Chromosoma 13: 385.
19. Clever, U. 1966. Am. Zool. 6: 33.
20. Berendes, H.D. 1965. Develop. Biol. 11: 371.
21. Breuer, M., and C. Pavan. 1955. Chromosoma 7: 371.

22. Becker, H.J. 1959. Chromosoma 10: 654.
23. Gabrusewycz-Garcia, N. 1964. Chromosoma 15: 312.
24. Berendes, H.D. 1965. Chromosoma 17: 35.
25. Kroeger, H. 1960. Chromosoma 11: 129.
26. Kroeger, H. 1964. Chromosoma 15: 36.
27. Ritossa, F.M. 1962. Experientia 18: 571.
28. Ritossa, F.M. 1964. Exp. Cell Res. 35: 601.
29. Ritossa, F.M., J.F. Pulitzer, H. Swift, and R.C. von Borstel. 1965. Chromosoma 16: 144.
30. Berendes, H.D., F.M.A. van Breugel, and T.K.H. Holt. 1965. Chromosoma 16: 35.
31. Clever, U. 1965. Chromosoma 17: 309.
32. Clever, U., and P. Karlson. 1960. Exp. Cell Res. 20: 623.
33. Panitz, R. 1960. Naturwiss. 47: 383.
34. Panitz, R. 1964. Biol. Zentr. 83: 197.
35. Becker, H.J. 1962. Chromosoma 13: 341.
36. Burdette, W.J., and R. Anderson. 1965. Genetics 51: 625.
37. Burdette, W.J., and M.W. Bullock. 1963. Science 140: 1311.
38. Clever, U. 1963. Develop. Biol. 6: 73.
39. Fedoroff, N., and R. Milkman. 1964. Biol. Bull. 127: 369.
40. Edström, J.-E., and W. Beermann. 1962. J. Cell Biol. 14: 371.
41. Berendes, H.D. 1965. Genen en Phaenen 10: 32.
42. Berendes, H.D., and T.K.H. Holt. 1964. Genen en Phaenen 9: 1.
43. Van Breugel, F.M.A. 1966. Genetica 37: 17.
44. Kroeger, H. 1963. Nature 200: 1234.
45. Kroeger, H. 1963. J. Cell. Comp. Physiol. 62, Suppl. 1: 45.
46. Kroeger, H. 1966. Exp. Cell Res. 41: 64.
47. Kroeger, H., and M. Lezzi. 1966. Ann. Rev. Entomol. 11: 1.
48. Ito, S., and W.R. Loewenstein. 1965. Science 150: 909.
49. Clever, U. 1964. Science 146: 794.
50. Clever, U., and C.G. Romball. 1966. Proc. Natl. Acad. Sci. U.S. (In press.)
51. Ellgaard, E.G., and R.G. Kessel. 1966. Exp. Cell Res. 42: 302.

52. Arnold, G. 1965. J. Morphol. 116: 65.
53. Reich, E., E.M. Franklin, A.J. Shatkin, and E.L. Tatum. 1961. Science 134: 556.
54. Goldberg, I.H., M. Rabinowitz, and E. Reich. 1962. Proc. Natl. Acad. Sci. U.S. 48: 2094.
55. Beermann, W. 1966. In "Cell Differentiation and Morphogenesis," North Holland Publ. Co., Amsterdam.
56. Siegel, M.R., and H.D. Sisler. 1964. Biochim. Biophys. Acta 87: 70, 83.
57. Ennis, H.L., and M. Lubin. 1964. Science 146: 1474.
58. Noll, H. 1965. Symp. Fundamental Cancer Res. 19th Houston 1965, 67.
59. Felicetti, L., B. Colombo, and C. Baglioni. 1966. Biochim. Biophys. Acta 119: 120.
60. Fiala, E.S., and F.F. Davis. 1965. Biochem. Biophys. Res. Commun. 18: 115.
61. Haidle, C.W., and R. Stork. 1966. Biochem. Biophys. Res. Commun. 22: 175.
62. Sussman, M. 1966. Proc. Natl. Acad. Sci. U.S. 55: 813.
63. Fukuhara, H. 1965. Biochem. Biophys. Res. Commun. 18: 297.
64. de Kloet, S.R. 1965. Biochem. Biophys. Res. Commun. 19: 582.
65. Casjens, S.R., and A.J. Morris. 1965. Biochim. Biophys. Acta 109: 677.
66. Chang, F.N., C.J. Sih, and B. Weisblum. 1966. Proc. Natl. Acad. Sci. U.S. 55: 431.
67. Colombo, B., L. Felicetti, and C. Baglioni. 1966. Biochim. Biophys. Acta 119: 109.
68. Yarmolinsky, M.B., and G.L. de la Haba. 1959. Proc. Natl. Acad. Sci. U.S. 45: 1721.
69. Jacob, F., and J. Monod. 1961. J. Mol. Biol. 3: 318.
70. Lewis, E.B. 1963. Am. Zool. 3: 33.
71. Welshons, W.J. 1965. Science 150: 1122.
72. Sadler, J.R., and A. Novick. 1965. J. Mol. Biol. 12: 305.
73. Garen, A., and S. Garen. 1963. J. Mol. Biol. 6: 433.
74. Bonner, J., and P. Ts'o, eds. 1964. "The Nucleohistones," Holden-Day, San Francisco.
75. Butler, J.A.V. 1965. Nature 207: 1041.

76. Swift, H. 1963. In "The Molecular Control of Cellular Activity," J.M. Allen, ed. McGraw-Hill, N.Y.
77. Robert, M., and H. Kroeger. 1965. Experientia 21: 326.
78. Pogo, B.G.T., V.G. Allfrey, and A.E. Mirsky. 1966. Proc. Natl. Acad. Sci. U.S. 55: 805.
79. Spirin, A.S., and M. Nemer. 1965. Science 150: 214.
80. Joklik, W.K., and Y. Becker. 1965. J. Mol. Biol. 13: 511.
81. McConkey, E.H., and J.W. Hopkins. 1965. J. Mol. Biol. 14: 257.
82. Beermann, W., and G.F. Bahr. 1954. Exp. Cell Res. 6: 195.
83. Stevens, B.J. 1964. J. Ultrastruct. Res. 11: 329.
84. Kalnins, V.I., H.F. Stich, and S.A. Bencosme. 1964. Can. J. Zool. 42: 1147.

Section III

The Exchange of Material Between Nucleus and Cytoplasm

Machinery for Exchange Across the Nuclear Envelope

A. R. Stevens

Department of Anatomy
University of Colorado Medical Center
Denver

I. INTRODUCTION

A vast amount of biochemical, genetic, and cytological evidence has provided the biologist with a comprehensive understanding of cellular protein synthesis. We are now aware that DNA exerts its influence on this important cellular activity by transcribing its information in the form of several species of RNA molecules. The role of each of these gene products in protein production has been well defined by biochemical analyses of subcellular fractions. Moreover, a correlation of in vitro studies with investigations on the ultrastructure of the cytoplasm has revealed the cellular machinery implicated in the assembly of amino acids into polypeptides. The ribosomes often found attached to the lipoprotein membranes in the cytoplasm are arranged in groups or clusters which constitute the functional protein-synthesizing organelles of the cell

(Gierer, 1963; Marks, Rifkind, and Danon, 1963; Warner, Knopf, and Rich, 1963; Mathias et al., 1964).

Early, in vivo, autoradiographical investigations demonstrated that RNA is synthesized in the nucleus before it appears in the cytoplasm (Goldstein and Plaut, 1955). Furthermore, most of this synthesis and transfer occurs continuously during interphase (Prescott, 1957); in late prophase, RNA production ceases with a subsequently, abrupt release of the RNA remaining in the nucleus (Prescott, 1964). However, the exact manner by which the various types of RNA molecules are transferred to the cytoplasm for participation in protein construction remains one of the most puzzling questions in cell biology. The purpose of this paper, therefore, is to present experimental observations of a unique nuclear structure that may be implicated in mediating the transfer of a particular type of RNA to the cytoplasm for its designated role in cellular protein synthesis.

II. THE NUCLEAR ENVELOPE

The major release of RNA occurs during interphase when the nuclear envelope is intact. Therefore, any discussion concerning the movement of RNA from the nucleus to the cytoplasm must consider the functional and structural integrity of the structure that separates the cell into two compartments.

The presence of a structure delimiting the contents of the nucleus from the remaining constituents of the cell was suspected as early as 1833 by Robert Brown but was confirmed only in this century by the micromanipulation experiments of Chambers and Fell (1931). Thereafter, investigations of the nuclear envelope were mainly of a physiological nature. Studies conducted to study the osmotic properties of isolated nuclei revealed that the envelope was permeable to simple salts and sugars but would not allow the entry of substances of higher molecular weight (Goldstein and Harding, 1950); however, utilization of the fluorescent-antibody technique to localize larger molecules in vivo demonstrated that albumins and gamma globulin could permeate the cell nucleus (Coons, Leduc, and Kaplan, 1951). Furthermore, Maisel and Lytle (1966) have shown recently that animal cells cultured in vitro concentrate nonimmune serum proteins in the nucleoli. Electrophoretic analysis of the serum indicates that the "nucleolar binding component is a globulin" (Maisel and Lytle, 1966). In view of the results of Coons and his associates (1951) and of Maisel and Lytle (1966), isolation of nuclei by the earlier methods apparently did not allow an accurate analysis of the permeability properties of the cell nucleus.

Some of the most significant information about the nuclear envelope has been provided by the electron microscope. Examination of envelopes of isolated nuclei (Callan and Tomlin, 1950) and ultrathin sections of intact cells (Watson, 1955; Beams, et al., 1957) show that the nuclear surface is bordered by two unit membranes that enclose a perinuclear cisterna and that join at certain intervals to define circular discontinuities or pores. The pores are approximately 300 to 500 A in diameter, as visualized in sections cut normal to the surface of the nuclear envelope, and presumably correspond to the ring-shaped structures or annuli observed in tangential sections (Watson, 1955; Haguenau and Bernhard, 1955; Pappas, 1956a). Another striking feature of the envelope frequently observed in micrographs of ultrathin sections is the continuity between the perinuclear space and the cavities of the endoplasmic reticulum (Watson, 1955; Marinos, 1960).

Electron microscope investigations have established that the basic nuclear envelope framework in almost all cells is a porous bilaminar structure (Wischnitzer, 1960); however, several variations that may represent specialization of the envelope have been consistently noted. Small cylinders that project a short distance on either side of the nuclear envelope are associated with the nuclear pores in some invertebrate (Afzelius, 1955; André and Rouiller, 1956) and vertebrate oocytes (Wischnitzer, 1958; Swift, 1958) and in a particular somatic cell (Dawson, Hossack, and Wyburn, 1955). Moreover, in several instances the walls of the cylinders or annuli have been resolved into a defined number of subannuli or microcylinders (Gall, 1956; Rebuhn,

1956; Wischnitzer, 1958; Swift, 1958).

Another example of possible specialization of a nuclear envelope was found very early in Amoeba proteus. The pioneering work of Bairati and Lehmann (1952) and Harris and James (1952) revealed that this protozoan possesses a thick honeycomb layer just inside the double nuclear membranes. This inner lamina is composed of closely packed hexagonal prisms (approximately 1400 A wide) that open into the surrounding nucleoplasm. Furthermore, each prism has been observed to terminate at the nuclear envelope "in a precisely centered pore" (Pappas, 1956a).

A structure comparable to the honeycomb layer in A. proteus has since been found in several other species of protozoa (Beams, et al., 1957; 1959) and in the neuron and glial cells of a leach (Coggeshall and Fawcett, 1964). Recently, Coggeshall and Fawcett (1964) have referred to this layer as the fibrous lamina because of its filamentous appearance in electron micrographs. Moreover, some evidence indicates that the layer may be present in other cell types in a less obvious form (Fawcett, 1966).

III. THE NUCLEAR ENVELOPE AND NUCLEOCYTOPLASMIC INTERACTIONS

The complex morphological features of the nuclear envelope as revealed by the electron microscope imply that this cellular organelle may play an active role in the mediation of nucleocytoplasmic interactions. As early as 1955, Watson stated that the nuclear envelope offered the nucleus two channels by which to communicate with its environment. The indirect route would be realized by the continuity between the perinuclear cisterna of the envelope and the cisternae of the endoplasmic reticulum. This avenue might allow the exchange of inorganic ions and small molecules. The direct route, for the transport of larger molecules, might be the nuclear pores, the dimension of which far exceeds the size of any substance that may be implicated in nucleocytoplasmic relationships (Watson, 1955). Substances may also be released from the nucleus to the cytoplasm by the blebbing of the nuclear membranes (Gay, 1955; Moses, 1956; Clark, 1960; Kessel and Beams, 1963; Kessel, 1964; Szollosi, 1965). However, it is still not possible to decide whether the blebbing phenomenon can be considered a concept of general significance for nucleocytoplasmic interplay in the cell (Swift, 1958).

Observations indicating the direct passage of substances through the nuclear pores make this route an attractive possibility for the transfer of the genetic information. The first convincing illustration showing well-defined material within the pores of the nuclear envelope was presented by Anderson and Beams (1956) from their investigations of the nurse cells of an insect ovary. The pore material, granular in texture, was in continuity with similar material present in both the nucleus and cytoplasm. Although the pore material bore a great similarity to the particulate component of the nucleolus, Anderson and Beams did not characterize the substance chemically.

More recently, light microscope cytochemical studies correlated with electron microscope examination of immature oocytes of a tunicate suggest that the dense granular material noted in the nuclear pores of this organism contains RNA (Kessel, 1966). The dense masses in the openings of the envelope have been observed in direct continuity with material on both the nuclear and cytoplasmic sides of the envelope. Furthermore, the particulate component of the granular masses located immediately adjacent to the nuclear pores on the cytoplasmic side bears a structural similarity to the cytoplasmic ribosomes and to the granular constituent of the nucleolus. Thus the observations of Kessel (1966) are compatible with cytological and biochemical evidence that implicate the nucleolus as the source of ribosomal RNA (Edström, 1960; Edström and Beermann, 1962; Scherrer and Darnell, 1962; Perry, 1962, 1963, 1964; Edström and Gall, 1963; Scherrer, Latham, and Darnell, 1963; McConkey and Hopkins, 1964) and possibly as the source of ribosomes (Bernhard and Granboulan, 1963; Lafontaine and Chouinard, 1963; Swift, 1963; Granboulan and Granboulan, 1964; B.J. Stevens, 1964; Karasaki, 1964, 1965).

Additional observations suggesting the presence of RNA within the nuclear pores have been presented recently by B.J. Stevens and Swift (1966). Ultrastructural examination of the salivary gland nuclei of Chironomi reveals that the Balbiani rings (RNA puffs) of the large chromosomes can be resolved into dense threads, granules, and chromatin fibrils. These authors believe that the threads and granules merely represent a different configurational state of the same entity, because both are ribonuclease digestible and electron micrographs occasionally reveal continuity between the threads and granules. Since only granules are found in regions other than the Balbiani ring, Stevens and Swift believe the threads condense into the granules at the site of the Balbiani ring. The granules then presumably migrate into the surrounding nucleoplasm and ultimately become elongated into rod like structures during passage through the nuclear pores. These results have led Stevens and Swift (1966) to suggest "that the granules represent the product of the Balbiani ring, possibly a messenger RNA bound to protein."

The experiments just described present the first clear indication that a specific species of RNA may assume a distinct ultrastructural configuration for transport from the nucleus to the cytoplasm. The experiments which will be discussed now concern another unique entity that may also represent the packaging of a particular RNA species for its efficient transport out of the nucleus.

IV. THE HELICES OF AMOEBA PROTEUS

Amoeba proteus has long been a favorite organism for cytological investigations, particularly in those studies concerned with nucleocytoplasmic interactions. In addition to many light microscope observations, various electron microscope studies have also been performed on this protozoan (Bairati and Lehmann, 1952; Harris and James, 1952; Pappas, 1956a, b; Cohen, 1957; Mercer, 1959; Roth, Obetz, and Daniels, 1960; Daniels, 1964a, b; Daniels and Breyer, 1965, 1966). Several such studies have revealed that the *Amoeba* nucleus varies in shape but is usually a large, slightly biconcave structure bordered by a complex honeycomb structure and porous double membranes (Figure 1). Large, granular "nucleoli" containing electron-dense (foamy) particles (Cohen, 1957) line the inside of the nuclear envelope, and in the more central regions of the nucleus, unusual arrays of helical clusters have been described (Pappas, 1956b; Mercer, 1959; Roth, Obetz, and Daniels, 1960). The remaining substance of the interphase nucleus has been tentatively defined as filamentous in texture (Mercer, 1959).

During the present investigations, however, several other distinct entities could be resolved in the *Amoeba* nucleus. Large, granular masses composed of particles of varying size and density are often evident in close proximity to the "nucleoli" (Figure 1). These masses usually display several large, electron-dense "mulberry" structures within their matrices (Figure 2). Another component of the nucleus is a network of condensed patches (Figure 1) that at higher magnifications appear to be comprised of a mass of electron-dense, tangled filaments (Figure 3)

The unusual clusters of helices are among the most striking and interesting structures in the *Amoeba* nucleus (Figures 1, 4, and 5). Because these structures were first described by Pappas (1956b) in the Feulgen-positive areas of the nucleus, the chemical nature of the helices has been frequently assumed to be DNA or deoxyribonucleoprotein. The configuration of the helices and speculation that they might contain DNA has led Taylor (1963) to cite the ameba helices as morphological evidence supporting a model of the interphase chromosome. In 1960, however, Roth and his colleagues performed an electron microscope study of the nuclear changes accompanying mitosis in *A. proteus* and found that the helices were present in interphase, disappeared by late prophase, and did not reappear until the nuclear reconstruction stage. As they report, the helices do not coexist with chromatin or with chromosomes during the mitotic sequence, and, thus, the "helices represent either a DNA configuration unique to interphase or are not DNA at all."

Because the role of the helices in the cellular activities of A. proteus is obscure, we have utilized cytochemical techniques coupled with electron microscopy to acquire information about the distribution and chemical composition of these nuclear structures. All electron microscope observations that will be reported were performed on amebae fixed with osmium tetroxide (with the additives sucrose and calcium chloride), dehydrated in a graded series of alcohols, and embedded in Epon or araldite (Stevens and Prescott, 1965). The sections were stained with uranyl acetate and lead citrate (Reynolds, 1963; Venable and Coggeshall, 1965).

Clusters of helices of the same size and form as those described by Pappas (1956b) have been observed consistently in our material (Figure 4). In agreement with the earlier observations, the helices often radiate from a common central core of electron-dense material. Contrary to previous reports, however, single helices and smaller, more dispersed groups of helices have been seen in the nucleus proper (Figure 5) and in areas adjacent to the thick honeycomb layer of the ameba nucleus (Figure 6).

Subsequent to locating the helices in the ameba nucleus, examination of the pore complex revealed one and sometimes two helices within a single opening of the honeycomb layer (Figure 7). Moreover, in rare instances, a helix was found touching the nuclear envelope precisely in the region of a nuclear pore (Figure 8). A careful inspection of the micrograph in Figure 8 reveals that the helix is uncoiled at the extreme tip that extends into the electron-opaque material of the pore.

The presence of ill-defined, electron-opaque material within the nuclear pores has been demonstrated previously in A. proteus (Feldherr, 1965) as well as in a variety of other cell types (André and Rouiller, 1956; Baud, 1959; Watson, 1959; Gall, 1964) and has been suggested to play a role in nucleocytoplasmic exchange (Watson, 1959; Feldherr, 1965). The presence of such material might retard the free passage of substances between the nucleus and cytoplasm.

Electron micrographs of helical structures within the honeycomb layer and touching the nuclear pores of

A. proteus suggested the possibility that the helices were moving through the nuclear membranes and therefore should be detectable in the cytoplasm. A careful survey of the cytoplasm did reveal several clearly recognizable helices (Figure 9), but, compared to the number in the nucleus, cytoplasmic helices were extremely rare. Their measurement showed that they are comparable in size to many of the helices located in the nucleus. Helices of the pore complex, nucleus, and cytoplasm can attain lengths of 7000 A, and the diameter of the coil making up the helix varies from 300 to 800 A. Generally, the increase in the diameter of the coil composing the helix seems to be accompanied by a corresponding decrease in the distance between successive coils.

Although the Amoeba nuclear pores have a diameter of 640 A in electron micrographs, Feldherr (1965) has shown that only those colloidal gold particles having a diameter of 145 A or less can penetrate the electron-opaque pore material when injected into A. proteus. On the basis of this evidence, the coiled helices with a diameter of 300 to 800 A, might not be able to pass through the nuclear pores. However, the diameter of the filament making up the helix is only about 120 to 130 A (Pappas, 1959). Therefore, if the helix were uncoiled, it might pass to the cytoplasm through a narrow channel in the pore. Stevens and Swift (1966) suggest such a channel as a route for the movement of the Balbiani ring product through the electron-dense material filling the nuclear pores in Chironomi salivary nuclei.

Subsequent experiments were conducted to gain some insight concerning the possible movement of the helices from nucleus to cytoplasm and/or vice versa. Determining the site of origin of the helices and the timing of their appearance in the postmitotic nucleus, the pore complex, and the cytoplasm, could provide a partial answer to this question.

Amebae were synchronized by the selection of dividers with a braking pipet in about the same stage of division, and groups from the synchronous population were fixed at half-hour intervals through the first 4 hr of interphase. Nuclei fixed ½ hr after the selection of the dividers were either in later anaphase or early telophase of mitosis. The condensed chromosomes were arranged in a definite pattern, and only fragments of the nuclear envelope could be discerned (Figure 10). Helices have been noted occasionally in the vicinity of the condensed chromosomes at this stage of the cell cycle, but they do not seem to have any specific relationship with these structures (Figure 11). The rarity of the helices and their less precise structural arrangement in dividing cells suggest that any helices present at the time of nuclear membrane breakdown disintegrate rapidly as they come into contact with the cytoplasm.

By ½ to 1 hr after the initiation of the experiment, karyokinesis and cytokinesis were complete. Cells fixed at this time display a completely reformed nuclear envelope, but the honeycomb layer has not been reformed. The "nucleoli" appear as irregular, granular masses more or less peripherally arranged in the nucleus (Figure 12). Neither single helices nor clusters of helices were ever found in the nucleus at this stage; thus, they must not be incorporated from the cytoplasm during nuclear reformation.

Subsequently, at 1 hr into interphase, the large masses of "nucleolar" material have largely dispersed into smaller bodies, and the honeycomb region of the nuclear envelope has been partially reformed (Figure 13). The clearly distinguishable granular masses have reappeared, are found in close association with the "nucleoli", and occasionally display large, dense, "mulberry" structures within their matrices. However, helices are still not apparent in any area of the nucleus.

Small clusters of helices are first noted in the nucleus at 1½ hr into interphase but are only evident in areas adjacent to the "nucleoli" (Figure 14). During the succeeding hour, the clusters of helices become more numerous in the nucleus and are observed not only in the vicinity of the "nucleoli" but also in close proximity to the "mulberry" structures (Figure 15). Moreover, in several instances, a helix appears attached at one end to a "mulberry". This latter observation may reflect a morphological transition of a "mulberry" into a helix (Figure 15).

Helices are first observed in the openings of the pore complex by 3 hr into interphase and subsequently in the cytoplasm by 3½ hr (Figures 16, 17, 18 and 19). The helices close to the nuclear membranes on the cytoplasmic side in these figures appear to have some type of substructure and may be in the process of disintegration. If the helices actually break up immediately after passage through the nuclear pores, the clearly recognized paucity of the helices in the cytoplasm would be explained.

Examination of cells fixed 4 hr into interphase and in very early G_2 show that the helices are still prevalent in the nucleus and in the honeycomb region. Thus, it seems that the ameba helices may be produced during most, or perhaps almost all, of interphase for their release to the cytoplasm.

We interpret the detection of helical structures in the cytoplasm of *A. proteus* as evidence that the helices are not DNA or a complex of DNA. On the contrary, the possibility that the helices contain RNA is very attractive, inasmuch as RNA is synthesized in the nucleus and released to the cytoplasm continuously during interphase (Prescott, 1957). Thus, ribonuclease and actinomycin D experiments were studied with autoradiographic analyses to determine whether the ameba helices contained RNA.

Living amebae were subjected to ribonuclease (0.1% solution made up in culture media for ameba) for 2 hr prior to osmium fixation. After the first hour of enzyme treatment, however, the culture was flooded with fresh medium to prevent cell death. When the sample was taken, the organisms were healthy and showed no sign of lysing.

The results of the enzyme experiments can be summarized as follows. No helical structures could be found in the nucleus, pore complex, or cytoplasm of the ribonuclease-treated organisms. Moreover, the large "nucleoli" showed definite signs of internal digestion (Figure 20), and the nucleoplasm had a rather homogeneous, dense, fibrous appearance. Material corresponding to the granular masses was noted occasionally, but the general morphology of these components had been greatly altered; the masses appeared as clumped material of rather indeterminate structure.

Since the synchronization experiments revealed that helices are first visible in the nucleus at 1½ hr after division, experiments were undertaken to determine if the formation of the helices could be inhibited. If the helices do contain RNA, then treatment of synchronized amebae in very early interphase with the antibiotic actinomycin D might prevent their formation or produce a modification in their general morphology.

A preliminary experiment was performed to ascertain the concentration of actinomycin D that would completely inhibit RNA synthesis in _A. proteus_. Various reports indicate that fairly low concentrations of this agent are required to block RNA synthesis in mammalian cells (Reich, et al., 1961; Franklin and Baltimore, 1962; Reich, et al., 1962; Perry, 1963); however, significantly higher concentrations of actinomycin D and long exposures are required to inhibit completely the incorporation of ^{3}H precursors into RNA of _A. proteus_ (G. Lorick, personal communication).

Amoeba in cytokinesis were selected and placed in culture media containing either 25 or 100 μg/ml of actinomycin D. A third group of organisms served as the control sample. After approximately 1 hr, _Tetrahymena_ (food organisms for ameba) labeled with ^{3}H uridine (specific activity of 14.7 c/mM) were added to label any RNA being synthesized in the ameba nucleus. Subsequently, at 1 hr intervals, samples of nuclei from each group were isolated in Triton X-100 (Prescott, et al., 1966) and counted in a windowless, gas-flow Geiger counter.

The results of the experiment are plotted in Figure 21. The graph illustrates that incorporation of the labeled precursor into RNA occurred in the control sample between 1 and 2 hr after the addition of the radioactive _Tetrahymenae_. Although RNA synthesis is reduced in the presence of 25 μg/ml of actinomycin, complete inhibition of RNA production in the ameba nucleus occurs only at a concentration of 100 μg/ml. Since a later experiment revealed that this high concentration of actinomycin caused no detectable inhibition of DNA synthesis, 100 μg/ml actinomycin D was used in our initial electron microscope studies to examine the effect of the antibiotic on the formation of the helices.

Amebae in division were exposed to actinomycin D (100 μg/ml) for 6 hr prior to their preparation for electron microscopy. A survey of the nucleus and pore complex in ultrathin sections of the experimental sample failed to reveal helices in either of these areas, whereas the control group fixed at an equivalent stage in interphase displayed many groups of helical clusters within the nucleus and helices within the openings of the honeycomb layer. The presence of helices in untreated amebae at 6 hr into interphase further substantiates our theory that the helices are formed in the nucleus and released to the cytoplasm over a major part of interphase.

A very striking effect of the antibiotic was noted on the "nucleoli". Many of these structures had become grossly fragmented (Figure 22) or were more spherical and electron dense than normal "nucleoli"; the characteristic granular appearance was difficult to discern. The remaining nucleoplasm of actinomycin-treated amebae was sparsely occupied by condensed material of indeterminate structure. Granular masses in the vicinity of "nucleoli" were noted occasionally (Figure 22), but these masses never possessed the unusual "mulberrry" structures within their matrices.

Observations on the alteration of nucleolar fine structure in actinomycin-treated amebae parallels those of Journey and Goldstein (1961) and Jones and Elsdale (1964), who investigated the effect of actinomycin D on nuclear fine structure in HeLa cells and amphibian embryonic cells, respectively. The nuclei of HeLa cells resistant to the antibiotic contain granular, osmiophilic nucleoli of fairly uniform shape. The nucleoli of HeLa strains sensitive to actinomycin D become fragmented and exhibit a greatly decreased electron density within the central nucleolar regions after the cells are exposed to the antibiotic (Journey and Goldstein, 1961). Differentiating amphibian embryonic cells normally exhibit nucleoli composed of characteristic large and small granules. After exposure to actinomycin D, however, the granular appearance of the nucleoli cannot be observed. According to Jones and Elsdale (1964), the "nucleolar remnant is roughly spherical and composed of a compact mass of dense substance of almost crystalline appearance."

More recent experiments performed to study the chemical composition of amebae helices have involved the use of electron microscope autoradiography. In one experiment, a random population of amebae was fed with Tetrahymenae labeled with ^{3}H uridine and ^{3}H cytidine (specific activities between 1 and 10 c/mM). Free ^{3}H uridine and ^{3}H cytidine were added simultaneously with the food to maintain the level of RNA labeling. After 5 hr incubation with the isotopes, the sample was fixed and prepared for electron microscope autoradiography (A.R. Stevens, 1966).

Thick sections of the labeled material examined with the light microscope indicated that the maximum amount of incorporation had occurred in the "nucleoli", the majority of which are peripherally located (Figure 23). Grains were noted in regions surrounding the nucleoli but were much less numerous.

After an emulsion-exposure time of approximately 5 months, ultrathin sections of the experimental material verified the interpretation of the light autoradiographs - i.e., the maximum incorporation of the ^{3}H precursors was in the "nucleoli" (Figure 24). This localization of RNA tends to justify the assumption that ameba nucleoli are analogous to nucleoli in other forms. In addition to the nucleolar label, however, silver grains were consistently noted over the clusters of helices (Figures 24 and 25).

After acquiring these results, we performed a second experiment to increase the amount of incorporated label and thereby reduce the required exposure time of the ultrathin sections. Synchronized amebae were exposed to Tetrahymena heavily labeled with ^{3}H uridine in the 5 position (specific activity approximately 22 c/mM). Uridine labeled in this position assures us that, even up to a labeling time of 24 hr in Tetrahymena, the incorporated precursor is more than 99% digestible with ribonuclease. By this mechanism of introducing uridine into amebae, only negligible amounts of the

^{3}H RNA precursor are diverted into non-RNA constituents.

The results of the second experiment on RNA labeling showed that an intense electron microscope autoradiograph (EM-ARG) could be obtained after the ultrathin sections had exposed for only 5 days. Furthermore, in addition to localization of nucleoside incorporation in the nucleoli (Figure 26), silver grains were present over the remaining nucleoplasm (chromatin areas) and were consistently detectable over the helices. Figure 27 shows an electron microscope autoradiograph (enlarged area of Figure 26) displaying several groups of labeled helices in close proximity to heavily labeled nucleoli.

Experiments have also been performed to determine the localization of DNA within the nucleus by labeling amebae with ^{3}H thymidine. The small total amount of DNA and its low concentration in _A. proteus_ make labeling the genetic material difficult. Thus, in order to obtain adequate labeling of DNA, amebae were fed for 5 days on _Tetrahymenae_ heavily labeled for 24 hr with ^{3}H thymidine (concentration 5 μc/ml; specific activity 16.7 c/mM). Initially, light microscope autoradiographs of thick sections revealed that the maximum incorporation had occurred in the central region of the nucleus, which corresponds to the Feulgen-positive area (Figure 28). After a 2-month exposure, electron microscope autoradiographs indicated that the ^{3}H precursor had been incorporated in the filamentous nucleoplasm (Figure 29) and might be localized to some degree in the condensed patches (Figures 29 and 30). However, no incorporated ^{3}H thymidine has ever been clearly assignable to the helices (Figure 30).

V. DISCUSSION AND CONCLUSIONS

The observations that the helices are consistently labeled with ^{3}H RNA precursors (Figures 24 - 27) but not with ^{3}H thymidine (Figure 30) suggest that the helices contain RNA but not DNA. The presence of the helices in the nucleus before their subsequent appearance in the openings of the honeycomb structure (Figures 7 and 8) and later in the cytoplasm (Figures 9, 16, 17, and 19) is consistent with the conclusion that the helices contain RNA, because RNA is synthesized in the nucleus before its appearance in the cytoplasm (Prescott, 1964). The absence of the helices in the nucleus and pore complex after living amebae are subjected to ribonuclease or actinomycin D also supports the contention that the helices contain RNA. Of course, none of these observations can rule out that the helices contain yet another macromolecular constituent, e.g., protein.

The presence of helical structures in *A. proteus* does not make this organism unique among the protozoa. The nucleus of *Pelomyxa carolinensis* contains helices with dimensions similar to those in *A. proteus*, but evidence for the passage of the *Pelomyxa* structures through the pore complex and into the cytoplasm has not been given (Pappas, 1959). The unusual formation of the chromatoid bodies within the cytoplasm of the parasite *Entamoeba invadens* during encystment, seems to reflect an aggregation of ribonucleoprotein units (approximately 200 A in diameter, Deutsch and Zaman, 1959) into an ordered array of helical structures. Barker and Svihla (1964) studied the chromatoid bodies in relation to growth and encystment and hypothesized from the experimental results that "the large crystalloids, the chromatoid bodies, are a manifestation of a special parasite host mechanism." These authors speculated that the chromatoid bodies may be merely an economic way for the encysted organisms to store ribosomes. Recently, electron micrographs of encysted *E. invadens* have demonstrated that the chromatoid bodies represent parallel rows of extremely elongated helices (Morgan and Uzman, 1966).

In addition to *E. invadens*, helical configurations also have been reported in the cytoplasm of various other cell types. The cytoplasm of developing pollen mother cells of *Ipomoea purpurea* contains helical structures that presumably represent ribosomal configurations (Echlin, 1965). Electron microscope observations of differentiating epithelial and connective tissue cells of the small intestine of rat fetuses suggest that some of the free ribosomes of these cells may also be arranged in helices (Behnke, 1963). The structures observed in the fetal tissue of the rat are very similar to those noted in the cytoplasm of differentiating muscle cells in the tail of *Rana pipiens* embryos (Waddington and Perry, 1963). The latter cells exhibit an exceedingly small amount of granular endoplasmic reticulum but have a large number of smooth-membrane surfaced vesicles. The majority of ribosomes are found detached in the cytoplasm, but occasionally helical structures are observed that Waddington and Perry (1963) interpret as ordered arrays of ribosomes.

A recent electron microscope study of HeLa cells combined with sucrose gradient analysis of the cell lysates indicates that the interphase cell contains within the cytoplasm helical structures that probably represent aggregates of polyribosomes (Scharff and Robbins, 1966). Since protein is synthesized at a high rate throughout interphase but is sharply reduced at mitosis, Scharff and Robbins suggest that the polyribosomes assume the helical configurations during active protein synthesis.

These reports, with the exception of Pappas's study of *P. carolinensis*, describe helical structures in the cytoplasm which are not localized in any particular cytoplasmic organelle; however, several investigators have observed helical structures within mitochondria (Mugnaini, 1964; Behnke, 1965). Astrocytic mitochondria of the corpus striatum of the rat display dilated intracristal spaces in which helical filaments can be discerned (Mugnaini, 1964). The diameter of the coil making up the helix is approximately 140 A, and the filament thickness is roughly 30 A. Although we cannot exclude the possibility that the helices might represent mitochondrial DNA, Mugnaini (1964) prefers the hypothesis that the helices are non-DNA macromolecules - e.g., protein - synthesized by the mitochondria. Similar filaments have been found in the mitochondria of liver cells that also exhibit dilated intracristal spaces (Behnke, 1965). Since lipid micelles can spontaneously aggregate into helical configurations, the helices may reflect some type of phospholipid that is synthesized by the mitochondria (Behnke, 1965).

The helices of A. proteus closely resemble the cytoplasmic structures in other cell types that have been suggested to be aggregates of ribosomes. However, ameba helices cannot be assumed to be strings of intact ribosomes for two reasons. First, the exact site at which the ultimate, functional ribosome is formed is not known in Amoeba, or, for that matter, in any other cell type. Second, the filament of the coil composing the ameba helices is approximately 120 to 130 A in diameter (Pappas, 1959). This filament dimension is not large enough to accomodate a string of intact ribosomes, which are usually considered to measure 150 A in diameter. Nevertheless, our results indicate indirectly that the RNA of the helices is of nucleolar origin and is thus probably ribosomal in nature. This contention is supported by the ribonuclease and actinomycin D experiments and the ultrastructural analyses of the ameba interphase nucleus.

At the time of their appearance in the nucleus and even at later hours of interphase, the helices consistently appear in close proximity to the nucleoli (Figure 14). After ribonuclease or actinomycin D treatment, the helices are absent from the nucleus; the nucleoli correspondlingly display an altered appearance which probably results from the absence of some macromolecular constituent - e.g., ribosomal RNA. The lack or diminution of nucleolar RNA could thus prevent the formation of the helices.

We now come to a point concerning the amebae helices that is completely unclear. If the helices do represent a packaging of ribosomal RNA, maybe complexed with protein, where do the helices assume their characteristic appearance? Undoubtedly this does not occur in the nucleolus for careful examination of many nucleoli has failed to reveal any helices within these structures. Since the helices are frequently noted in the vicinity of the granular masses and also close to the electron-dense "mulberry" structures (Figure 15), these two components may be implicated in some way in the construction of the helices. The formation of the granular masses in close proximity to the nucleoli and the presence of "mulberries" in these structures (Figure 13) precede the appearance of clusters of helices within the interphase nucleus. Moreover, the granular masses are reduced in number and have an altered fine structure after ribonuclease and actinomycin D treatment of amebae; the electron-dense "mulberries" have not been seen after such treatments.

Although Scharff and Robbins (1966) feel that the HeLa cell helices actually represent polyribosomal aggregates active in protein synthesis, our electron micrographs suggest that the ultimate fate of the amebae helices is disintegration into particles of a smaller size after their immediate passage through the nuclear envelope (Figures 16, 17 and 19). Therefore, the hypothesis is presented that the amebae helices represent some type of packaging of nascent or incomplete ribosomes. These nascent ribosomes would be formed ultimately in the nucleoli but subsequently accumulate in adjacent areas - i.e., the granular masses. Thereafter, the nascent ribosomes would aggregate into the "mulberry" structures which eventually undergo conversion to form the helices. The helices would thus serve as a convenient mode for transferring the nascent ribosomes through the nuclear envelope for their participation in the synthesis of cellular proteins.

The evidence presented supports reasonably well the hypothesis that the ameba helices represent machinery by which nascent or incomplete ribosomes are mobilized for transport to the cytoplasm. It is still an hypothesis, however, and it is possible that the nuclear helices of *A. proteus* are machinery for transport of another species of RNA - e.g., messenger RNA.

ACKNOWLEDGMENTS

The author acknowledges with deep gratitude and appreciation Dr. D.M. Prescott for his guidance in the course of this study and in the preparation of the manuscript. The work reported in this article was supported by a National Science Foundation grant to Dr. D.M. Prescott.

The author's present address is: Institute for Developmental Biology, University of Colorado, Boulder.

REFERENCES

Afzelius, B.A. 1955. Expt. Cell Res. 8: 147.

Anderson, E., and H.W. Beams. 1956. J. Biophys. Biochem. Cytol., 2: Suppl. 439.

André, J., and C. Rouiller. 1956. In "Proceedings of the Stockholm Conference on Electron Microscopy," F.S. Sjöstrand and J. Rhodin, eds. Academic Press, N.Y. 162 p.

Bairati, A., and F.E. Lehmann. 1952. Experientia 8: 60.

Barker, D.C., and G. Svihla. 1964. J. Cell Biol. 20: 389

Baud, C.A. 1959. In "Problèmes d'ultrastructures et de fonctions nucléaires," J.A. Thomas, ed. Masson et Cie., Paris 1 p.

Beams, H.W., T.N. Tahmisian, R.L. Devine, and E. Anderson. 1957. Exp. Cell Res. 13: 200.

Beams, H.W., T.N. Tahmisian, R.L. Devine, and E. Anderson. 1959. Exp. Cell Res. 18, Suppl. 7: 366.

Behnke, O. 1963. Exp. Cell Res. 30: 597.

Behnke, O. 1965. Exp. Cell Res. 37: 687.

Bernhard, W., and N. Granboulan. 1963. Exp. Cell Res., Suppl. 9: 19.

Callan, H.G., and S.G. Tomlin. 1950. Proc. Roy. Soc., London Ser. B. 137: 367.

Chambers, R., and H.B. Fell. 1931. Proc. Roy. Soc., London Ser. B. 109: 380.

Clark, W.H. 1960. J. Biophys. Biochem. Cytol. 7: 345.

Coggeshall, R.E., and D.W. Fawcett. 1964. J. Neurophysiol. 27: 229.

Cohen, A.I. 1957. J. Biophys. Biochem. Cytol. 3: 859.

Coons, A.H., E.H. Leduc, and M.H. Kaplan. 1951. J. Exp. Med. 93: 173.

Daniels, E.W. 1964a. Z. Zellforsch. Mikroskop. Anat. 64: 38.

Daniels, E.W. 1964b. J. Protozool. 11 (2): 281.

Daniels, E.W., and E.P. Breyer. 1965. J. Protozool. 12 (3): 417.

Daniels, E.W., and E.P. Breyer. 1966. Z. Zellforsch. Mikroskop. Anat. 70: 449.

Dawson, I.M., J. Hossack, and G.M. Wyburn. 1955. Proc. Roy. Soc. London Ser. B. 144: 132.

Deutsch, K., and V. Zaman. 1959. Exp. Cell Res. 17: 31(

Echlin, P. 1965. J. Cell Biol. 24: 150.

Edström, J. 1960. J. Biophys. Biochem. Cytol. 88: 47.
Edström, J., and W. Beermann. 1962. J. Cell Biol. 14: 371.
Edström, J., and J.G. Gall. 1963. J. Cell Biol. 19: 277.
Fawcett, D.W. 1966. In "Atlas of Fine Structure. The Cell, Its Organelles and Inclusions," D.W. Fawcett, ed. W.B. Saunders, Co. Phila., Penna.
Feldherr, C.M. 1965. J. Cell Biol. 25: 43.
Franklin, R.M., and D. Baltimore. 1962. Cold Spring Harbor Symp. Quant. Biol. 27: 175.
Gall, J.G. 1956. J. Biophys. Biochem. Cytol., 2: Suppl. 393.
Gall. J.G. 1964. Protoplasmatologia 5: 4.
Gay, H. 1955. Proc. Natl. Acad. Sci. U.S. 41: 370.
Gierer, A. 1963. J. Mol. Biol. 6: 148.
Goldstein, L., and G.V. Harding. 1950. Federation Proc. 9: 48.
Goldstein, L., and W. Plaut. 1955. Proc. Natl. Acad. Sci. U.S. 41: 874.
Granboulan, N., and P. Granboulan. 1964. Exp. Cell Res. 34: 71.
Haguenau, F., and W. Bernhard. 1955. Bull. Cancer 42: 537.
Harris, P., and T.W. James. 1952. Experientia 8: 384.
Jones, K.W., and T.R. Elsdale. 1964. J. Cell Biol. 21: 245.
Journey, L.J., and M.N. Goldstein. 1961. Cancer Res. 21: 929.
Karasaki, S. 1964. J. Ultrastruct. Res. 11: 246.
Karasaki, S. 1965. J. Cell Biol. 26: 937.
Kessel, R.G. 1964. J. Ultrastruct. Res. 10: 498.
Kessel, R.G. 1966. J. Ultrastruct. Res. 15: 181.
Kessel, R.G., and H.W. Beams. 1963. Exp. Cell Res. 32: 612.
Lafontaine, J.G., and L.A. Chouinard. 1963. J. Cell Biol. 17: 167.
Maisel, J.C., and R.I. Lytle. 1966. J. Cell Biol. 29: 461.
Marinos, N.G. 1960. J. Ultrastruct. Res. 3: 328.
Marks, P.A., R.A. Rifkind, and D. Danon. 1963. Proc. Natl. Acad. Sci. U.S. 50: 336.
Mathias, A.P., R. Williamsen, H.E. Huxley, and S. Page.

1964. J. Mol. Biol. 9: 184.
McConkey, E., and J. Hopkins. 1964. Proc. Natl. Acad. Sci. U.S. 51: 1197.
Mercer, E.H. 1959. Proc. Roy. Soc. London Ser. B. 150: 216.
Morgan, R.S., and B.G. Uzman. 1966. Science 152: 214.
Moses, M.J. 1956. J. Biophys. Biochem. Cytol., 2: Suppl. 397.
Mugnaini, E. 1964. J. Cell Biol. 23: 173.
Pappas, G.D. 1956a. J. Biophys. Biochem. Cytol., 2: Suppl. 431.
Pappas, G.D. 1956b. J. Biophys. Biochem. Cytol. 2: 221.
Pappas, G.D. 1959. Ann. N.Y. Acad. Sci. 78: 448.
Perry, R.P. 1962. Proc. Natl. Acad. Sci. U.S. 48: 2179.
Perry, R.P. 1963. Exp. Cell Res. 29: 400.
Perry, R.P. 1964. J. Natl. Cancer Inst. 15: 73.
Prescott, D.M. 1957. Exp. Cell Res. 12: 196.
Prescott, D.M. 1964. Progr. Nucleic Acid Res. 3: 33.
Prescott, D.M., M.V.N. Rao, D.P. Evenson, G.E. Stone, and J.D. Thrasher. 1966. In "Methods in Cell Physiology," D.M. Prescott, ed. Academic Press, N.Y. Vol. II., 131.
Rebhun, L.I. 1956. J. Biophys. Biochem. Cytol. 2: 93.
Reich, E., R.M. Franklin, A.J. Shatkin, and E.L. Tatum. 1961. Science 134: 556.
Reich, E., R.M. Franklin, A.J. Shatkin, and E.L. Tatum. 1962. Proc. Natl. Acad. Sci. U.S. 48: 1238.
Reynolds, E.S. 1963. J. Cell Biol. 17: 208.
Roth, L.E., S.W. Obetz, and E.W. Daniels. 1960. J. Biophys. Biochem. Cytol. 8: 207.
Scharff, M.D., and E. Robbins. 1966. Science 151: 992.
Scherrer, K., and J.E. Darnell. 1962. Biochem. Biophys. Res. Commun. 7: 486.
Scherrer, K., H. Latham, and J.E. Darnell. 1963. Proc. Natl. Acad. Sci. U.S. 49: 240.
Stevens, A.R. 1966. In "Methods in Cell Physiol," D.M. Prescott, ed. Academic Press, N.Y. vol. II., 255.
Stevens, A.R., and D.M. Prescott. 1965. Exp. Cell Res. 40: 204.
Stevens, B.J. 1964. J. Ultrastruct. Res. 11: 329.
Stevens, B.J., and H. Swift. 1966. J. Cell Biol. 31: 55.
Swift, H. 1958. In "A Symposium on the Chemical Basis

of Development," W.A. McElroy and B. Glass, eds. Johns Hopkins Press, Baltimore, Md. 103 p.
Swift, H. 1963. Exp. Cell Res., Suppl. 9: 54.
Szollosi, D. 1965. J. Cell Biol. 25: 545.
Taylor, J.H. 1963. In "Molecular Genetics," J.H. Taylor, ed. Academic Press, N.Y. pt. 1, 65.
Venable, J.H., and R. Coggeshall. 1965. J. Cell Biol. 25: 407.
Waddington, C.H., and M.M. Perry. 1963. Exp. Cell Res. 30: 599.
Warner, J.R., P.M. Knopf, and A. Rich. 1963. Proc. Natl. Acad. Sci. U.S. 49: 122.
Watson, M.L. 1955. J. Biophys. Biochem. Cytol. 1: 257.
Watson, M.L. 1959. J. Biophys. Biochem. Cytol. 6: 147.
Wischnitzer, S. 1958. J. Ultrastruct. Res. 1: 201.
Wischnitzer, S. 1960. Intern. Rev. Cytol. 10: 137.

Figure 1. Ultrathin section of A. proteus showing large area of the nucleus. The thick honeycomb layer, which constitutes part of the nuclear envelope in this organism, can be visualized in several different planes of sectioning. A small cluster of helices is situated close to the honeycomb region and is denoted by h. N represents nucleolus, a single arrow, granular mass, and a double arrow, condensed patch. Magnified ca. 6000 X.

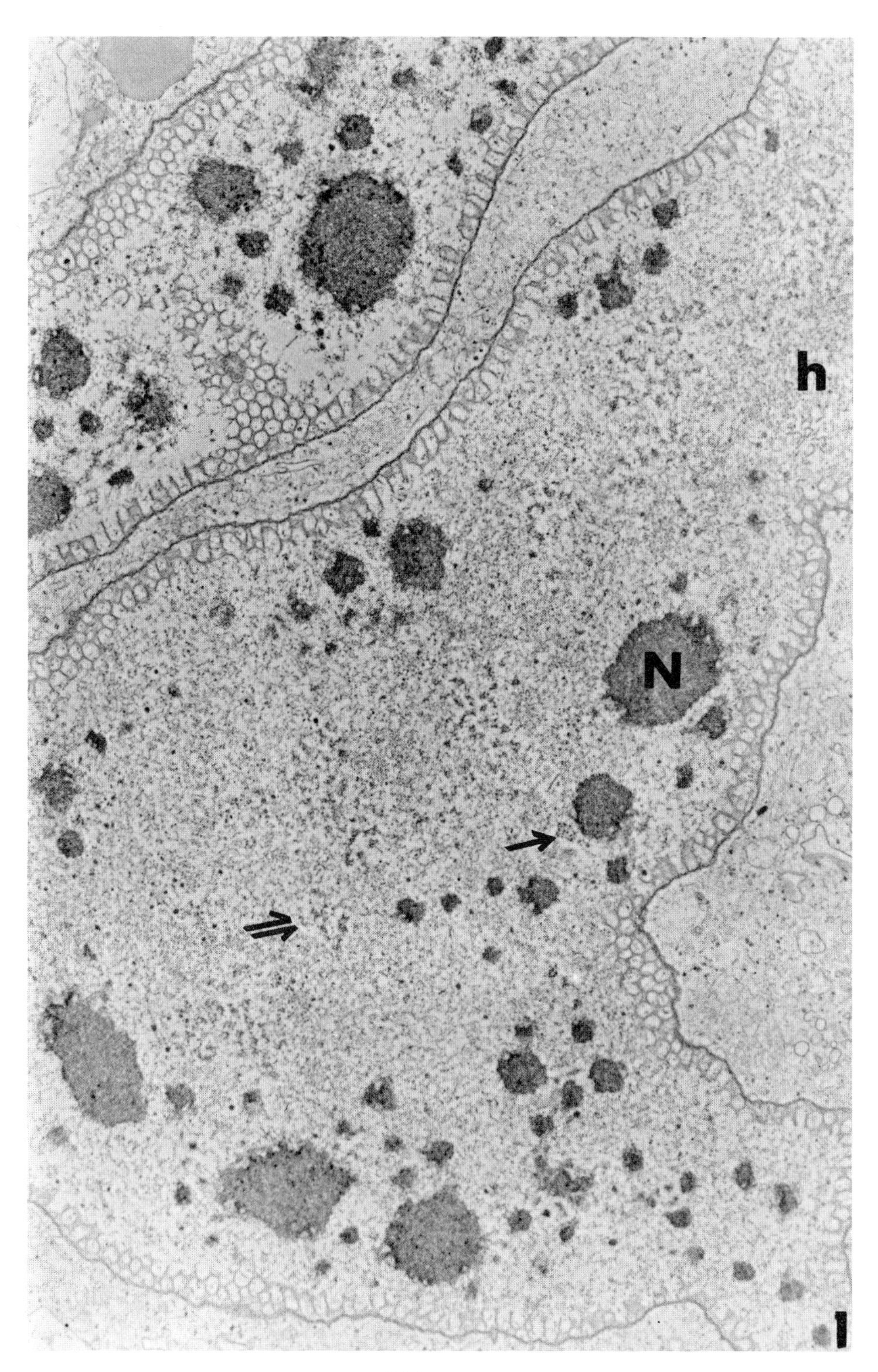
h
N
l

Figure 2. Ultrathin section of amebae nucleus. The granular mass (G) displays an electron-dense "mulberry" (double arrows). Singel arrow represents clusters of helices. Magnified ca. 27,700 X.

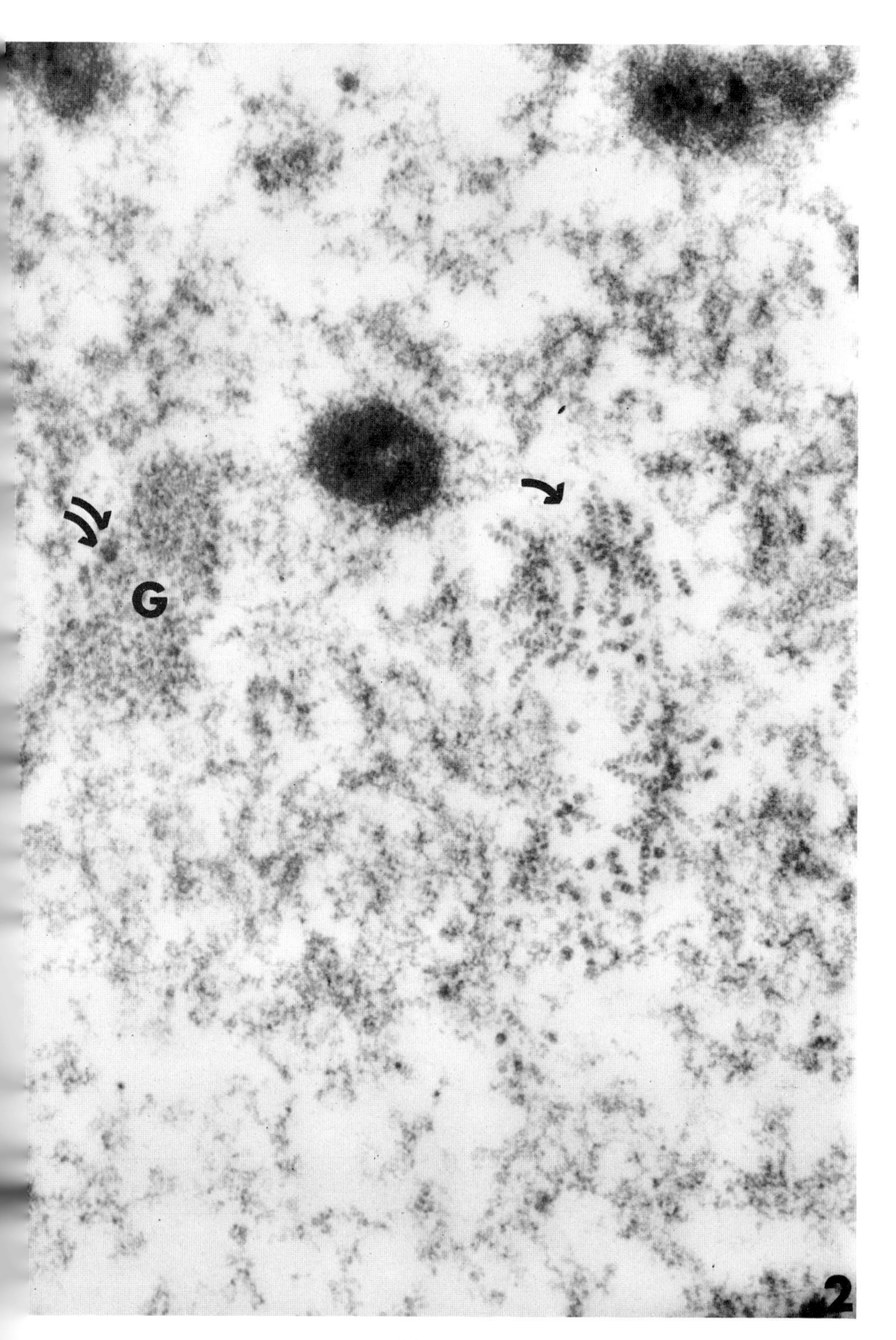
G
2

Figure 3. Ultrathin section of a highly magnified area of an ameba nucleus showing a condensed patch (Cp) and small cluster of longitudinally and cross sectioned helices (h). Magnified ca. 63,200 X.

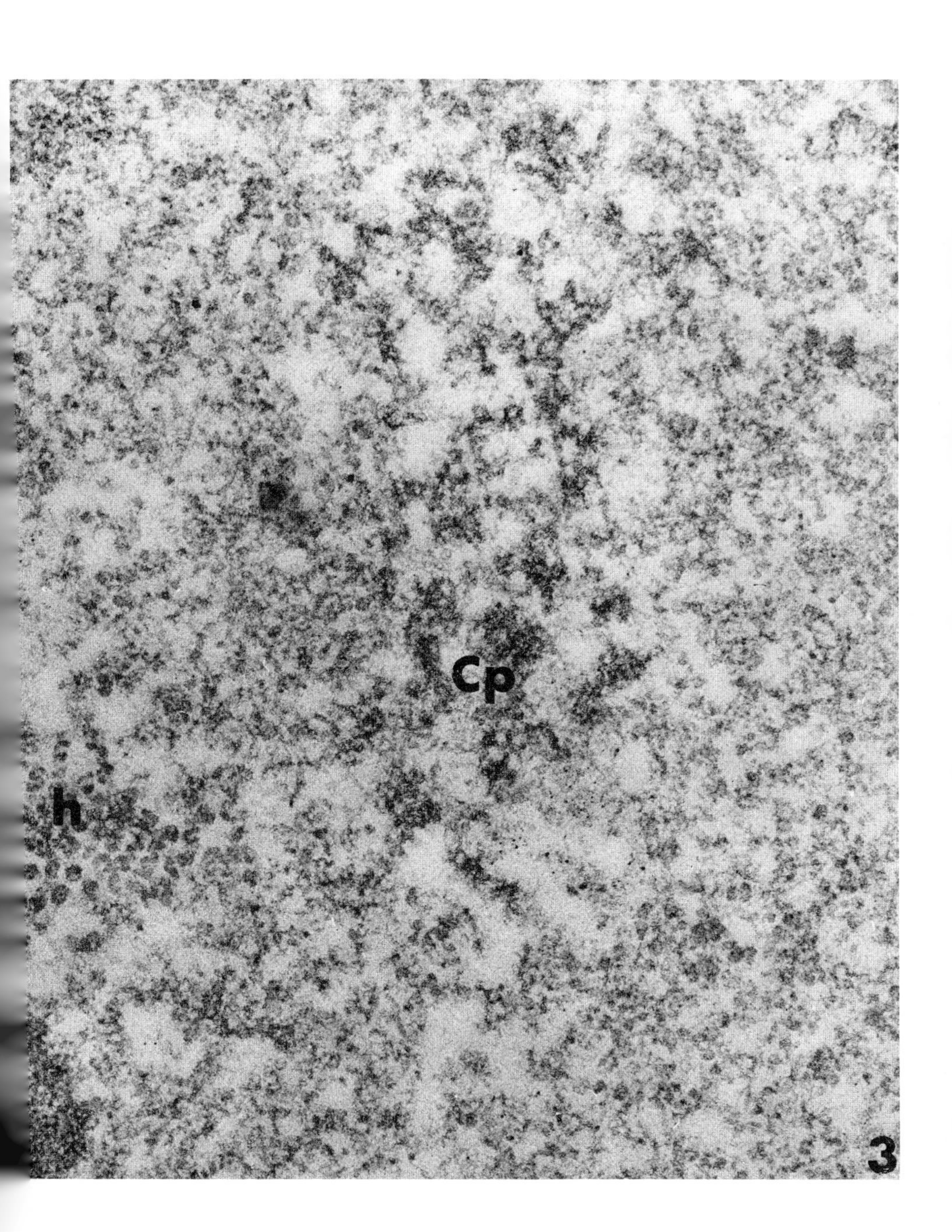
Cp
h
3

Figure 4. Ultrathin section of ameba nucleus showing large cluster of longitudinally oriented helices that are radiating from a common core of electron-opaque material (arrow). Magnified ca. 43,200 X.

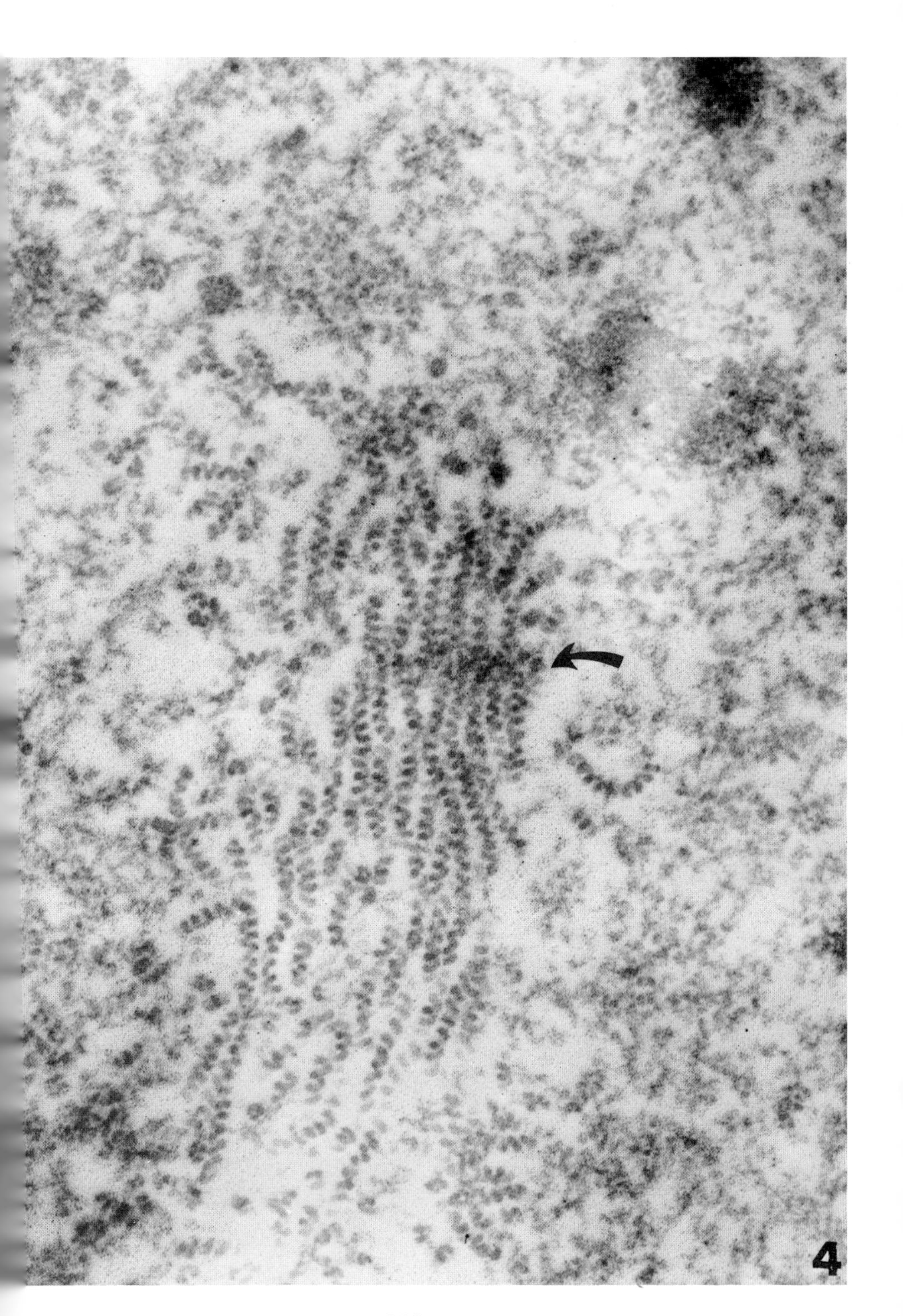
4

Figure 5. Ultrathin section of ameba nucleus displaying helical clusters (h) and helices not attached to a common core (arrow). Magnified ca. 81,200 X.

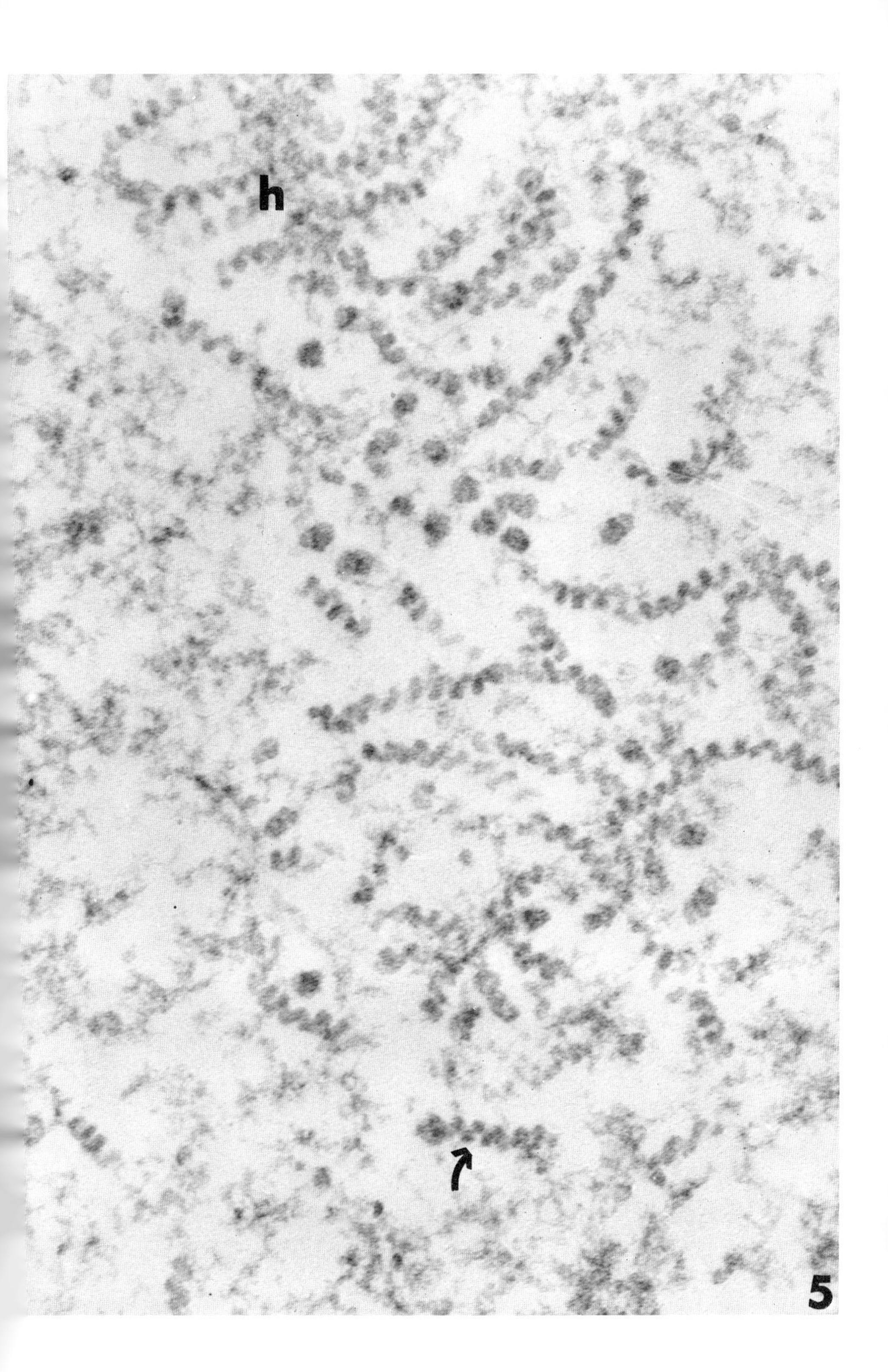
h
5

Figure 6. Ultrathin section of ameba displaying helices in close proximity to the honeycomb layer (H) of the nuclear envelope. C represents cytoplasm, N, nucleoli. Magnified ca. 68,000 X.

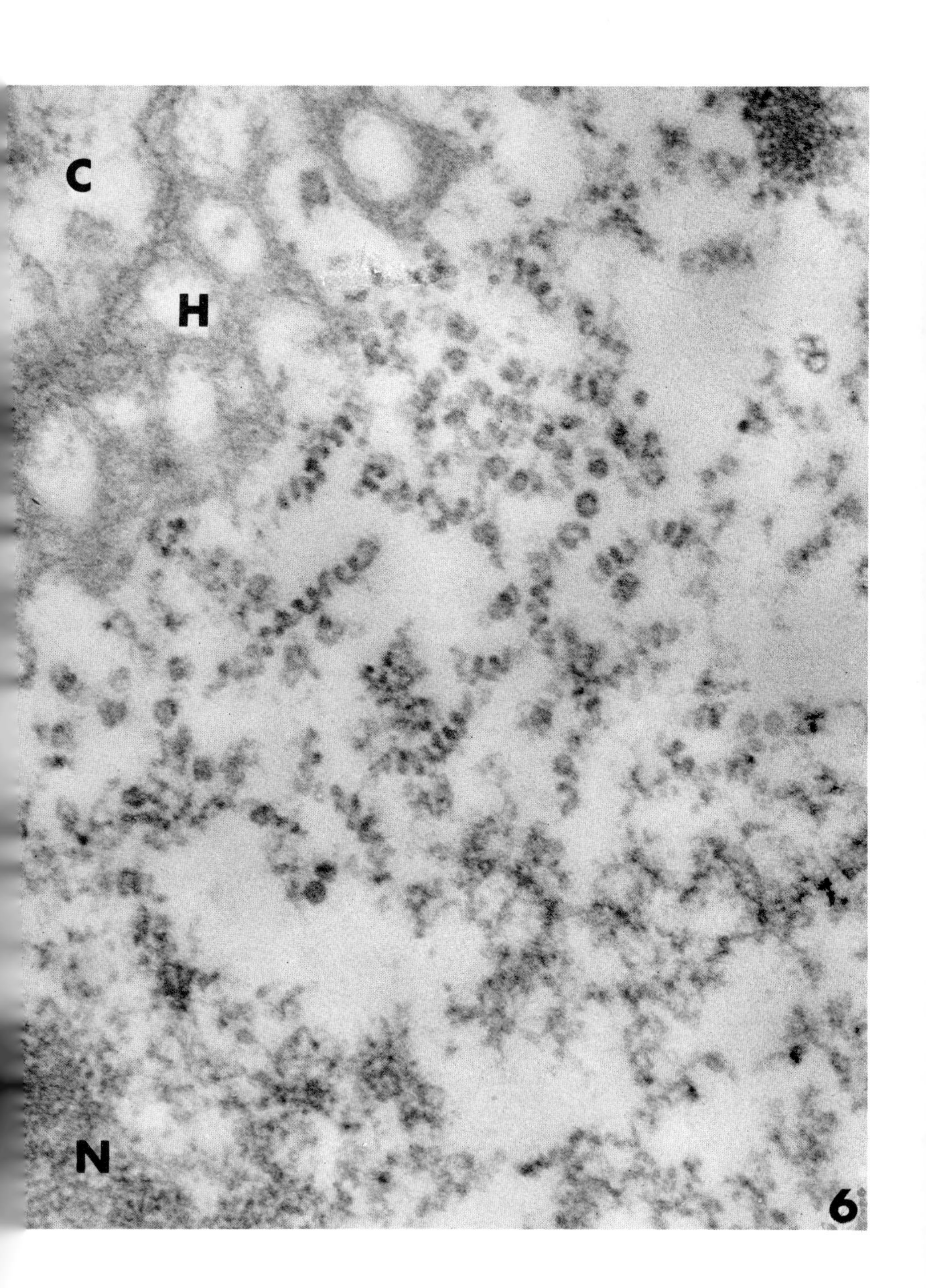
C
H
N
6

Figure 7. Ultrathin section of ameba demonstrating helices in close proximity to the honeycomb layer of the nuclear envelope. Several of the individual openings of the honeycomb region contain helices. Two helices are seen in one opening. C represents cytoplasm, N, nucleoli. Magnified ca. 71,600 X.

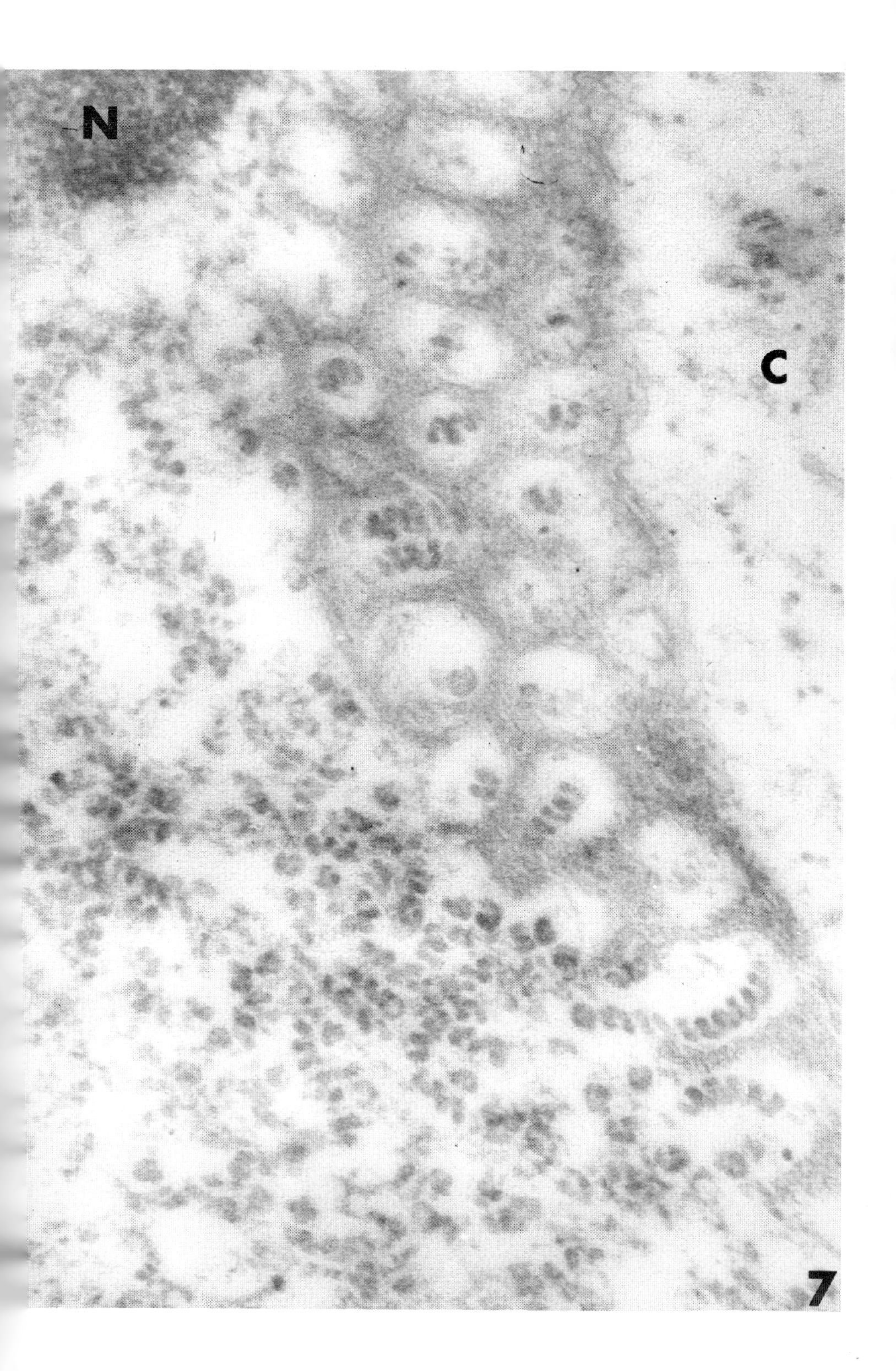
N
C
7

Figure 8. Ultrathin section of ameba that presents a single helix touching the nuclear envelope precisely in the region of a nuclear pore. C represents cytoplasm, Nu, nucleus. Magnified ca. 110,000 X.

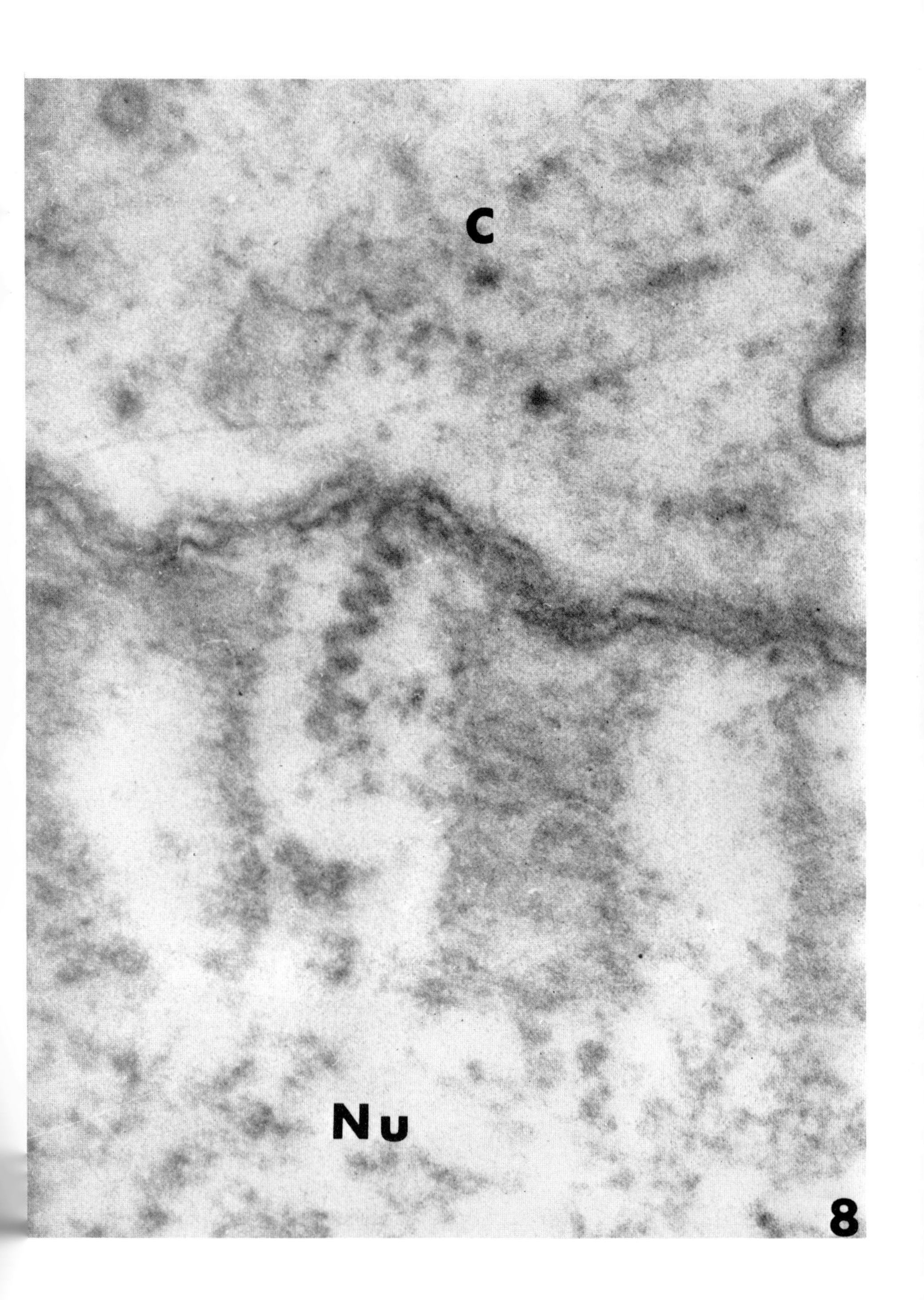
C
Nu
8

Figure 9. Ultrathin section of ameba cytoplasm demonstrating a single helix in this area of the cell. R represents part of a rickettsial particle. Magnified ca. 102,000 X.

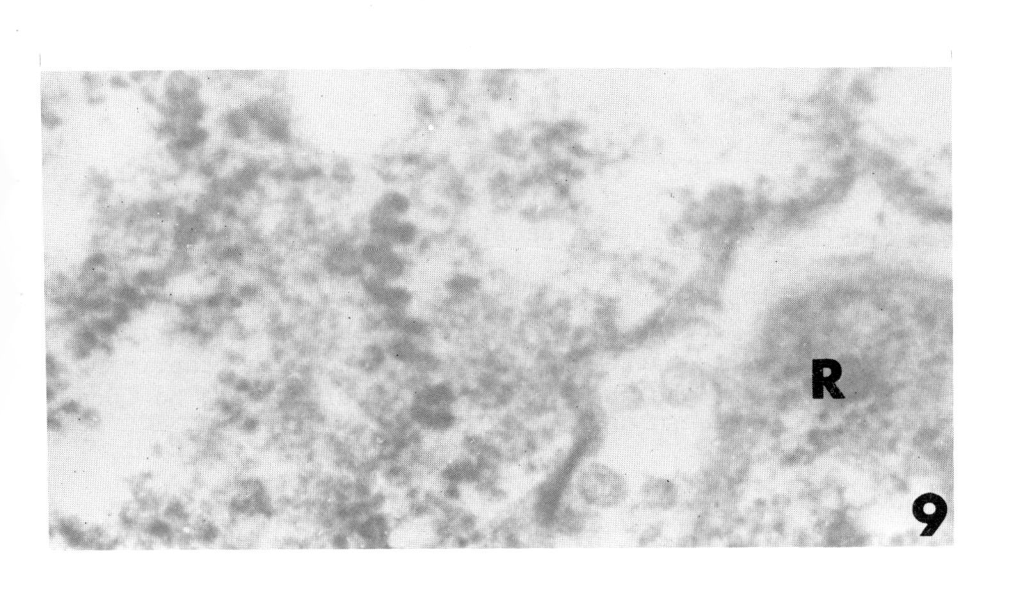
R
9

Figure 10. Ultrathin section of an ameba undergoing mitosis. The cell was either in late anaphase or early telophase of the mitotic cycle at the time of fixation. The condensed chromosomes (Cx) are arranged in a definite pattern with respect to each other. Only fragments of the nuclear envelope (arrow) can be found. Magnified ca. 60,000 X.

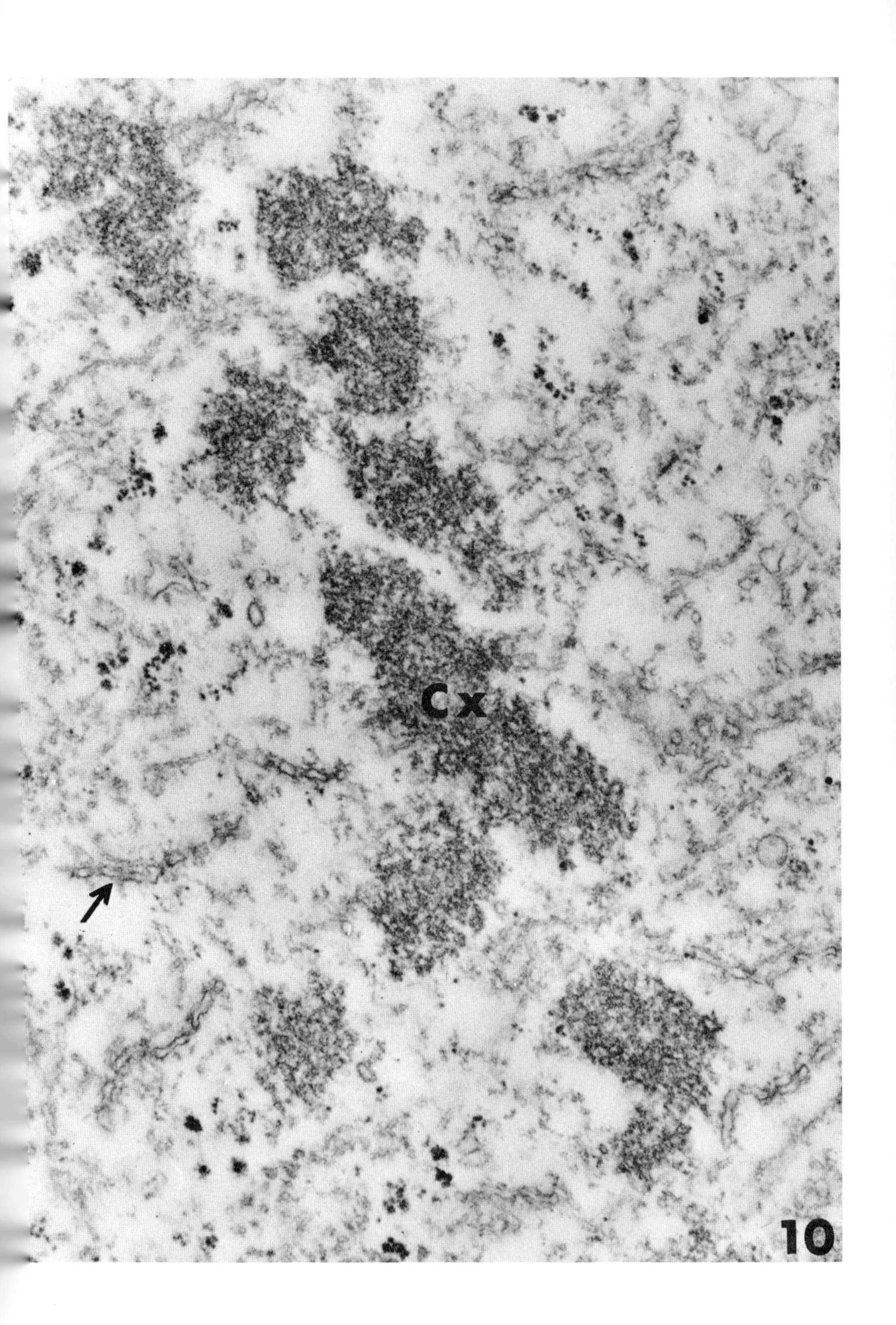
Cx
10

Figure 11. Ultrathin section of ameba fixed during late anaphase or early telophase. A helix (arrow) that may be in the process of disintegration is located close to a rather diffuse mass of material. The latter may represent a nucleolus that did not dissociate completely during mitosis or that is in the process of reforming. Cx represents condensed mitotic chromosome. Magnified ca. 57,000 X.

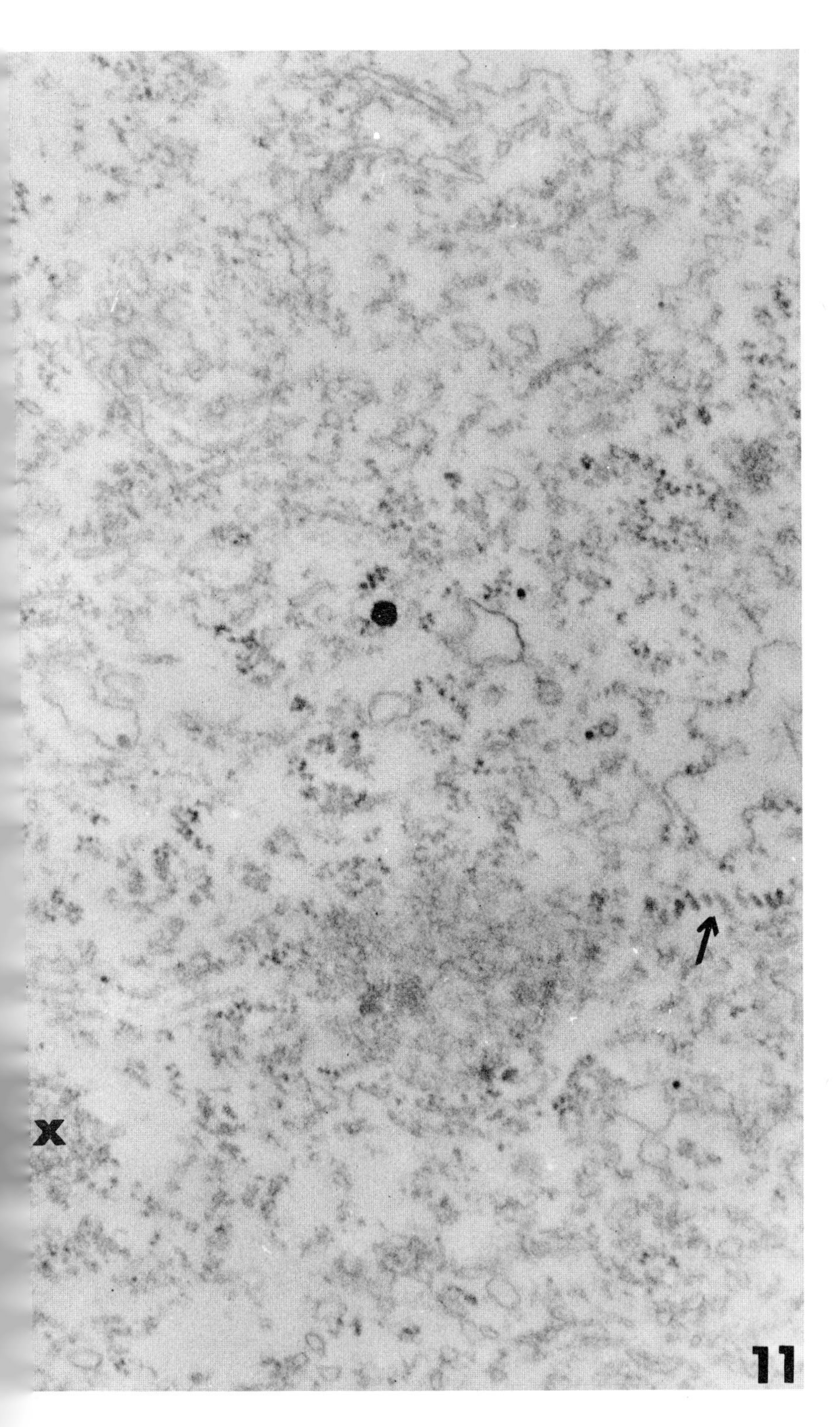
x
11

Figure 12. Ultrathin section of ameba fixed ½ to 1 hr into the DNA synthetic period (S period). The nucleus is completely enveloped by the nuclear membranes, and the nucleoli (N) have been reformed; however, the honeycomb layer of the nuclear envelope has not been reformed at this stage of the nuclear cycle. C represents cytoplasm. Magnified ca. 16,700 X.

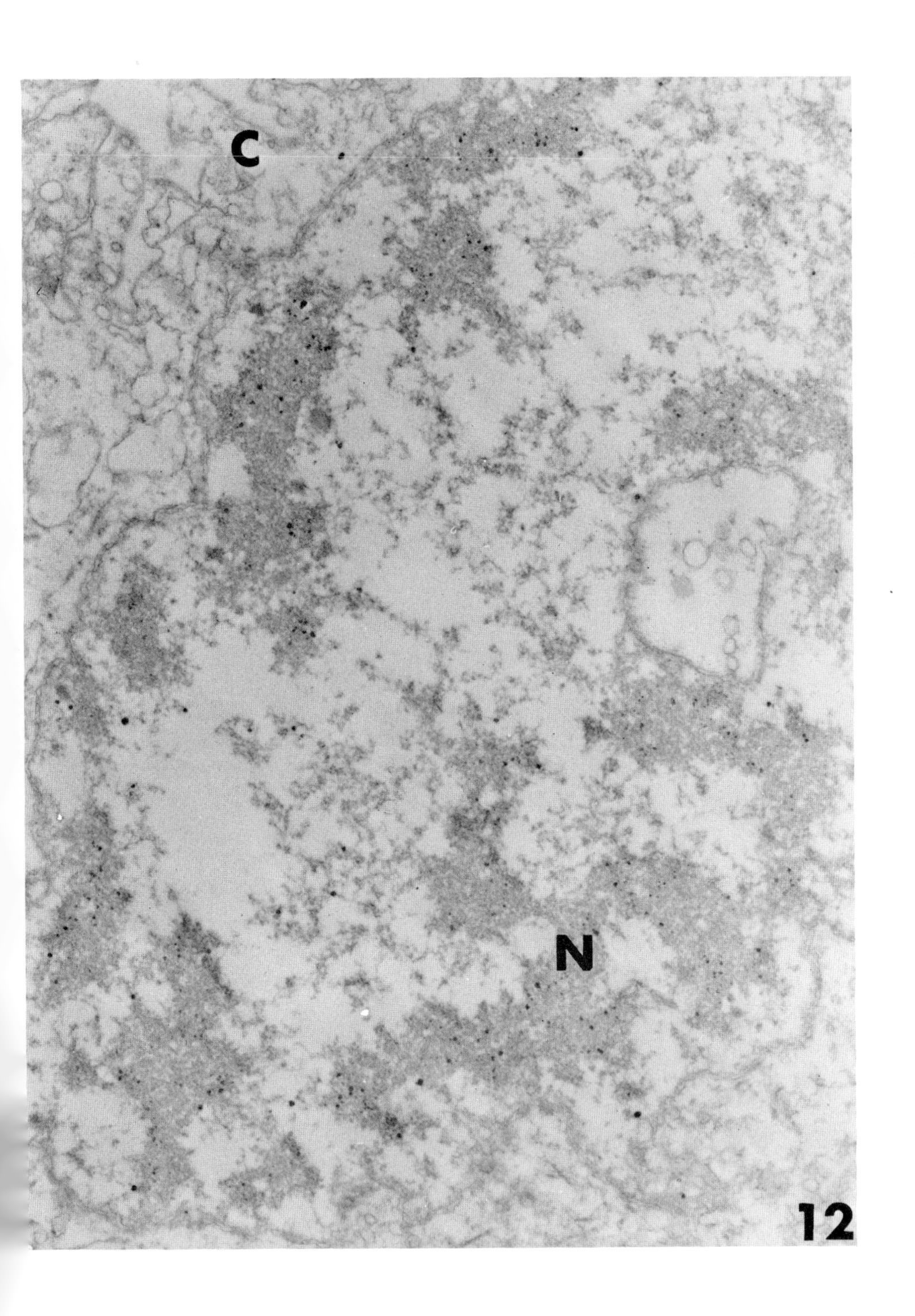
C
N
12

Figure 13. Ultrathin section of ameba fixed 1 hr into the S period of interphase. The honeycomb layer of the nuclear envelope has been partially reformed. The granular masses (G) displaying the electron-dense "mullberries" within their matrices have reappeared in the nucleus by this stage of the nuclear cycle and lie in the vicinity of the nucleoli (N). C represents cytoplasm. Magnified ca. 16,800 X.

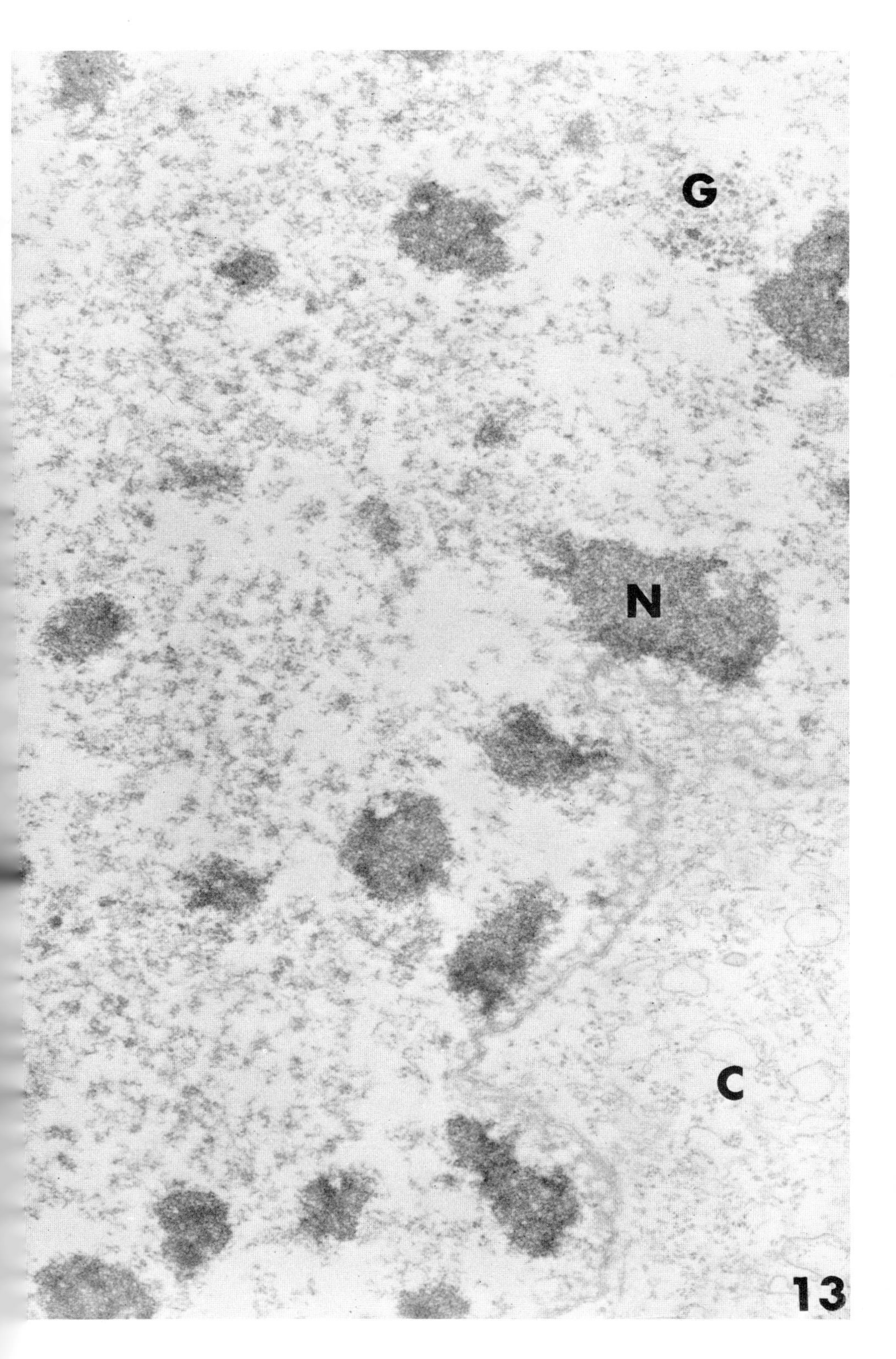
G
N
C
13

Figure 14. Ultrathin section of ameba fixed 1½ hr into interphase. The helices (h) have reappeared in the nucleus at this stage of development. C represents cytoplasm, N, nucleoli. Magnified ca. 45,500 X.

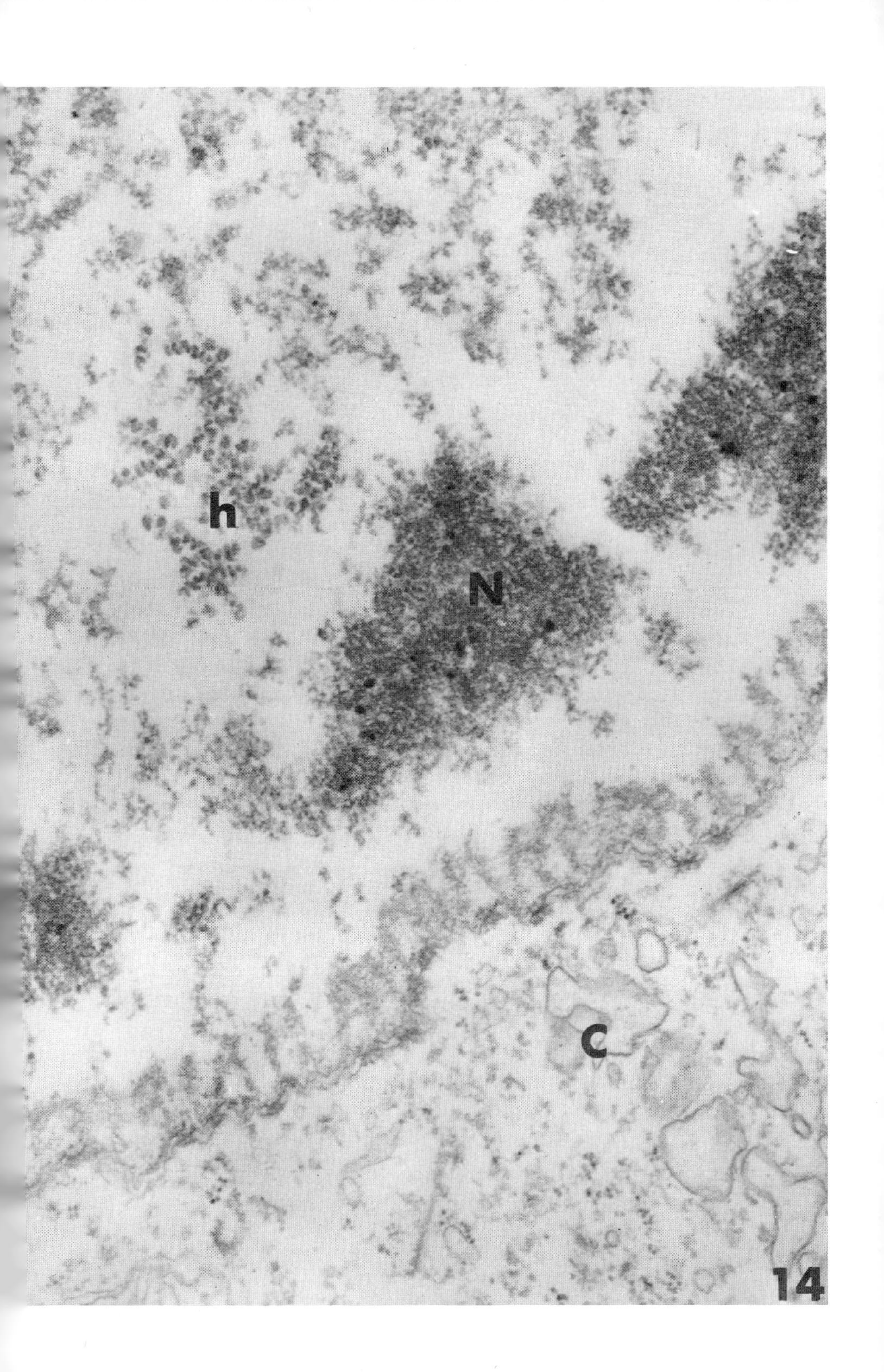
h
N
C
14

Figure 15. Ultrathin section of ameba fixed 2½ hr into interphase. The helices and the "mullberries" (m) are situated in close proximity to the nucleolus (N). In several instances, helices appear to be attached to the electron-dense mulberries (single arrow). The very electron-opaque structures in the nucleolus have been termed foamy particles (Cohen, 1957). Double arrows represent cross-sectioned helices. Magnified ca. 69,000 X.

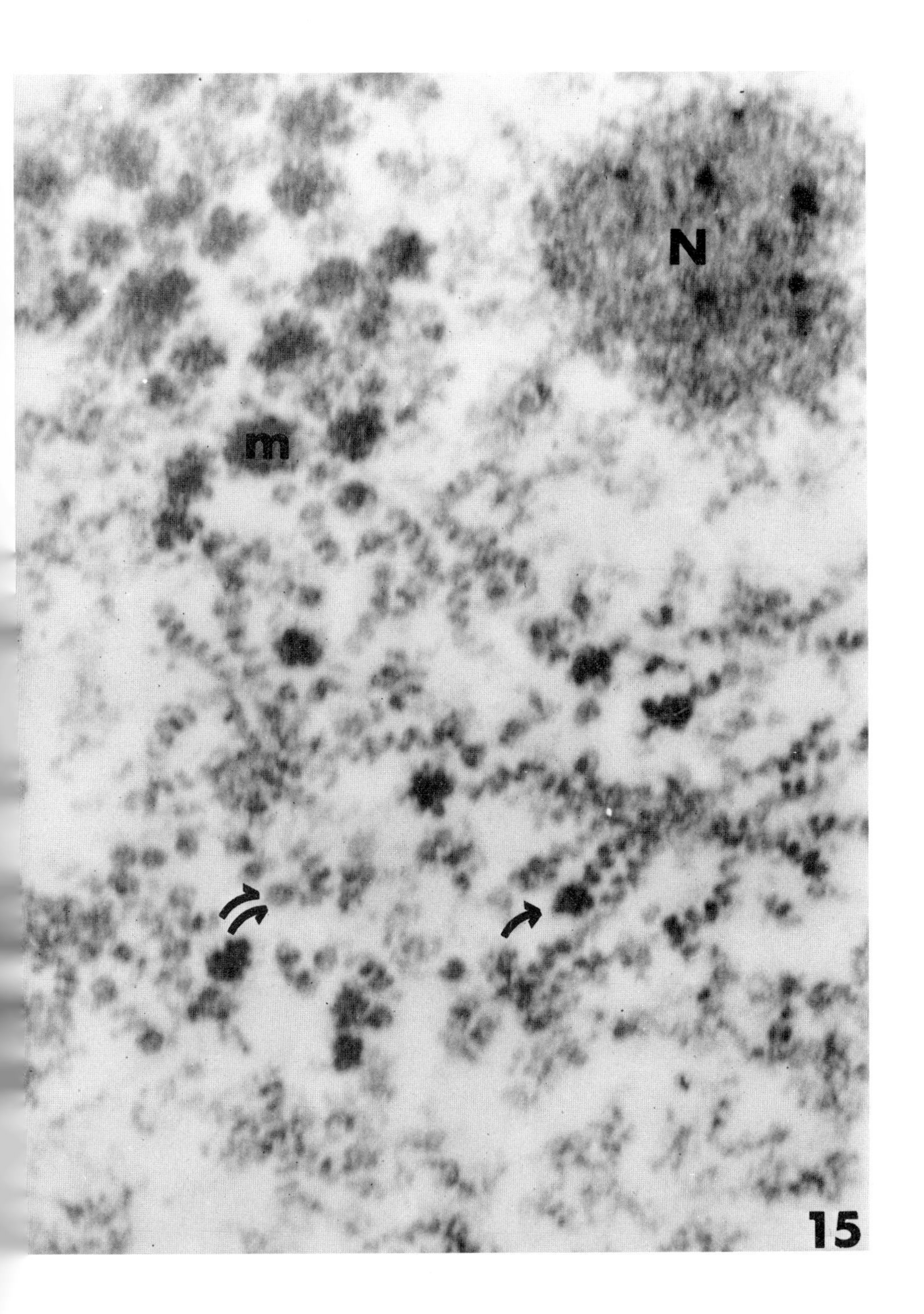
N
m
15

Figure 16. Ultrathin section of ameba fixed 3½ hr into interphase. A helix that appears to be in the process of disintegration is located in close proximity to the nuclear envelope on the cytoplasmic side (C). Magnified ca. 82,000 X.

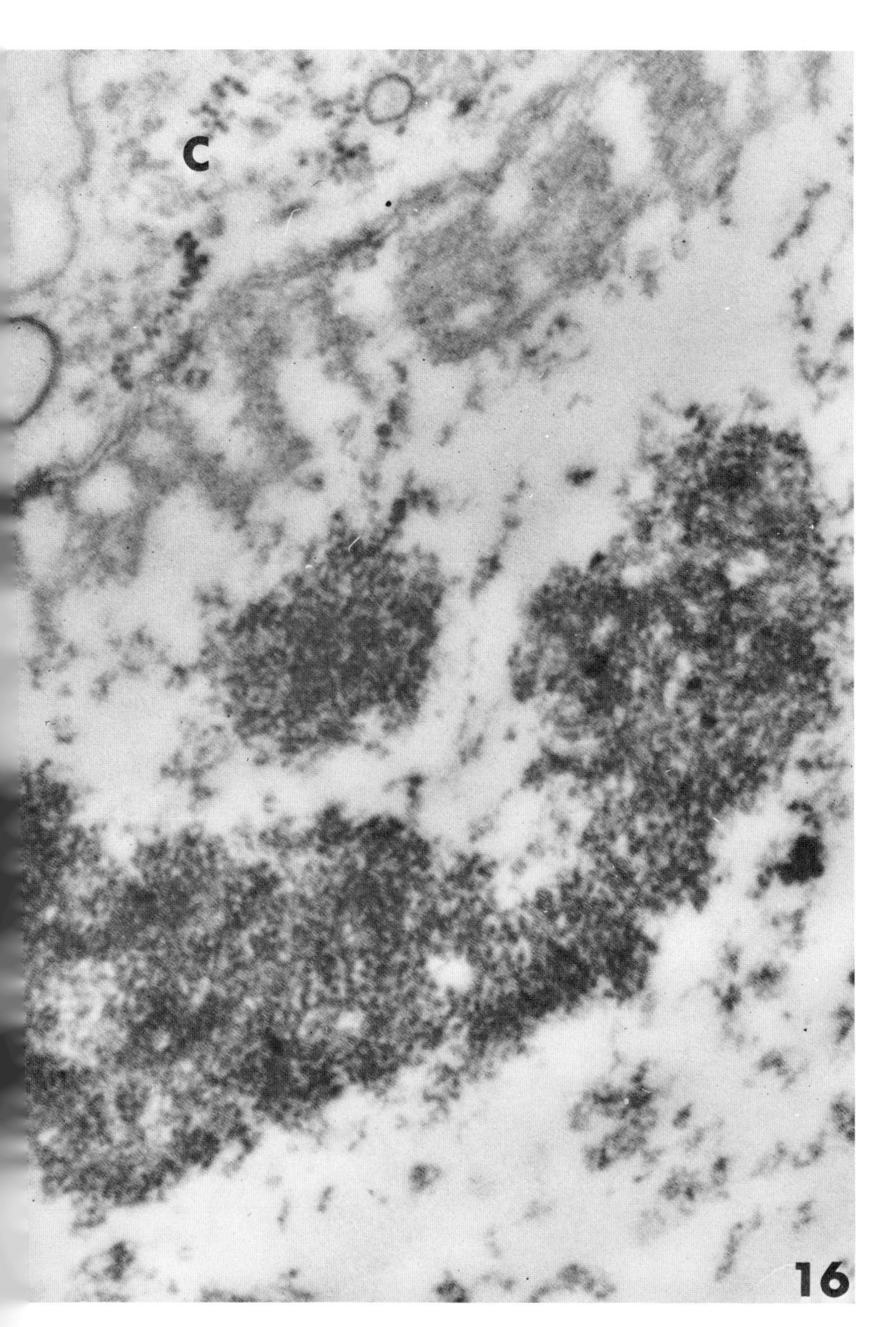
C
16

Figure 17. Ultrathin section of ameba fixed 3½ hr into interphase. A helix is located close to the nuclear envelope on the cytoplasmic side (C) and may be in the process of disintegration. Magnified ca. 69,500 X.

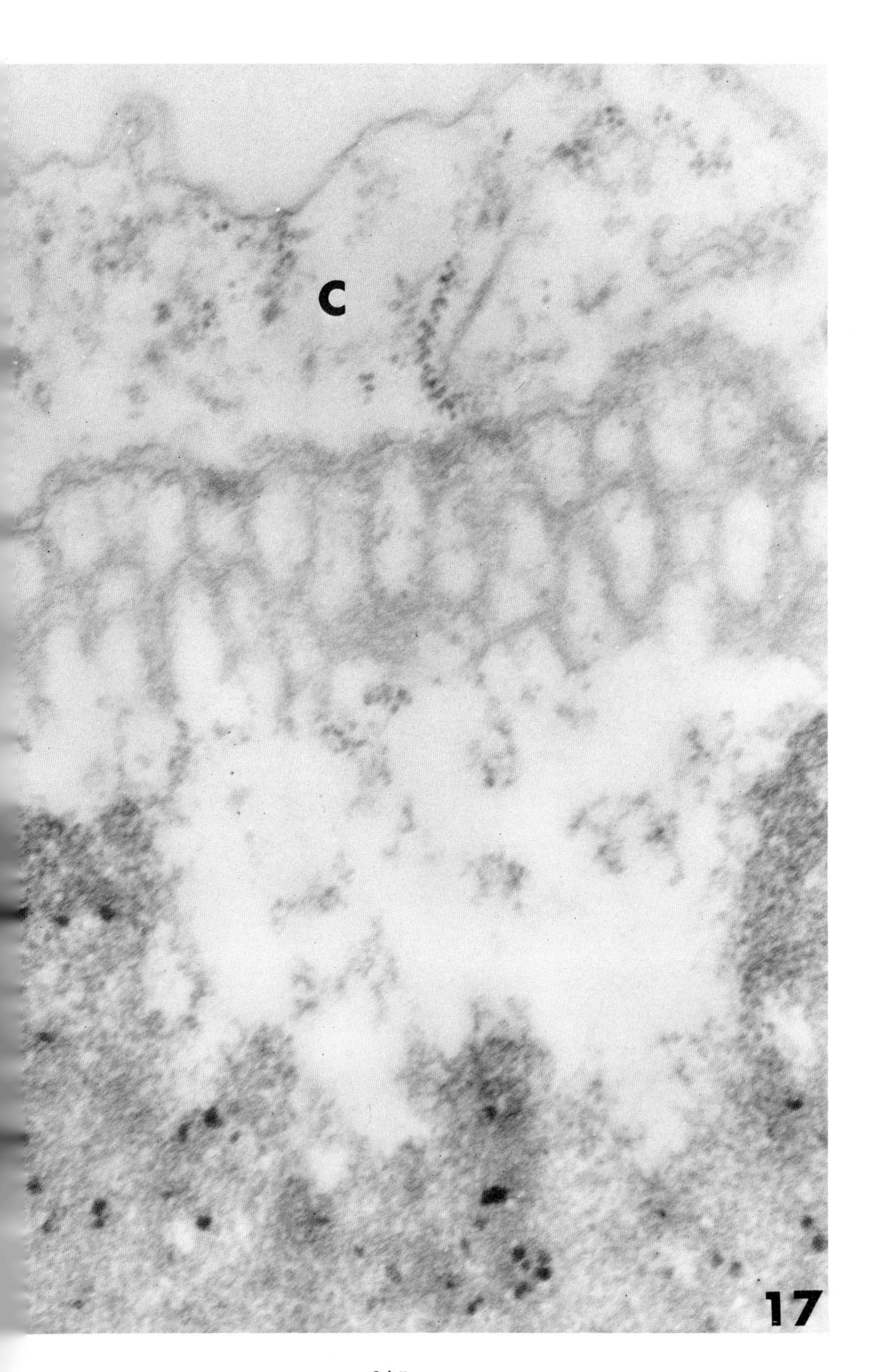
c
17

Figure 18. Ultrathin section of ameba showing groups of helices (h) in the nucleus and a single helix (arrow) outside the nuclear envelope. Magnified ca. 27,500 X.

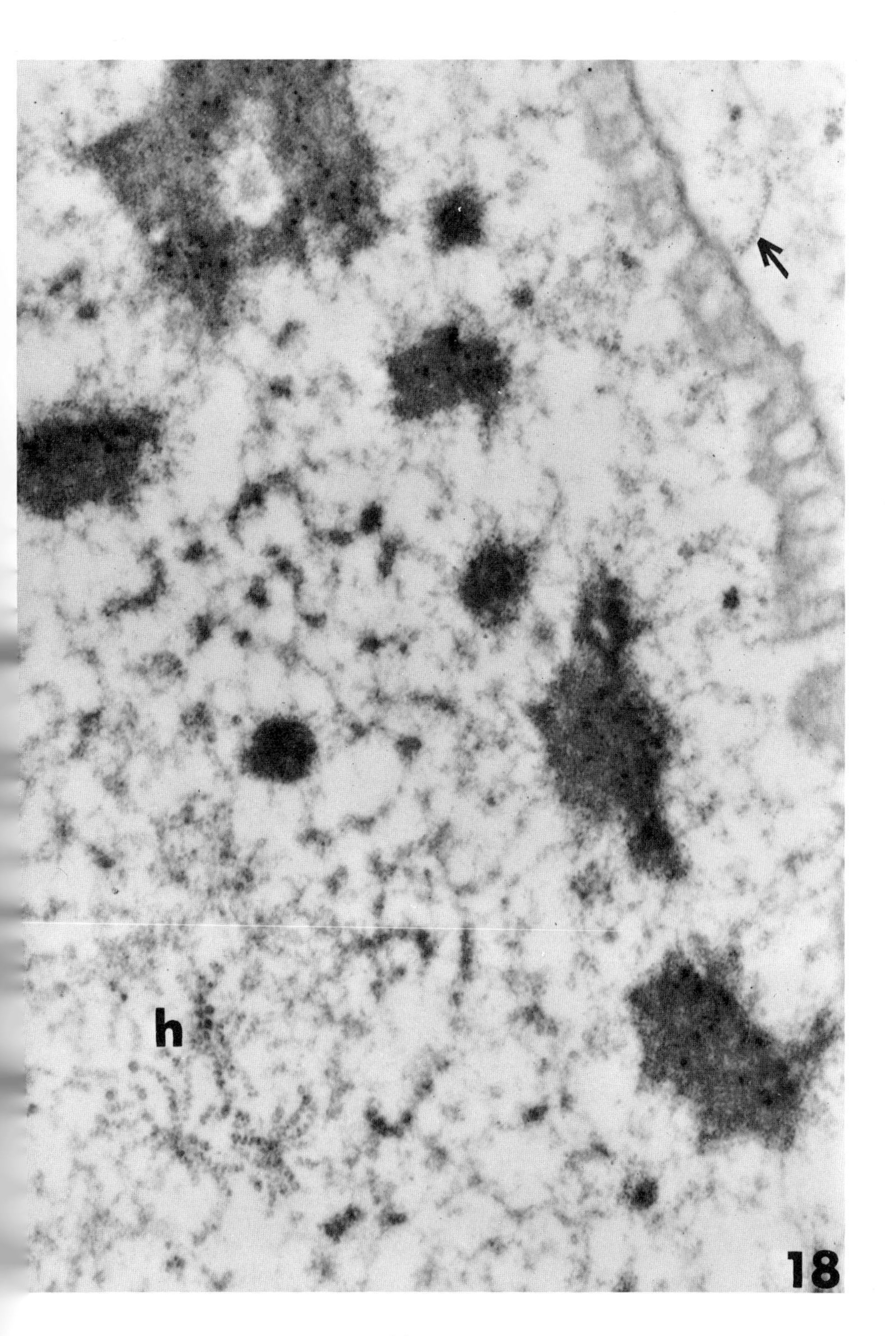
h
18

Figure 19. High magnification of helix seen in Figure 18. The helix (arrow) appears to have some type of substructure that may represent its disintegration into smaller units. Magnified ca. 41,000 X.

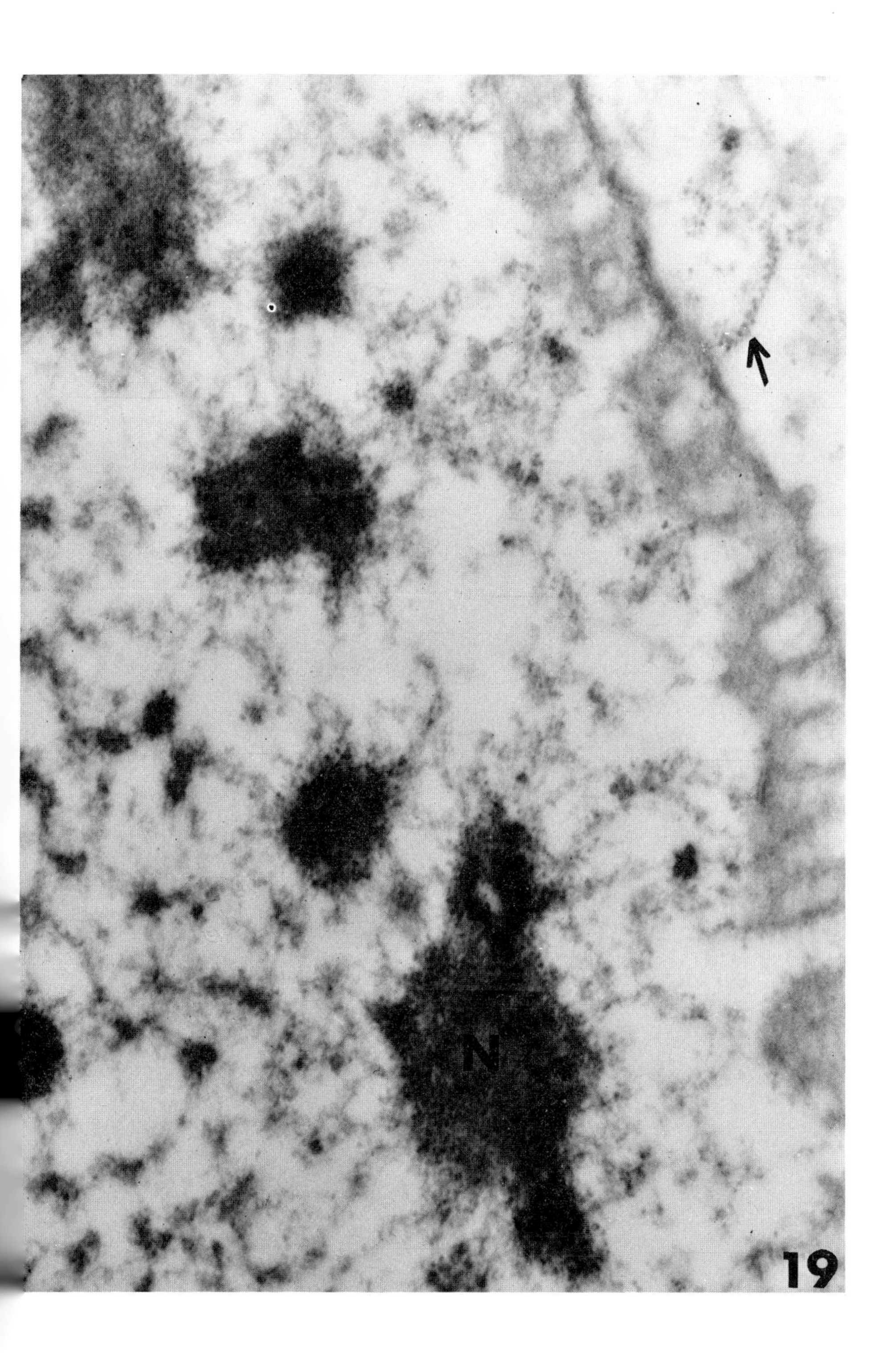
N
19

Figure 20. Ultrathin section of ameba treated with ribonuclease. The nucleoli (N) show signs of internal digestion. Magnified ca. 19,400 X.

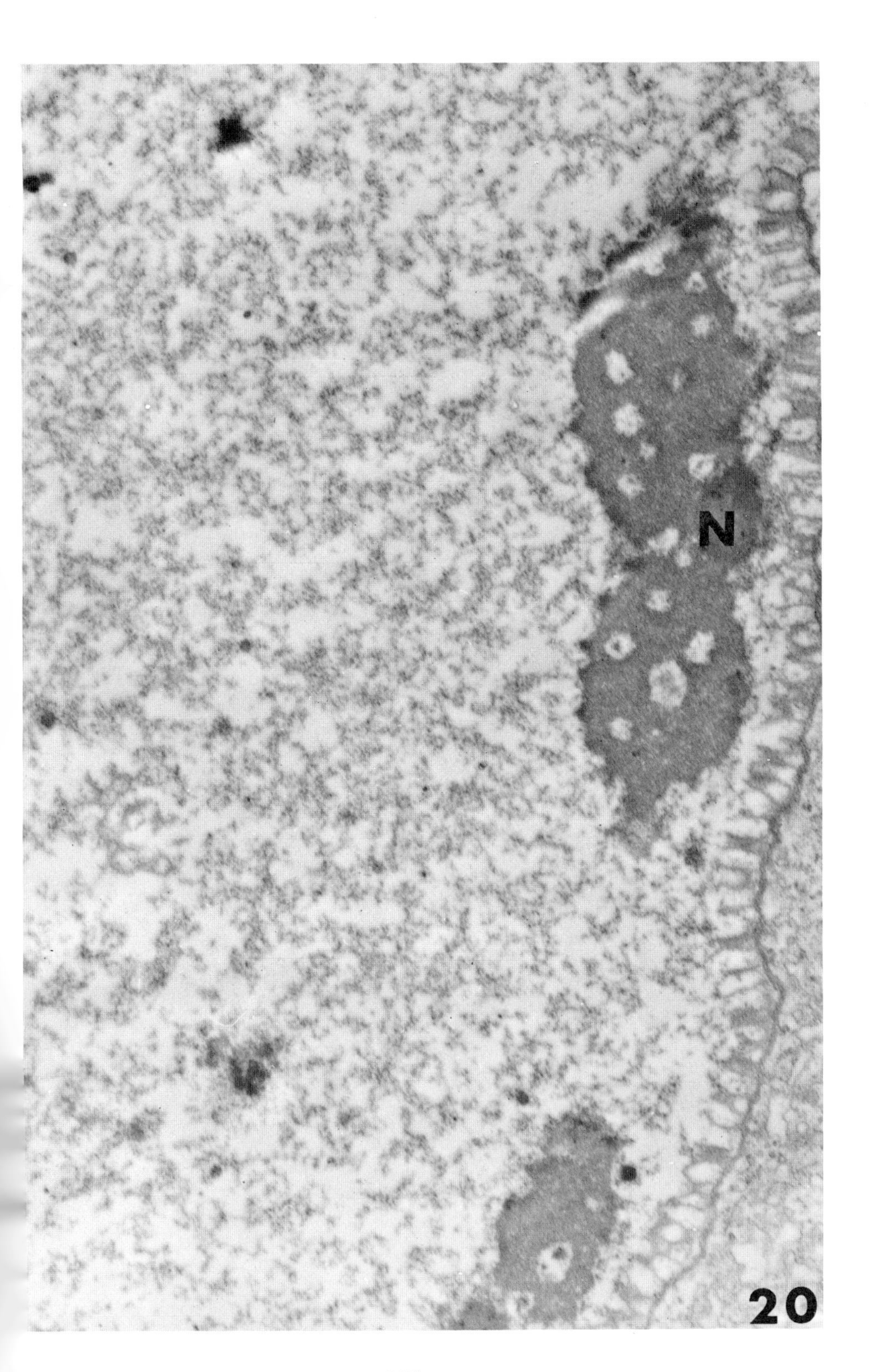
N
20

Figure 21. Graph illustrating the effects of two concentrations of actinomycin D on the incorporation of ^{3}H uridine into nuclear RNA of *Amoeba* during early interphase.

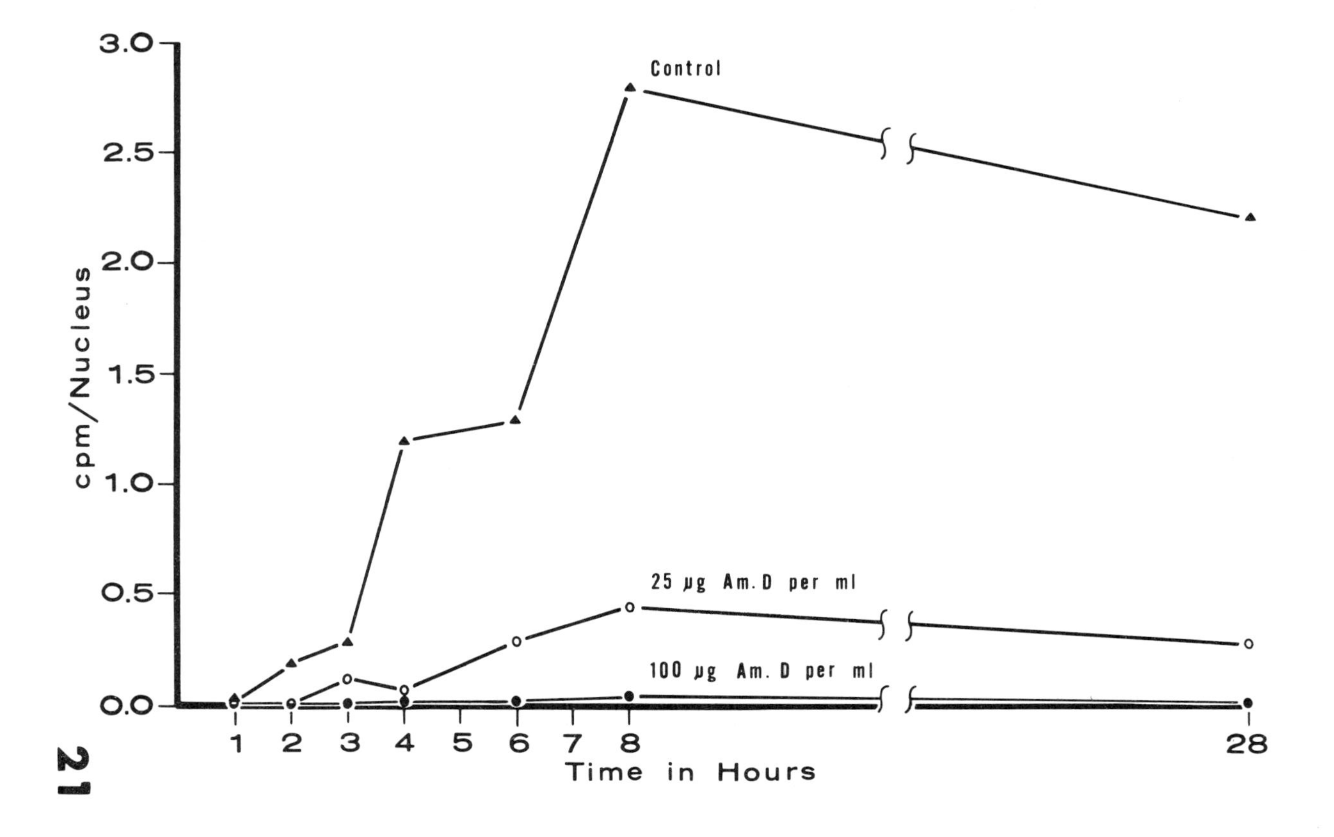

cpm/Nucleus
3.0
2.5
2.0
1.5
1.0
0.5
0.0
Control
25 µg Am. D per ml
100 µg Am. D per ml
1
2
3
4
5
6
7
8
28
Time in Hours
21

Figure 22. Ultrathin section of ameba treated with 100 μg/ml actinomycin D for 6 hr. The nucleoli have become fragmented or appear more electron-dense and spherical than normal nucleoli. The arrow indicates what may be an atypical granular mass. Magnified ca. 18,000 X.

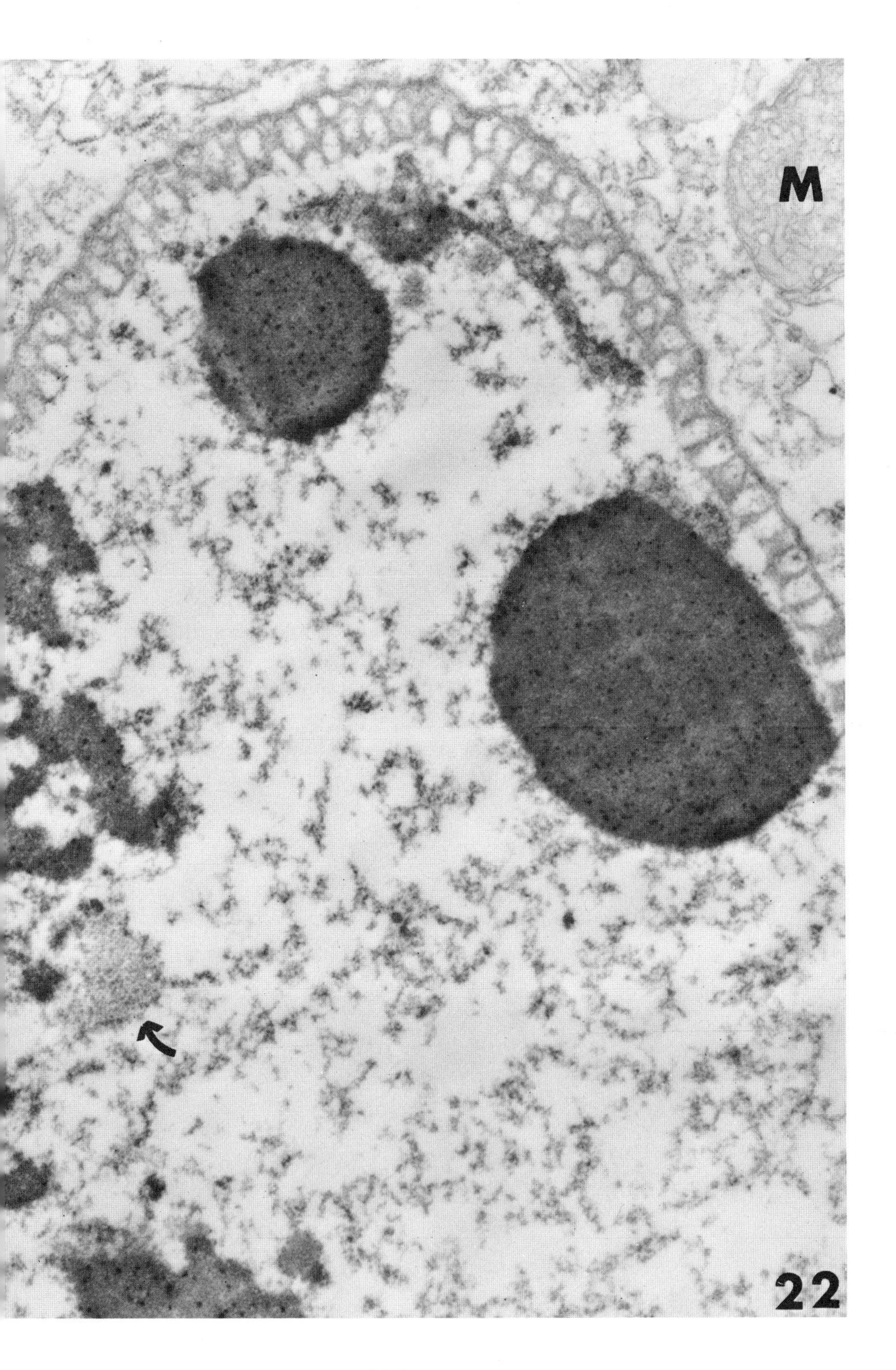
M
22

Figure 23. Light microscope autoradiograph of a section of ameba labeled with ^{3}H uridine and ^{3}H cytidine for 5 hr. The incorporated labeled precursor is well localized in the nucleoli. The very heavily labeled cytoplasmic structures are _Tetrahymenae_ food vacuoles. Nu represents nucleus. Magnified ca. 1620 X.

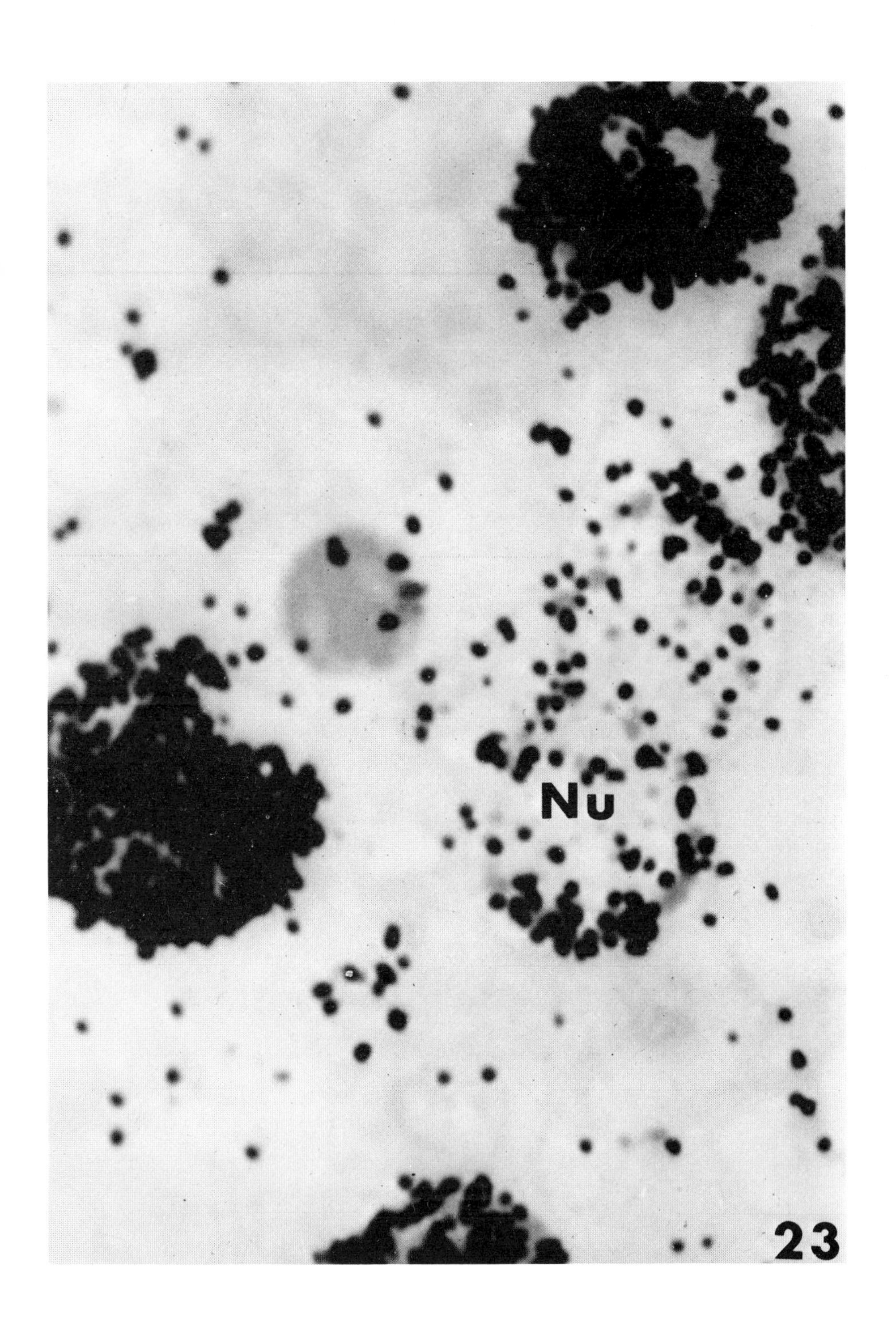
Nu
23

Figure 24. Electron microscope autoradiograph (EM-ARG) of an ameba nucleus. The incorporated ^3H RNA precursors are maximally localized in the peripherally located nucleoli (N). Silver grains are also detectable over the helices (h). Magnified ca. 8000 X.

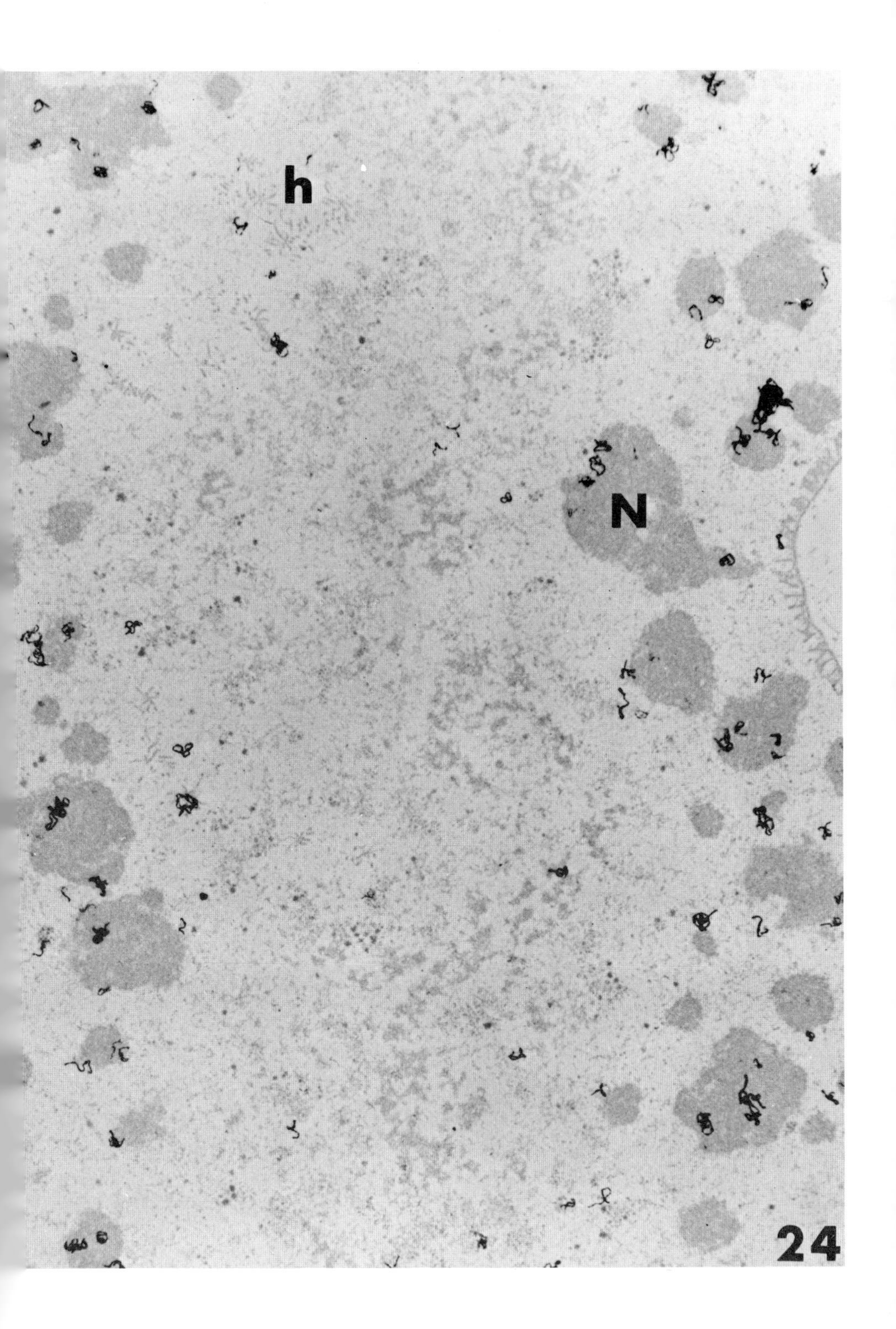
h
N
24

Figure 25. EM-ARG of an ameba that shows a different but closely adjacent section of the nucleus seen in Figure 24. Incorporated ^3H uridine and ^3H cytidine are localized in the nucleoli (N) and the helices. Magnified ca. 22,000 X.

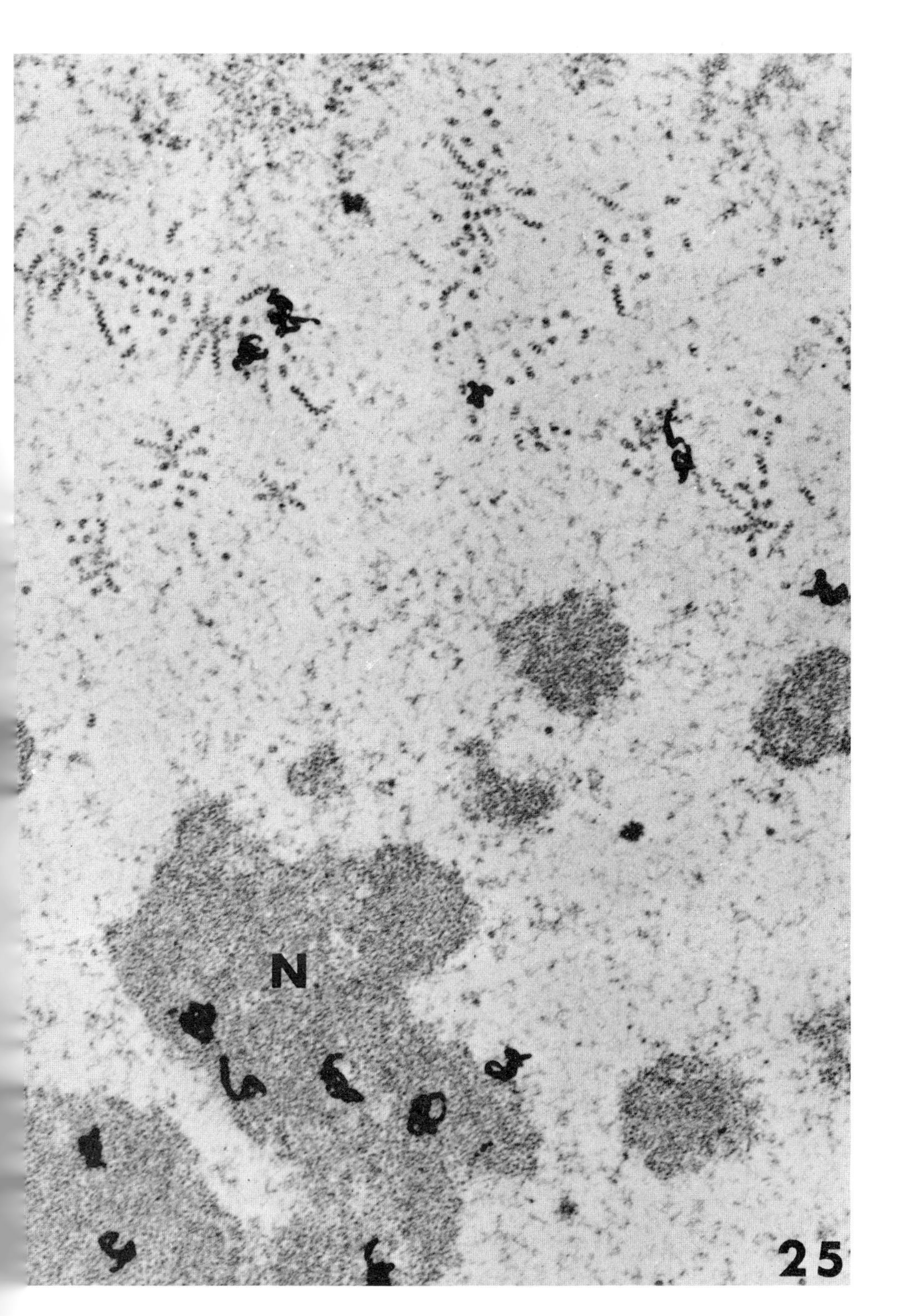
N
25

Figure 26. EM-ARG of an ameba that was labeled with ^{3}H uridine during the first 6 hr of interphase. The incorporated label is maximally localized in the nucleoli and to a lesser extent in the remaining nucleoplasm. The arrow in the lower right quadrant indicates a group of labeled helices. Magnified ca. 18,000 X.

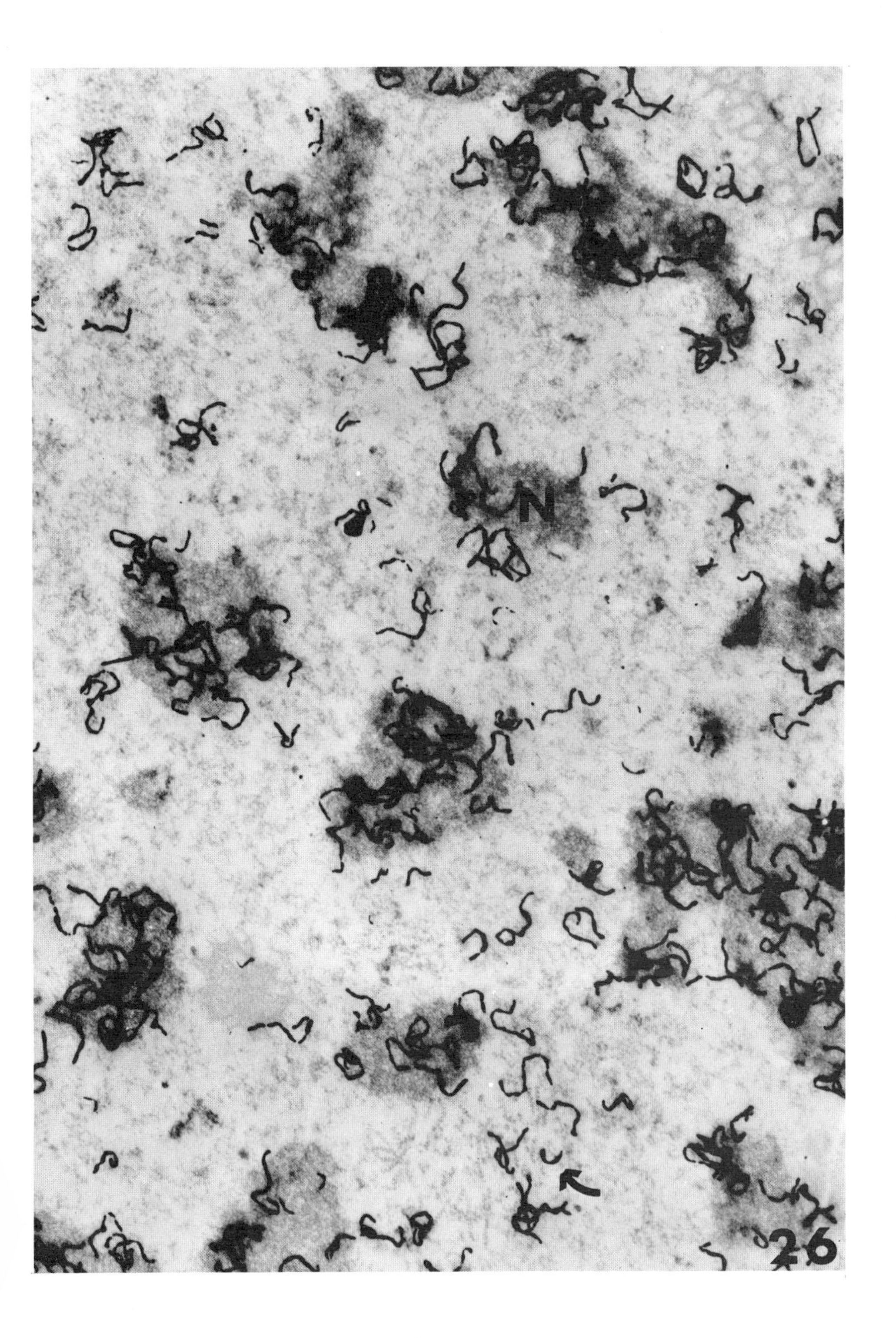
N
26

Figure 27. Higher magnification of a different area of the nucleus seen in Figure 26. Several large groups of helices are labeled and lie in the vicinity of the heavily labeled nucleoli (N). Magnified ca. 24,300 X.

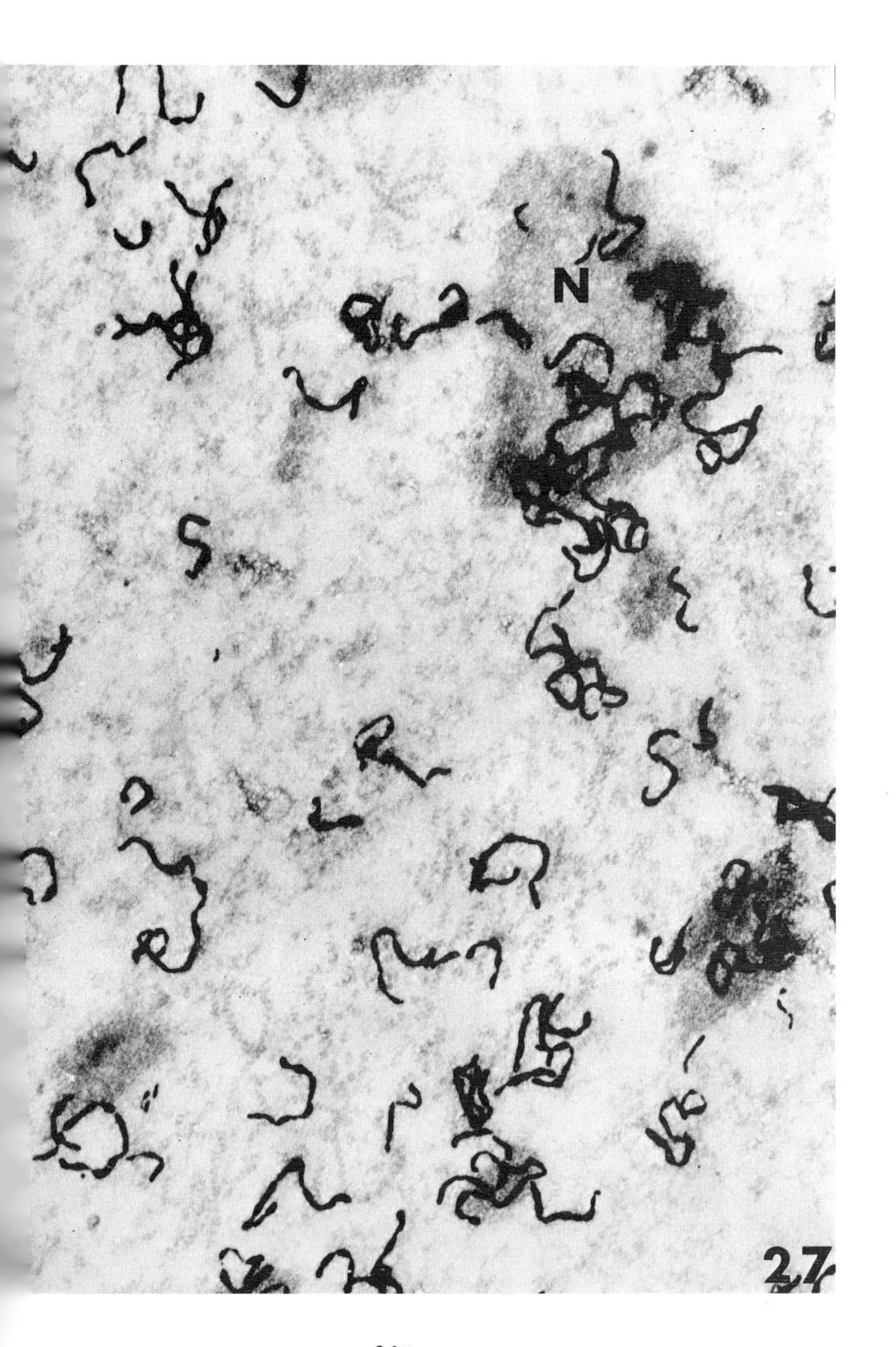
N
27

Figure 28. Light microscope autoradiograph of a section of an ameba labeled with ^3H thymidine. The incorporated ^3H precursor is localized in the more central regions of the nucleus (n), which correspond to the Feulgen-positive areas of the nucleus. Magnified ca. 1240 X.

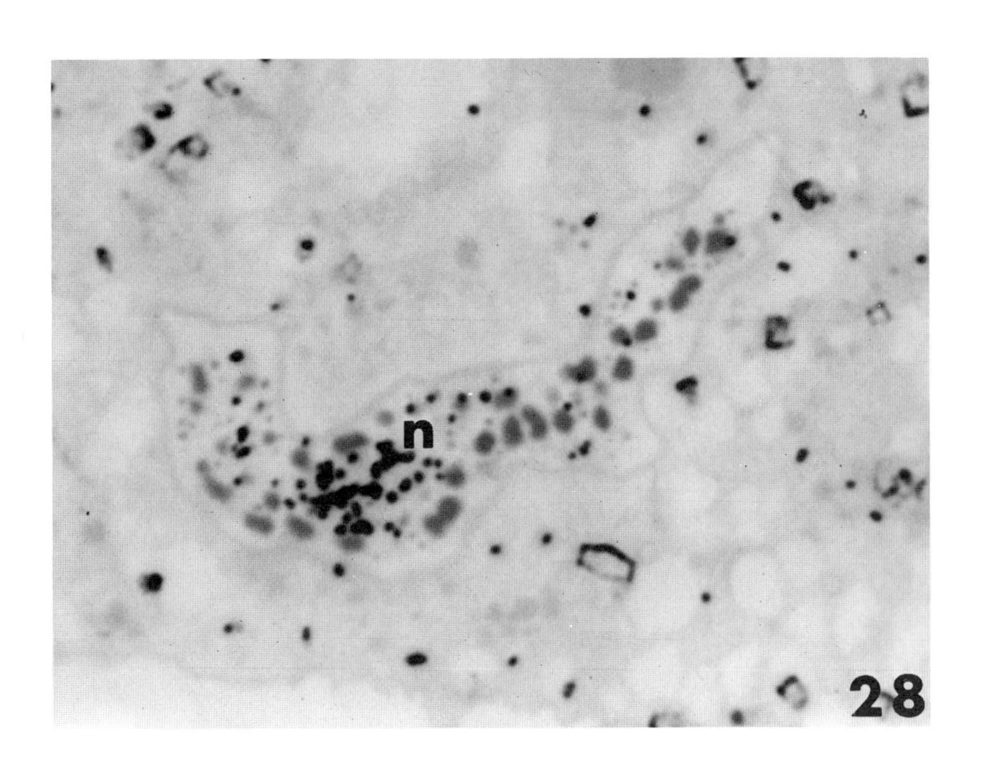
n
28

Figure 29. EM-ARG of an ameba that was labeled with ^{3}H thymidine. The ^{3}H DNA precursor has been incorporated in the more central regions of the nucleus. Little or no ^{3}H thymidine is associated with the peripherally located nucleoli (N). C represents cytoplasm. Magnified ca. 13,000 X.

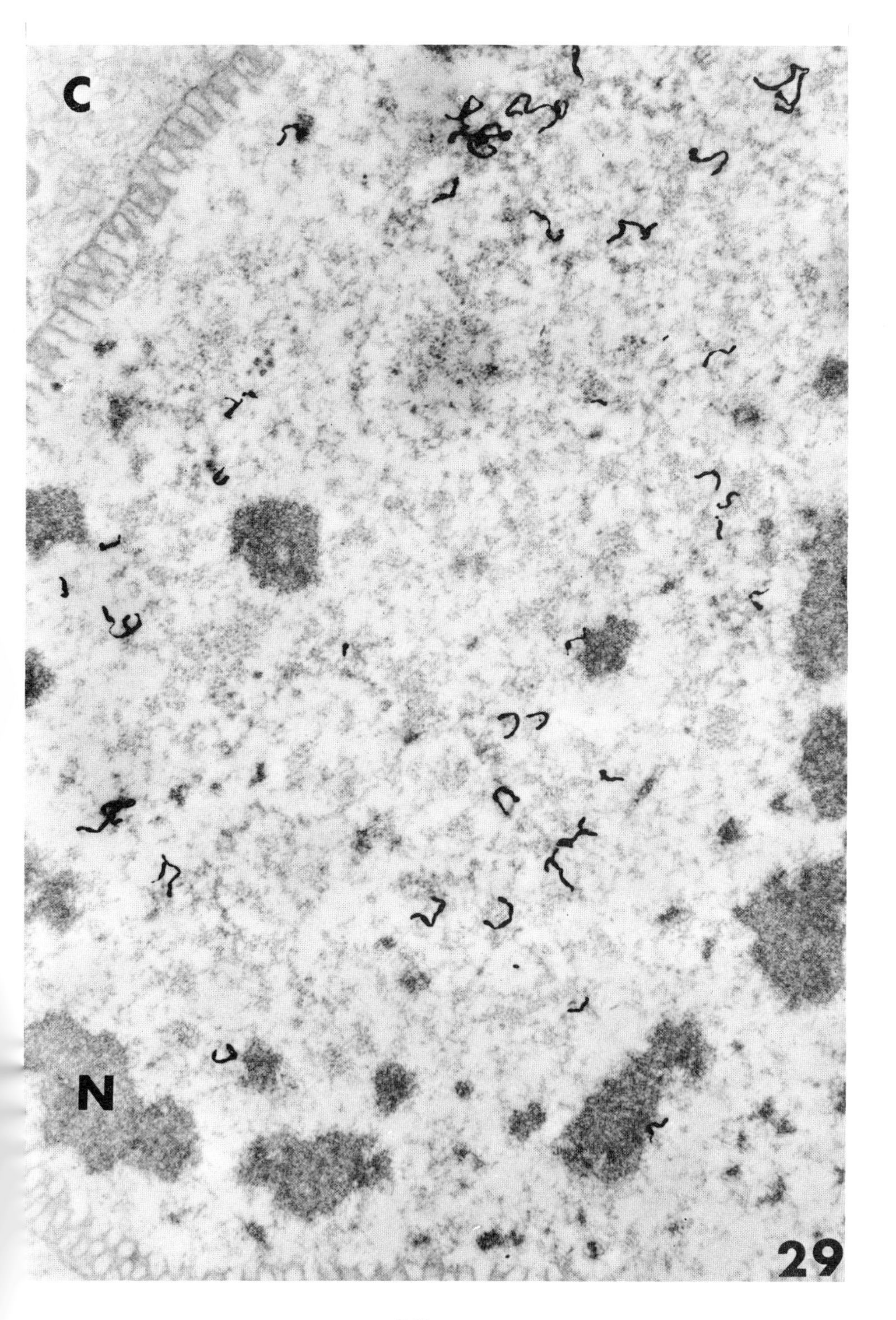
C
N
29

Figure 30. EM-ARG of an ameba that was exposed to ^{3}H thymidine. The incorporated ^{3}H DNA precursor appears to be localized to some degree in the condensed patches (Cp) but is not detectable in either the helices (h) or the granular masses (G). Magnified ca. 24,700 X.

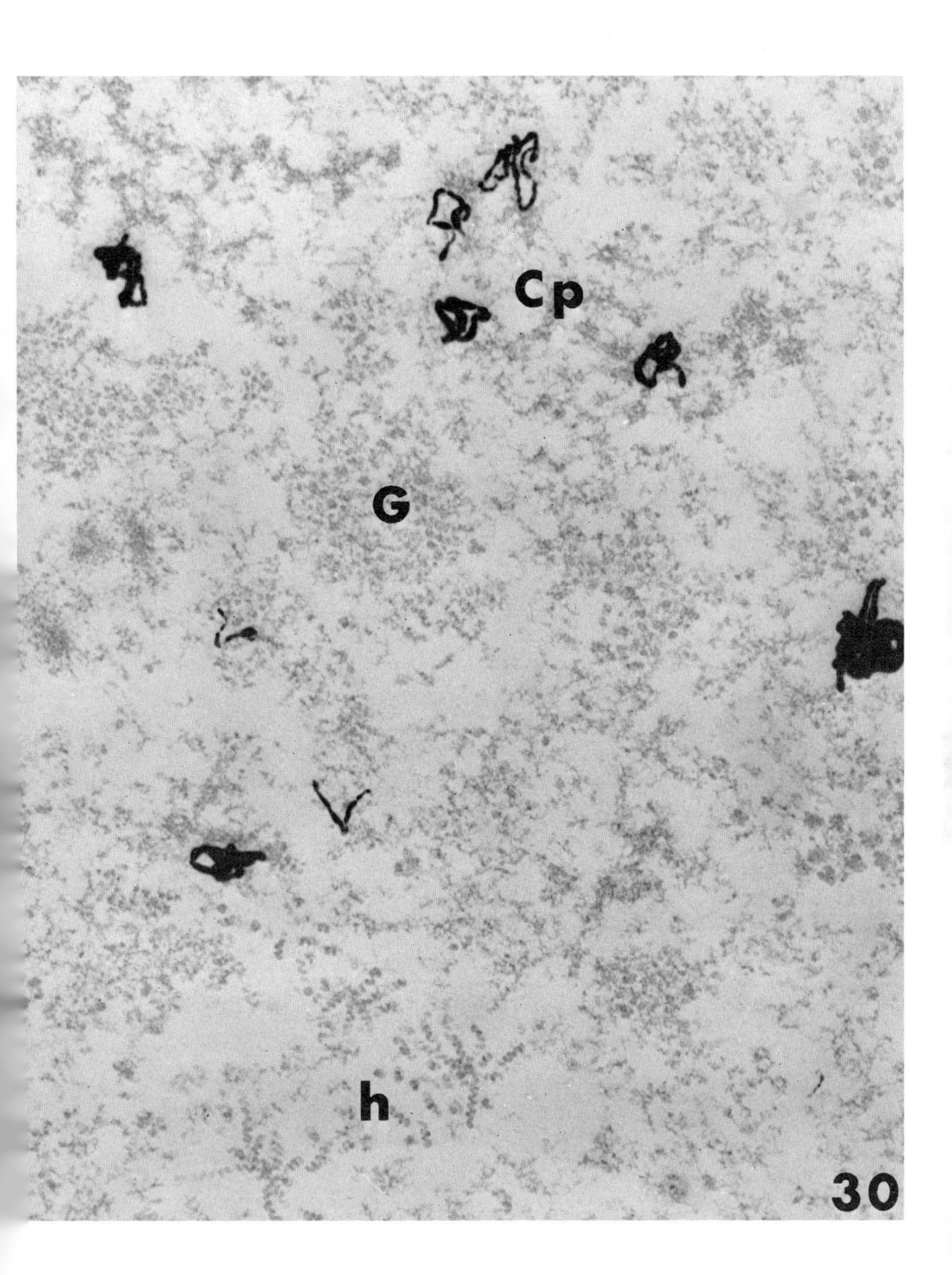
Cp
G
h
30

*Protein Interactions Between Nucleus and Cytoplasm**

Lester Goldstein

Department of Biology
University of Pennsylvania
Philadelphia

and

David M. Prescott

Institute for Developmental Biology
University of Colorado
Boulder

Despite much attention to nuclear proteins - presumably because their localization implies that they are importantly involved in chromosomal replication and/or transcription - our ignorance of the roles they play in the physiology of the cell is almost complete. Because of the presumed involvement in replication and/or transcription we, too, have been interested in the nuclear proteins, and, in contrast to most other studies, have been investigating primarily the physiologic behavior of these molecules.

Although we have studied nuclear proteins for several years, the work of the past year has entered a new and more fruitful phase, largely a result of highly reliable techniques for the quantitative assay of the

*Supported by a grant from the National Science Foundation to David M. Prescott and a grant from the U.S. Public Health Service to Lester Goldstein.

proteins we are examining. From our earlier studies on nuclear proteins in Amoeba proteus, three facts stand out as particularly important. First, this ameba contains a class of proteins that is constantly migrating back and forth between nucleus and cytoplasm, although the concentration in the nucleus far exceeds that in the cytoplasm. Second, the remainder of the nuclear proteins seemed not to migrate at all - at least in short-term experiments. The third fact, seeming to contradict the second, is that under suitable methods of long-term observation, essentially all the nuclear proteins appeared to turn over. That is, no significant fraction of protein has the nuclear permanence shown by chromosomal DNA.

Recent, quantitatively more reliable work confirms most of what had been learned earlier but has provided information of more subtle details; consequently, we have reclassified the nuclear proteins into two major groups. One, called rapidly migrating proteins, or RMP, corresponds to the class that is constantly shuttling back and forth between nucleus and cytoplasm. These proteins behave in a fashion that might be predicted for agents mediating cytoplasmic influences on genetic transcription. All other nuclear proteins are placed in a group called slow turnover proteins, or STP. This latter group also leaves the nucleus but at a rate considerably slower than that for RMP. The question of whether STP return to the nucleus after passage to the cytoplasm will be considered later. Within the STP group, we expect to find proteins of the following kinds: nuclear envelope proteins, structural proteins of the nucleolus, proteins of nascent ribosomes, various chromosomal proteins, etc.

In this report, we shall cover the following matters:

1. the basic quantitative considerations of the distribution of the nuclear proteins in the cell;
2. the effect on the distribution, localization, and movement of the nuclear proteins as a consequence of time, growth, and cell divisions;
3. structural factors affecting the distribution of the nuclear proteins;
4. some beginning experiments dealing with the role of these proteins in the physiology of the cell.

MATERIAL AND METHODS*

The cells used throughout the experiments reported were free-living amebae, _A. proteus_.†

The amebae were labeled by feeding them - usually for 2 or 3 cell generations - on _Tetrahymena_ grown on synthetic medium in which ten ^3H amino acids were substituted for their unlabeled counterparts. The labeled amebae were either fasted for a minimum of 24 hr or fed unlabeled _Tetrahymena_ for at least 12 hr before they were used for experimental purposes. Thus, the labeled pool was always "chased." One isolated nucleus from such an ameba registered 300 to 500 CPM in a windowless, gas-flow Geiger counter. We assume that all the proteins, under these conditions, are essentially uniformly labeled, and that the amount of radioactivity is a close approximation of the amount of protein.

A nucleus was transplanted from one ameba to another in the traditional manner - i.e., pushed with a microprobe from one cell into the other directly through both cell membranes. To amputate a piece of cytoplasm from a cell, we used a sharp-edged microtool as a knife to cut the cell into two parts, each of which seals up immediately. The result is one nucleate fragment and one enucleate fragment, both still viable.

We isolated a nucleus by placing an ameba into an aqueous solution of the detergent Triton X-100 and spermidine-HCl, and then drawing the cell in and out of a narrow-tipped pipet until the cell was ruptured. The nucleus was rinsed free of cytoplasm and handled singly, if necessary, for further processing. We have determined that nuclei isolated in this fashion lose approximately 20% of their protein content, but this

*See first article of this volume for additional details.

†The evidence presented in this paper is necessarily rather sketchy. Greater detail on many of the points raised will be found in papers by the authors to be submitted for publication (4, 5, 8, 9).

seems to be a general loss rather than one from a specific fraction, and thus does not materially affect our conclusions.

To measure the ^3H radioactivity, we placed nuclei or cytoplasm (in groups of one or more) on a planchet and treated them with formic acid. The acid disrupted the preparations and spread material into a layer thin enough to make self-absorption negligible. When dry, the planchet was counted in a low-background, gas-flow, windowless counter that assayed ^3H with an efficiency of 17 to 18%.

RESULTS

Basic Quantitative Considerations

The presence of RMP still is most clearly demonstrated by autoradiographic methods, as was first evident some years ago (2) (Figure 1). Because we have found that the quantitation of the radioactivity of isolated nuclei by Geiger counting is far superior to quantitation from autoradiographs, we have reexamined the distribution of the labeled proteins as shown in Figure 2. From this kind of experiment, we can determine the distribution of RMP between nuclei, the proportion of protein in STP, and the relative proportion of RMP in the cytoplasm.

In the first part of one such experiment, (we performed many as parts of a variety of investigations), we obtained the results shown in Table 1. These data, however, are not derived from isolated nuclei but are taken from the entire cell into which the nucleus was grafted. That is, the cell in Figure 2 that received nucleus A1 and the cell that received nucleus A2 at the second transfer were immediately fixed whole and assayed as such. We note that the mean ratio of activity between the nuclei is 6.4 to 1, which is the approximate ratio obtained regardless of whether the nuclei are isolated. The mean ratio generally ranged between 5 to 1 and 7 to 1.*

*For the remainder of this paper, whenever reference is made to the "ratio," it is the ratio obtained in this way - with or without nuclear isolation.

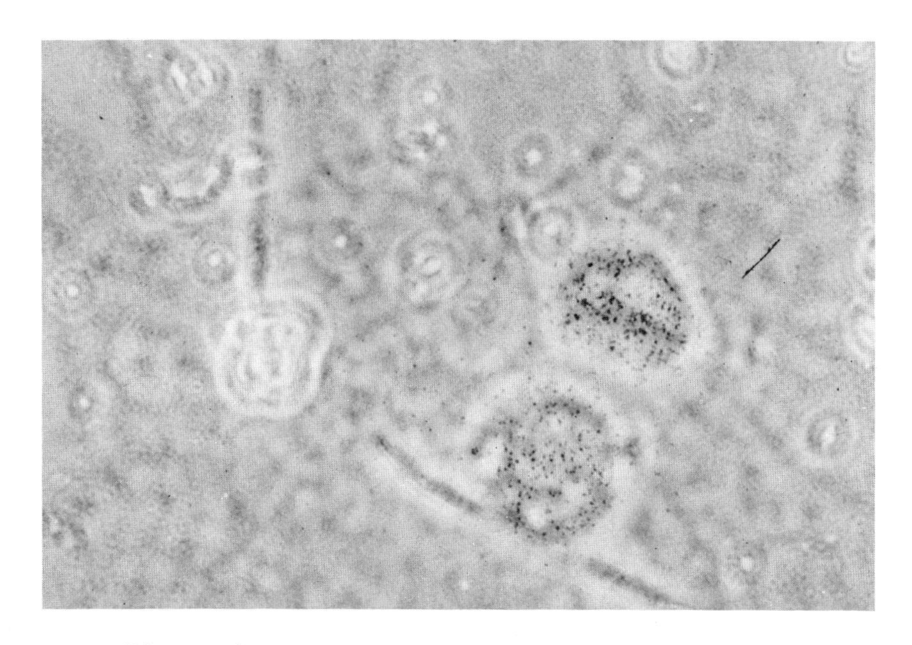

Figure 1. Autoradiograph of part of an ameba (out of focus) into which was grafted a lysine-1-^{14}C-labeled nucleus 20 hr before the cell was fixed. Radioactivity is almost completely localized over grafted nucleus and host cell nucleus. The most reasonable interpretation is that there exists a class of proteins (RMP) shuttling back and forth between the nucleus and the cytoplasm, but which is present in the former in a much higher concentration than in the latter.

Examination of the actual counts following transfer of an ^{3}H nucleus into a nonradioactive cell shows that 11% of the total cell activity is in RMP in each nucleus (since we assume the more radioactive nucleus has as much RMP as the less radioactive one). The cytoplasm (enucleate) has 20% of the activity, which we assume is all RMP label. In most experiments, contrary to what is illustrated here, the amount of RMP in the cytoplasm is only slightly greater than that in either nucleus. However, the concentrations in nucleus and

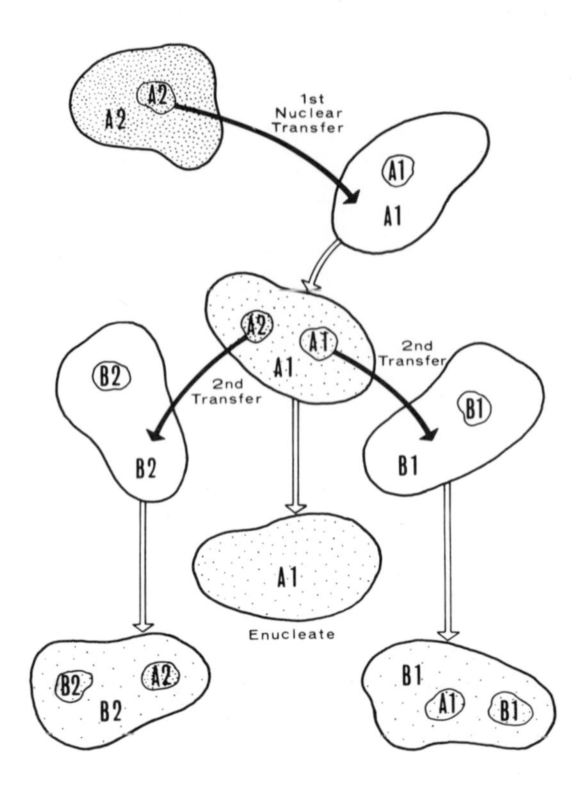

Figure 2. A nucleus (A2) from a ^{3}H protein cell is grafted into an unlabeled cell (A1) for the first nuclear transfer. The next day, nucleus A2 is grafted into unlabeled cell B2 and nucleus A1 is grafted into unlabeled cell B1. Enucleate A1 is saved for assay. Either the two cells after the second transfer are immediately fixed whole to assay for total activity of nucleus A2 and of nucleus A1, or the four nuclei are isolated the next day to determine the distribution of ^{3}H protein between nuclei B2, A2, A1, and B1.

cytoplasm are much different because the nucleus is only ca. 2% of the volume of the cytoplasm.

The reasonableness of our conclusions about the two classes of protein is demonstrated in Table 2, part of the same experiment as that just described. In this

TABLE 1

Distribution of nuclear protein label
(without nuclear isolation)

Cell	Nuclei	CPM	Ratio	% total
	A2	207		69
1	A1	26	8.0:1	9
	enucleate	68		23
	A2	264		72
2	A1	47	5.6:1	13
	enucleate	55		15
	A2	226		69
3	A1	38	5.9:1	12
	enucleate	62		19
	A2	199		66
4	A1	50	4.0:1	17
	enucleate	51		17
	A2	215		63
5	A1	27	8.0:1	8
	enucleate	101		29
	A2	259		67
6	A1	32	8.1:1	8
	enucleate	94		25
	A2	299		67
7	A1	55	5.4:1	12
	enucleate	94		21
	A2	330		75
8	A1	32	10.3:1	7
	enucleate	78		18
	A2	219		-
9	A1	49	4.5:1	-
	enucleate	lost		-
	A2	192		80
10	A1	25	7.7:1	11
	enucleate	22		9

$\overline{X}$ ratio = 6.4
$\overline{X}$ % in host nucleus = 11
$\overline{X}$ % in enucleate = 20
$\overline{X}$ CPM for less active nucleus (RMP) = 38
$\overline{X}$ CPM more active nucleus minus that of less active nucleus (STP) = 203

TABLE 2

Distribution of nuclear protein label after triple transfer (with nuclear isolation)*

Cell	Nuclei	CPM	Ratio
	A2	191	17.4:1
	B2	11	
11	A1	21	1.6:1
	B1	13	
	enucleate	53	
	A2	103	6.9:1
	B2	15	
12	A1	17	2.1:1
	B1	8	
	enucleate	124	
	A2	259	12.3:1
	B2	21	
13	A1	15	1.9:1
	B1	8	
	enucleate	lost	
	A2	157	11.2:1
	B2	14	
14	A1	22	2.8:1
	B1	8	
	enucleate	90	
	A2	180	10.6:1
	B2	17	
15	A1	10	1.4:1
	B1	14	
	enucleate	47	
	A2	152	6.9:1
	B2	22	
16	A1	9	2.0:1
	B1	18	
	enucleate	lost	
	A2	218	11.5:1
	B2	19	
17	A1	7	2.3:1
	B1	16	
	enucleate	57	

$\bar{X}$ ratio "hotter" pair = 11.0
$\bar{X}$ ratio "cooler" pair = 2.0
($\bar{X}$ ratio after 1st transfer, Table 1 = 6.4)
$\bar{X}$ CPM in nuclei A1 plus B1 = 27
$\bar{X}$ CPM in nucleus A2 minus B2 (STP) = 163

*Nuclei from these cells were isolated a day after the cells of Table 1 were fixed.

case, however, the nuclei were isolated the next day and then assayed for radioactivity. As expected, for one pair of nuclei the ratio is markedly greater than 6.4 to 1 - reflecting a decreased proportion of radioactivity in RMP. For the other pair of nuclei, also as expected, the ratio is considerably lower than 6.4 to 1 and, in fact, close to the expected 1 to 1 if the original host nucleus contained label only in RMP. (Since we do not know which nucleus is A1 and which is B1, and since any deviation from equality for whatever reason would be scored as greater than 1 to 1, we can not consider the observed 2 to 1 to be truly different from 1 to 1.) When the absolute counts for each compartment and protein type of the experiment's two parts (Tables 1 and 2) are compared, the values for RMP are as expected if the appropriate corrections are made. The value for STP, however, is reduced by ca. 20% for the second part assayed a day later, which proved to be the first indication that STP moves from the nucleus under normal circumstances.

We can summarize this section by noting two quantitative relations derived from the data.

1. The nucleus and the cytoplasm each normally have approximately half the cell's total of RMP, signifying that the nuclear concentration is almost 50 times that of the cytoplasm.
2. Approximately 40% of the nuclear proteins is RMP and the remaining 60% is STP.

Effect of Time, Growth, and Cell Division

We next turned to a study of the behavior of these proteins in time, under different growth conditions, and under conditions of cell multiplication.

"Turnover" under starvation conditions. A study of the effect of starvation on the protein content of the nucleus in a cell uniformly labeled with ^{3}H protein (Figure 3) reveals that apparently no net turnover of these proteins occurs over a period of ca. 5 weeks. It is important to remember this fact in dealing with questions of turnover in other experiments in this series.

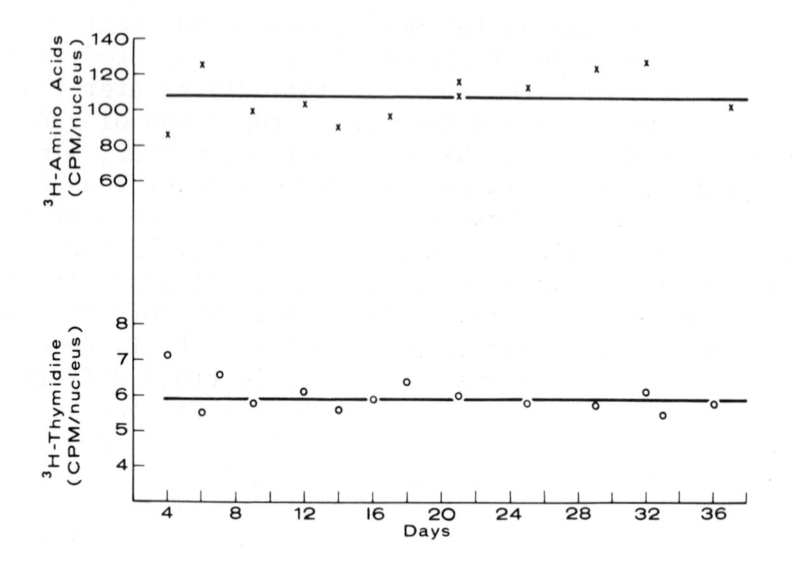

Figure 3. Upper curve shows pattern of change of ^{3}H protein content with time during starvation. Lower curve shows pattern of change of ^{3}H DNA content with time during starvation. Between 25 and 50 nuclei were isolated, pooled, and assayed for each point. Curves drawn by eye.

Distribution of nuclear proteins with time in the absence of growth. A study of the rate at which the labeled proteins distribute between the nuclei after a ^{3}H protein nucleus is grafted into an unlabeled cell yields the kinetics shown in Figure 4. As anticipated, the ratio between the nuclei falls rapidly until about 3 hr after the operation, at which time an abrupt change in rate takes place. This observation is in approximate agreement with earlier work, but, in contrast, these data suggest the ratio continues to

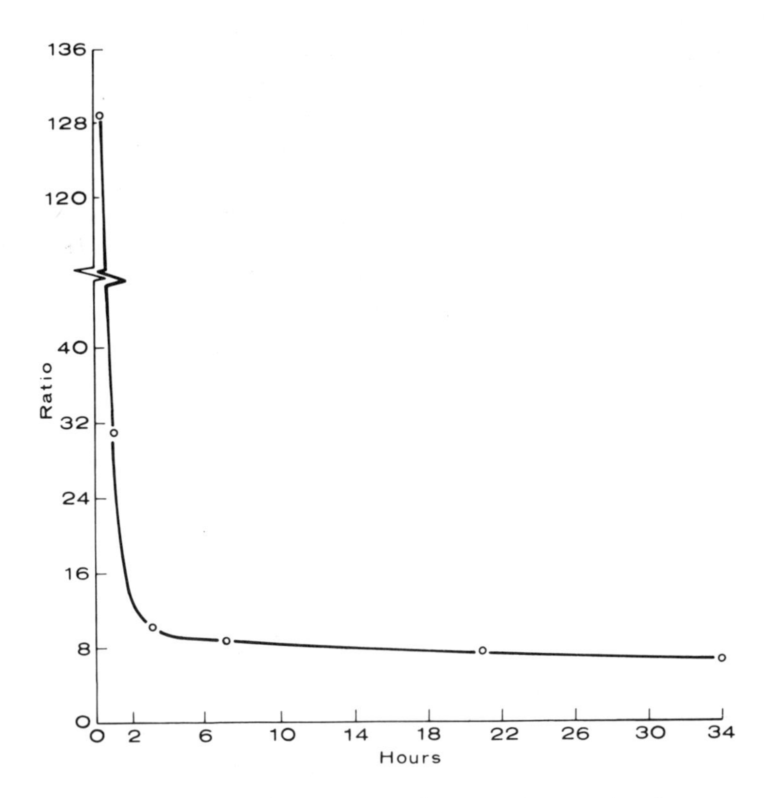

Figure 4. Pattern of change in ratio between donor and host nuclei following the implantation of a ^{3}H protein nucleus into an unlabeled cell. Nuclei from 10 to 20 cells isolated for each point; each point represents the mean of the ratios of the pairs of nuclei of the 10 to 20 cells.

fall, albeit at a slow rate, even after the first 3 hr. In another experiment over a longer time period we find this observation to be true (Figure 5).

Examination of the actual counts of such an experiment reveals that most of the post-3-hr fall in the ratio is a result of the loss of STP activity from the grafted nucleus, although the data suggest that some additional label (return of STP?) is being acquired by the host cell nucleus. It may also be significant that feeding seems to increase the rate at which the ratio falls, and again, the decrease seems to result largely from the loss of labeled STP from the grafted nucleus.

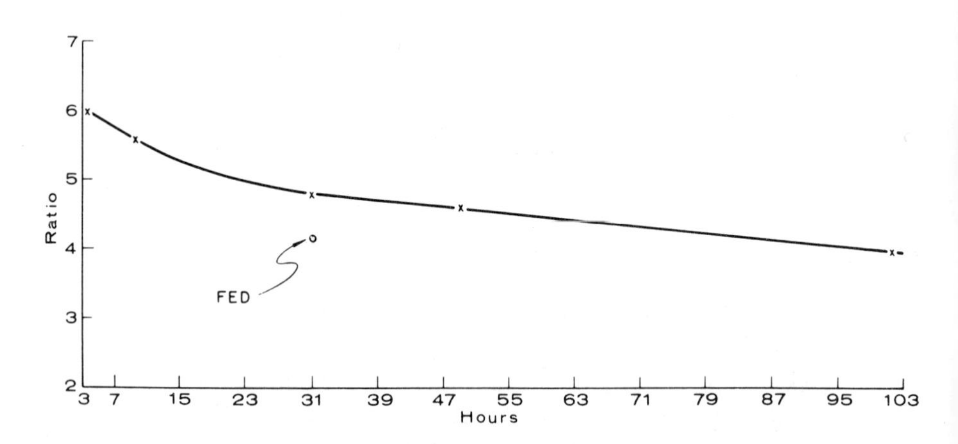

Figure 5. Similar to experiment shown in Figure 4, except the nuclei are isolated at intervals over a longer time period. Cells were unfed during the course of the experiment, except for those of FED point.

Distribution of nuclear proteins during growth without cell division. That labeled STP does leave the nucleus is firmly established by experiments in which a cell composed of a ^3H protein nucleus grafted into unlabeled, enucleate cytoplasm is allowed to grow for weeks on unlabeled food in the absence of cell division. Cell division is prevented by amputating

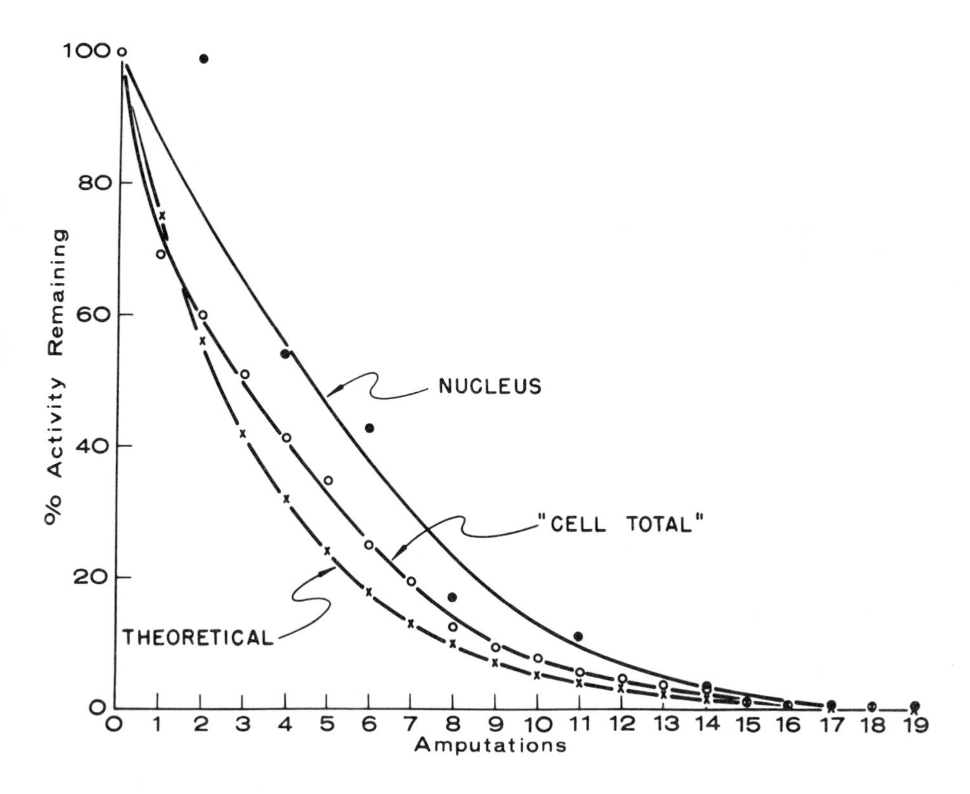

Figure 6. Experiment showing rate of loss of nuclear proteins during repeated cytoplasmic amputations and refeeding on unlabeled food. At the start of the experiment, approximately 150 cells were prepared by grafting a ^3H protein nucleus into an unlabeled enucleate cell. Each point for the NUCLEUS curve is based on the assay of approximately 15 nuclei; each point for the CELL TOTAL curve is based on extrapolations from assay of cytoplasmic fragments cut away or from assays of cytoplasmic fragments cut away plus isolated nuclei. The THEORETICAL curve is based on the loss of 25% of the remaining radioactivity at each amputation. All curves drawn by eye.

approximately 50% of the cytoplasm every time a cell has reached an almost full-grown size (i.e., double the size of a freshly divided cell). Upon refeeding on unlabeled food, the cell "regenerates" its cytoplasm by normal growth.

Figure 6 shows the loss rate of labeled protein from nucleus and cytoplasm. (The cell total is calculated from assays of the fragments cut away and samples of the nuclei that were taken for each nuclear determination.) We expect, of course, a continuous loss of labeled RMP because it rapidly equilibrates between nucleus and cytoplasm. These data show, however, that over 99.7% of radioactivity in protein (the limits of our assay at that time) is eventually lost. Since RMP accounts for only 40% of the labeled material, STP label must be lost as well. Interestingly, the loss rates from nucleus and cytoplasm are not far from a theoretical loss of 25% at each amputation, which is the rate expected of RMP, because approximately half the cell total of RMP is in the cytoplasm and approximately half the cytoplasm is removed with each amputation.

The rate of loss of STP is illustrated in an experiment similar to that just described, but in which nuclei from amputated cells were transferred to unlabeled cells after every 3 amputations so that we could determine how the remaining labeled protein was apportioned between RMP and STP. (In this particular experiment, amputations were begun on fully labeled cells that were refed on unlabeled _Tetrahymena_.) Figure 7 shows that the ratio of activity between the nuclei changes hardly at all with repeated amputations, indicating that the rate of loss from the nucleus of labeled STP and labeled RMP is essentially the same under these conditions. If STP were lost more slowly, our original expectation, the ratio should have increased with repeated amputations. This information, when considered with the earlier data, signified that ca. 20 to 25% of the STP leaves the nucleus with each doubling in cell size.

Distribution of nuclear proteins during growth and division. A study of the distribution of the labeled nuclear proteins during growth and cell division produced a few surprises. Fully labeled cells were fed

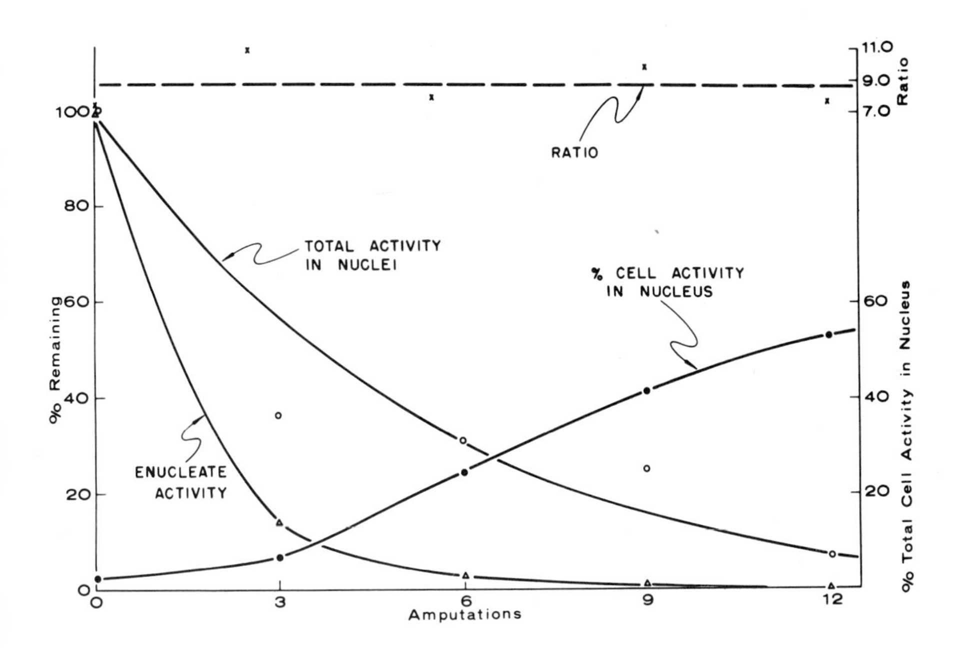

Figure 7. Experiment showing change in distribution of ^{3}H proteins during course of repeated cytoplasmic amputations and refeeding on unlabeled food. At the outset, the cells were fully labeled with ^{3}H amino acids. Procedure was much like that for the experiment described in Figure 6, except that to obtain the "ratio" data, we transplanted the nuclei from amputated cells to unlabeled cells after every third amputation. Pairs of nuclei from 10 to 20 such cells were isolated for each point, and means for ratios of all pairs are plotted.

unlabeled Tetrahymena, and after each division in the nonlabeled medium, we grafted the nucleus of one sister cell into an unlabeled host to assay the distribution of nuclear protein. We allowed the other to resume growth on unlabeled food. In addition, we determined the radioactivity of the enucleate donor as a measure of the inequality, if any, of each division. The data of two such experiments are illustrated in Table 3.

We see at once that the ratio falls with each division, an unexpected event in light of our other data. The reasons for this pattern of ratio change are also surprising. Values for STP fall by more than 50% between the first and second divisions, but thereafter only a 50% reduction occurs at each division, presumably a reflection of ordinary growth dilution. This evidence - i.e., an early, rapid loss of labeled STP resulting from the first cell divisions after labeling - and the earlier evidence that all STP is ultimately lost from the nucleus at a slow rate, even without dilution from cell multiplication in nonlabeled growth media, suggest that at least two classes of STP movement from the nucleus exist. Since growth dilution only occurs after the second division and all STP label eventually leaves the nondividing nucleus, we can also conclude that a good deal of STP is returning to the nucleus and that what we observe after the later divisions is an equilibrium condition for one class of labeled STP molecules shuttling between cytoplasm and nucleus.

The behavior of RMP label in these experiments is also surprising; except for one point, the amount of labeled RMP per nucleus after each division is more than half that for the nuclei before the prior division. Thus, growth dilution is less than the expected 50%. Such data seem most reasonably interpreted as reflecting the conversion of some material into "new" labeled RMP.

In summarizing this section, we can note that RMP migrates rapidly between nucleus and cytoplasm, but the precise rate has not yet been calculated. There is apparently a pool of some material that is slowly converted to the migrating form of RMP. STP, which was formerly thought to be nonmigrating, has been shown to be moving from nucleus to cytoplasm at a slower rate. The evidence suggests, moreover, that while there may be only a one-way passage for one part of STP, another portion of STP is returning to the nucleus. The fraction that seems not to return is evidently liberated in an accelerated fashion as a

TABLE 3

Effect of growth and cell division on the distribution of labeled proteins

Division*	No. cells	$\overline{X}$ ratio	$\overline{X}$ CPM in RMP[†]	$\overline{X}$ CPM in STP[§]	$\overline{X}$ CPM in enucleate donor
Exp. 16/5					
1st	19	6.4:1	18	98	9,300
2nd	14	4.4:1	12 (78)[¶]	35 (42)[¶]	3,950 (42.5)[¶]
3rd	11	3.6:1	6.5 (50)	15 (21)	1,650 (18)
Exp. 7/7					
1st	48	6.4:1	24.0	120.4	14,080
2nd	39	5.9:1	10.7 (49)[¶]	50.2 (45.5)[¶]	6,420 (45.6)[¶]
3rd	28	4.4:1	7.8 (36.5)	23.7 (22)	3,130 (22)
4th	30	3.6:1	4.9 (23)	12.2 (11)	1,570 (11)

*The division after cells were placed on unlabeled food. Nuclear transplantation was performed after indicated division.

†In each of grafted and host cell nucleus.

§In grafted nucleus.

¶Figures in parentheses are percentages of the first-division corrected for the division inequalities. RMP and STP percentages are corrected for the relative amount of cytoplasm shown by the $\overline{X}$ CPM for enucleate donors.

consequence of cell division.*

Structural Considerations of the Distribution of Nuclear Proteins

The unusual behavior patterns of these proteins must have some interesting relations to cell structure, and we have been curious about their nature. We early realized that we could take advantage of the behavior of these proteins during mitosis in designing experiments to explore matters relating to structure.

A few years ago, we showed in two separate experimental investigations (1, 7) that essentially all the nuclear proteins of the ameba were liberated to the cytoplasm during mitosis and returned to the daughter nuclei after the completion of cytokinesis. In a more recent quantitative study, we have found that the return takes about 3 hr and that 100% of the proteins present before prophase return to the daughter nuclei. Since from the onset of mitosis the nuclear envelope undergoes marked morphological changes, the nucleoli disappear, and the chromosomes condense, it is probable that the behavior of the nuclear proteins reflects at least some of these structural alterations.

Effects of an excess or reduced amount of nuclear protein. We have taken advantage of the distribution of the nuclear proteins during mitosis to modify the interphase distribution by cutting a metaphase cell in half. This surgery results in an enucleate half-cell, which can be considered to be relatively enriched with nuclear proteins because all the nuclear proteins are present in the cytoplasm at the time of cutting, and a pair of half-size sister nucleate cells (following mitosis, which usually proceeds normally), which are depleted in their normal supply of nuclear proteins. With this material, we have carried out the experiment

*Other experiments show that when an unlabeled nucleus is implanted into ^{3}H protein cytoplasm of an interphase cell, that nucleus will pick up some labeled STP. Whether that STP was formerly in a nucleus or whether it is newly synthesized is not known.

illustrated in Figure 8. The data of this experiment are too complex to consider here in detail, but they can be briefly summarized with these conclusions. When an excess of STP is present, the nucleus will take up almost all that is available even though it already may have a normal supply. If less than the normal amount of STP is present, the nucleus does not take up all that is available, which suggests that a factor normally responsible for the full return of STP after mitosis has also been affected by the amputation.

When an excess of RMP is present, most of that excess moves to the nucleus. When the normal amount is depleted, virtually all of the cell's RMP goes into the nucleus, leaving the cytoplasm almost devoid of those proteins.

Some electron microscope observations. We recently have begun an electron microscope investigation of nuclear-protein-enriched and nuclear-protein-deprived cells in collaboration with Dr. A.R. Stevens. The first low-power pictures already show striking differences in nuclear morphology. The enriched cells show relatively huge nucleoli and the depleted cells show nucleoli much smaller than normal. Earlier autoradiographic evidence of cells centrifuged following the implantation of a ^{3}H protein nucleus (Figure 9) had already shown that some part of STP is associated with the nucleoli.

Very recent, and as yet unconfirmed, studies suggest that when an excess of nuclear proteins are present (as when an interphase nucleus is grafted into an enucleate fragment of mitotic cell), the helices normally found in the nucleus (see chapter by A.R. Stevens in this volume) are no longer detectable. In view of these preliminary observations, we eagerly look forward to the results of higher resolution electron microscopy, for we feel that in addition to nuclear RMP, a substantial portion of nuclear STP is associated with the nonnucleolar regions of the nucleus. Thus, a variety of new structural relations may be revealed.

A Role of the Nuclear Proteins in Protein Synthesis

Finally, let us examine some relative preliminary experiments that may provide a clue to the physiological role of some of the nuclear proteins. These experiments deal with the effect on amino acid incorporation of altering the cellular content of nuclear proteins. The first experiment (Table 4) shows that the greater is the depletion of nuclear proteins, the higher is the rate of ^3H amino acid incorporation.

The next experiment (Table 5), shows also that the ability of enucleate fragments to incorporate amino acids is not influenced by the amount of nuclear proteins present. (In the absence of a nucleus, cells

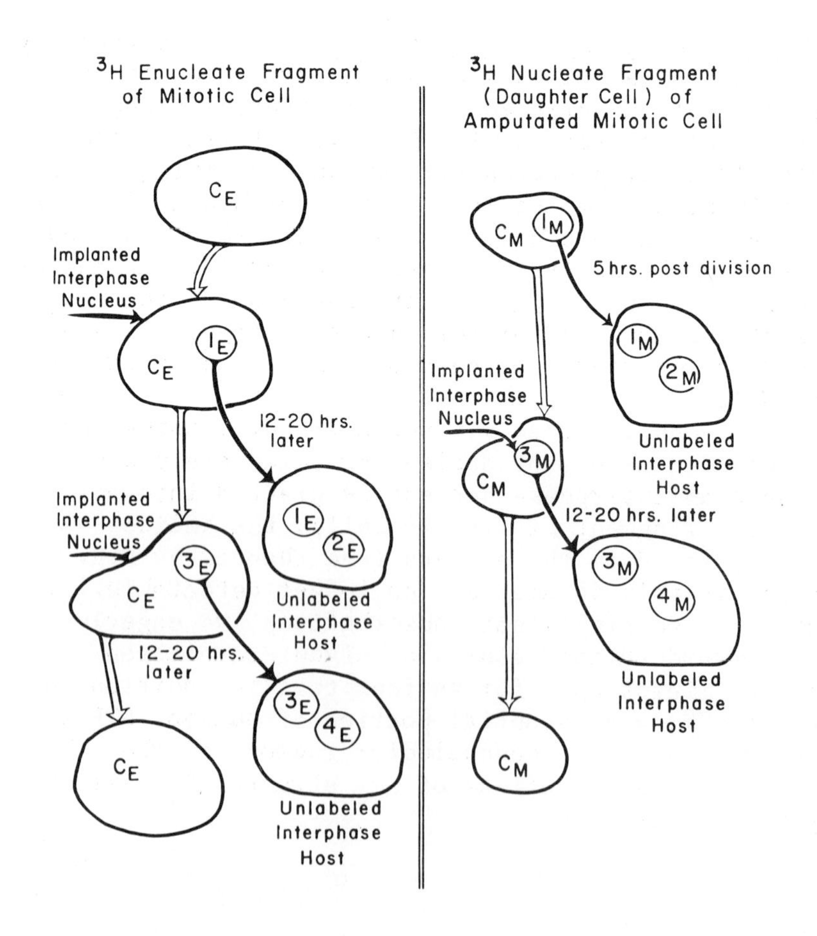

always exhibit a reduced ability to synthesize protein (6).

The third, and final experiment (Table 6), shows approximately the same information as Tables 4 and 5, but much more dramatically. When a nucleate cell is enriched with nuclear proteins, its ability to incorporate ^3H amino acids is reduced to that of a nonnucleate cell. We can tentatively conclude, therefore, that the capacity to synthesize protein is inversely proportional to the amount of nuclear protein present and that the effect of these proteins appears to be on some nuclear mechanism, despite the fact that essentially all protein synthesis occurs in the cytoplasm. It is not yet possible to say whether the effect is caused by STP or RMP, or both.

In closing, we should mention that we have not neglected the question of the role of histone. That

---

Figure 8. (Opposite page.) Experiment to determine effect of depleted and increased amount of nuclear proteins on the distribution of nuclear proteins. On the left we begin with the enucleate fragment of a mitotic cell, which is enriched for amount of ^3H nuclear proteins. An unlabeled interphase nucleus (1E) is grafted into unlabeled cell 2E. Immediately following that operation, another unlabeled interphase nucleus (3E) is grafted into the again enucleate cytoplasm (C_E). The next day, nucleus 3E is grafted into unlabeled cell 4E. Assays of radioactivity were performed on enucleate C_E at the end, and on isolated nuclei 1E, 2E, 3E, and 4E. On the right, we begin with a daughter of a mitotic cell that had been amputated. It is therefore depleted in its normal supply of ^3H nuclear proteins. About 5 hr after division, the nucleus (1M) is grafted into unlabeled interphase cell 2M; immediately thereafter, another unlabeled, interphase nucleus (3M) is implanted into the now enucleate, labeled cytoplasm (C_M). The next day, nucleus 3M is transplanted into unlabeled, interphase cell 4M. Assays of radioactivity were performed on enucleate C_M at the end of the experiment, and on isolated nuclei 1M, 2M, 3M, and 4M.

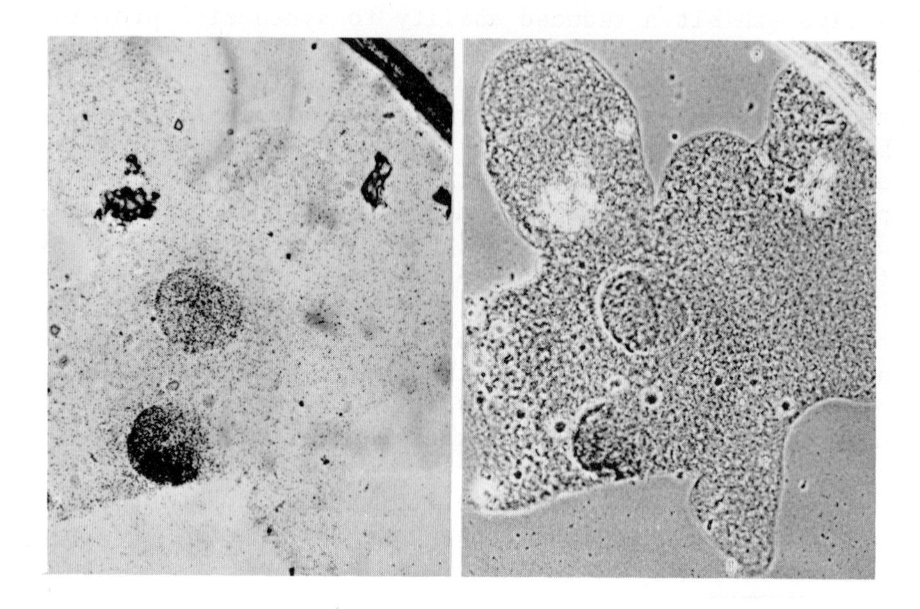

Figure 9. Autoradiograph (left) and phase-contrast view (right) of part of a fixed ameba into which was grafted a ^{3}H protein nucleus approximately 24 hr before centrifugation. Fixation of the cell followed immediately. The cell was centrifuged at 14,000 × g for 20 min. The centrifugal end of the cell is at the left; the lower nucleus is the grafted one. Only ^{3}H in the lower nucleus is stratified, and the stratification approximates the position of nucleoli (which also have been stratified). Since this stratification is seen only in the more radioactive nucleus, it is assumed that only STP is stratified.

story is too complex and lengthy to discuss here, but we can say that by generally accepted criteria, histone is apparently present in STP and RMP, and its behavior, by the criteria discussed in this paper, does not differ detectably from the other nuclear proteins.

TABLE 4

Effect of nuclear protein depletion on protein synthesis*

Cytoplasm amputated from cell in mitosis	No. cells	Relative activity (no. of AR† grains/unit area)
Control (sham cut)	8	75
5-10%	7	93
15-20%	4	131
25-30%	9	127
35-45%	2	167
35-45%, but cell still divided:		
Larger sister	5	92
Smaller sister	5	131

*The left-hand column gives the estimated amount of cytoplasm amputated during mitosis. Controls were similarly treated, but amputation was not completed. Five of the cells with 35 to 45% cytoplasm amputated proceeded through cytokinesis, but unequally; thus, the larger sister would have more nuclear proteins than the smaller, although the amount of chromosomal material presumably would be the same. Beginning approximately 3 hr after the amputations, the cells were incubated for 4 hr in a mixture of 6 ^{3}H amino acids, each present at ca. 25 μc/ml. At the end of the incubation, the cells were fixed on slides, extracted with acid, and subjected to autoradiography with NTB-2.

†AR, autoradiographic.

TABLE 5

Effect on protein synthesis of altering the concentration of nuclear proteins in the cell*

Cell fragment	No. cells	Relative activity	Condition§
Enucleate fragment of interphase cell	12	17.0	Normal
Enucleate fragment of mitotic cell	16	17.5	Enriched
Nucleate fragment of interphase cell	19	23.5	Normal
Nucleate fragment of mitotic cell:†			
Nondividers	12	34.0	Depleted
Dividers	22	28.5	Depleted

*Where relevant, the procedures described for the experiments of Table 4 apply here also. For the nucleate fragments of the amputated mitotic cells, those cells that proceeded through division were pooled in one group and those that were inhibited by the operation were pooled in another group. This latter group were therefore binucleate.

†30 to 40% of cytoplasm was amputated.

§With respect to nuclear protein content.

TABLE 6

Effect on protein synthesis of altering the concentration of nuclear proteins in the cell*

Cell fragment	No. cells	Relative activity	Condition†
Nucleate fragment of interphase cell	14	31.0	Normal
Enucleate fragment of interphase cell	8	21.0	Normal
Enucleate fragment of mitotic cell	6	22.5	Enriched
Renucleated fragment of interphase cell	8	27.5	Normal
Renucleated fragment of mitotic cell	11	22.5	Most Enriched

*Where relevant, the procedures described for the experiments of Table 4 apply here. Both the interphase and mitotic cells were cut so that ca. 1/3 was an enucleate fragment and ca. 2/3 was a nucleate fragment. "Renucleation" refers to the implantation of an ordinary interphase nucleus into an enucleate fragment. When the enucleate host originated from an interphase cell, renucleation presumably resulted in a relatively normal interphase cell; when the enucleate host was from a mitotic cell, it resulted in a nucleate cell much enriched with nuclear proteins.

†With respect to nuclear protein content.

REFERENCES

1. Byers, T.J., D.B. Platt, and L. Goldstein. 1963. The cytonucleoproteins of amebae II. Some aspects of cytonucleoprotein behavior and synthesis. J. Cell Biol. 19: 467.
2. Goldstein, L. 1958. Localization of nucleus-specific protein as shown by transplantation experiments in *Amoeba proteus*. Exp. Cell Res. 15: 635.
3. Goldstein, L. 1965. Interchange of protein between nucleus and cytoplasm. Symp. Intern. Soc. Cell Biol. 4: 79.
4. Goldstein, L., and D.M. Prescott. 1967. Proteins in nucleocytoplasmic interactions I. The fundamental characteristics of the rapidly migrating proteins and the slow turnover proteins of the *Amoeba proteus* nucleus. J. Cell Biol. (Manuscript submitted.)
5. Goldstein, L., and D.M. Prescott. Proteins in nucleocytoplasmic interactions II. Turnover and changes in nuclear protein distribution with time and growth. (In preparation.)
6. Mazia, D., and D.M. Prescott. 1955. The role of the nucleus in protein synthesis in *Amoeba*. Biochim. Biophys. Acta 17: 23.
7. Prescott, D.M. 1963. RNA and protein replacement in the nucleus during growth and division and the conservation of components in the chromosome. Symp. Intern. Soc. Cell Biol. 2: 111.
8. Prescott, D.M., and L. Goldstein. Proteins in nucleocytoplasmic interactions III. Redistribution of nuclear proteins during and following mitosis. (In preparation.)
9. Prescott, D.M., and L. Goldstein. Proteins in nucleocytoplasmic interactions IV. The turnover of acid-soluble nuclear proteins, acid-insoluble nuclear proteins, and histone in *Amoeba proteus*. (In preparation.)

Nuclear-Nuclear Interactions in Ameba

A. L. Judin

Institute of Cytology
USSR Academy of Sciences
Leningrad

The study of heterokaryons is one of the more interesting, although relatively infrequently used, methods for the investigation of nuclear activity and nucleocytoplasmic relationships in the cell. Perhaps only in the study of the genetics of some fungi has it become a usual experimental practice. Since heterokaryons in fungi may be produced naturally, they can be obtained with little difficulty. In other organisms, however, heterokaryons can be obtained only artificially, most frequently by means of micrurgic transplantation of nuclei, a difficult method now possible for only a few kinds of cells.

Various aspects of interactions between two or more different nuclei in common cytoplasm are of primary, if not exclusive, interest when heterokaryons are studied. It is reasonable to think that such interaction is confined solely to a joint participation of the different nuclei in the determination of the phenotype of the heterokaryotic cell. An interaction of this type might be called physiological in the sense that, as a result of their joint occupancy in common cytoplasm, the genetic characteristics of these nuclei remain unchanged.

Analysis of the physiological interaction of nuclei in heterokaryons enables us to obtain various kinds of information, primarily concerning the role of the nucleus in determining the phenotype. The bulk of publications on heterokaryons is devoted to this aspect of genetics, and we should mention numerous investigations of complementation in heterokaryons of fungi before we discuss our work. The most interesting are the recently reported cases of discordance between the phenotype of heterkaryons and that of heterozygous diploids genetically identical to the heterokaryons (Pontecorvo, 1963; Roberts, 1964; Apirion, 1966). Studies on nuclear morphogenetic activity done on interspecific heterokaryons of Acetabularia are well known (see review by Hammerling, 1963), and similar investigations have been made on amebae (Commandon and deFonbrune, 1942; Kalinina, 1964). Under appropriate conditions, heterokaryons derived from a mixed culture of somatic cells of various vertebrate species can be produced in vitro (Harris and Watkins, 1965; Yaffe and Feldman, 1965). Interesting data concerning the regulation of syntheses in nuclei were obtained from such heterokaryons (Harris, 1965, 1966).

Is the only kind of interaction possible between nuclei in a heterokaryon a physiological one? Can we observe, at least in some cases, an interaction that induces changes in the genetic properties of the nuclei, the consequences of which may be noted not only in the phenotype of the heterokaryon itself, but also in mononucleate progeny many generations later? Such an interaction might be called, provisionally, genetical (in the broad sense of the term).

Some facts suggest that this type of nuclear-nuclear interaction does occur under certain circumstances - e.g., in heterokaryons of fungi in cases of so-called somatic recombination. Our interest here is not, however, in somatic recombination occurring via karyogamy and parasexual cycles in a heterokaryotic mycelium. Disregarding this extensive material, we are left with relatively few instances of somatic recombination, the mechanisms of which are not clear but in which fusion of nuclei seems improbable for one reason or another (see, e.g., Weijer and Dowding, 1960; Crowe, 1961; Garber et al., 1961; Parag, 1962).

Sometimes a substitution of the "old" macronucleus for a "new" one after the sexual process in ciliates is regarded as a peculiar analog of heterokaryosis (Nanney, 1963). In this case, genetic interaction between nuclei is evident, when the old macronucleus directs the differentiation of the new one.

A study of examples of genetic nuclear-nuclear interactions in heterokaryons may extend our knowledge about the behavior of the cell nucleus. In this paper, I shall summarize briefly the main results obtained in our laboratory from studies of the genetic interaction between nuclei in amebae heterokaryons. This work is being carried out at the Institute of Cytology in Leningrad by Dr. L.V. Kalinina, Dr. G.V. Nikolayeva, and myself under the guidance of Prof. Yu. M. Olenov.

We have at our disposal a collection of Amoeba proteus strains of various origins, which were found to differ in a number of hereditary characteristics. As was shown by nuclear transfer according to the method of Commandon and deFonbrune, the inheritance of these traits is determined exclusively by the nucleus (Judin, 1961, 1964, 1965; Sopina and Judin, 1965; Judin et al., 1966). We selected two characteristics as genetic markers for the study of heterokaryons:

1. resistance to the toxic effects of methionine;
2. resistance to the toxic effects of ethyl alcohol.

All or nearly all strain-L amebae died by the end of 18 to 20 hr incubation in 0.15 M methionine solution, whereas more than half strain-B amebae remained alive under the same experimental conditions. We made similar observations after amebae were incubated for 5 min in 7% ethyl alcohol. Histograms illustrating the limits of variability for each strain after numerous tests in both solutions are shown in Figure 1. The

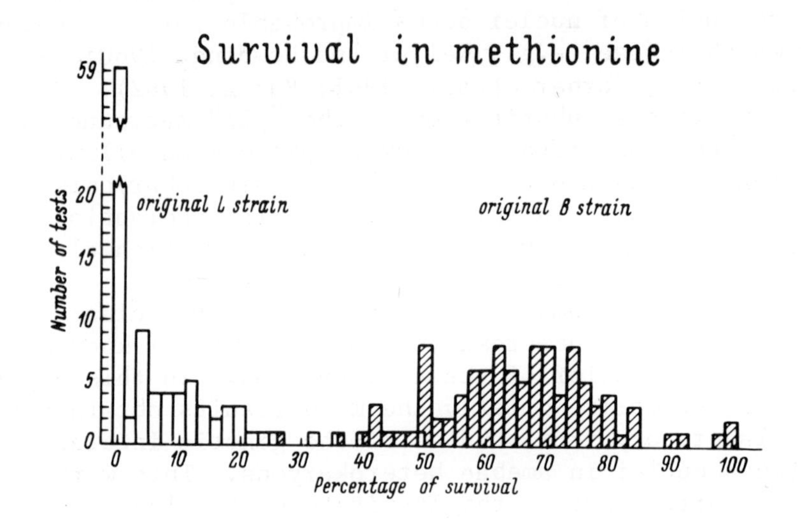

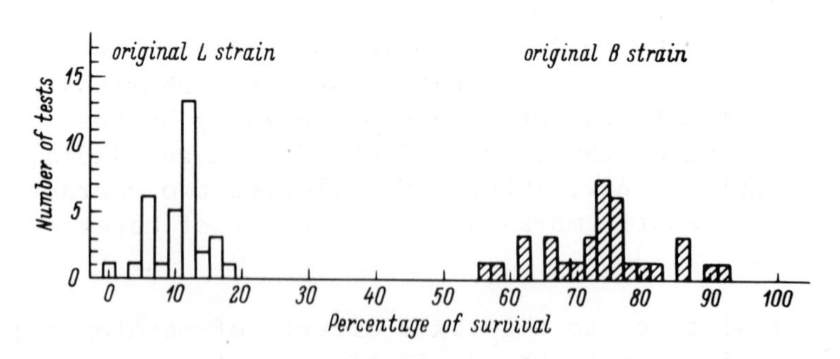

Figure 1

difference between L strain and C strain in resisting these two agents is even more strongly pronounced (Figure 2).

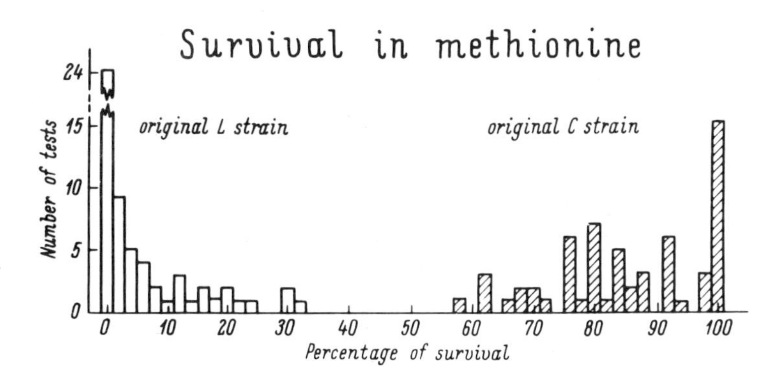

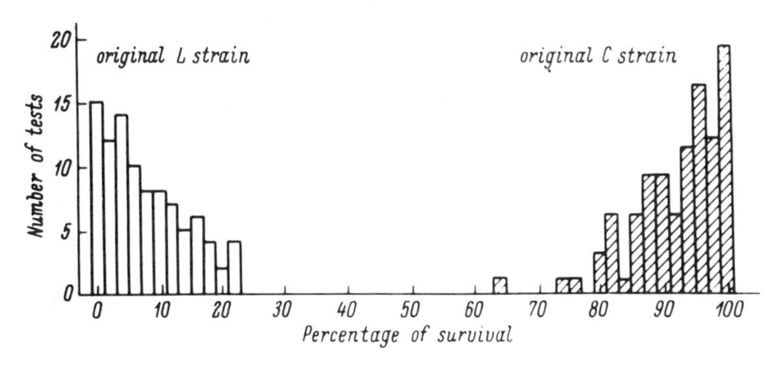

Figure 2

With respect to the given characters, these ameba strains are relatively stable. Each has definite limits of survival. The characteristic resistance level invariably has been reproduced at repeated tests for several years, upon recloning of strains, upon transplantation of their nuclei into enucleate cytoplasm of other strains, etc. Moreover, for each of the original clones, certain survival levels are never seen under given experimental conditions.

The genetic basis of these characteristics is not as yet clear. The differences between strains may be either genetic (in the narrow sense of the word, i.e., of mutational origin) or epigenetic. In the latter case, it may be, for example, that the inherited differences are concerned with the activity regulation of the corresponding genes. The possibility that these differences are connected with intranuclear symbionts, episomes, etc., does not seem probable in our case, as we shall try to show. As is well known, all these causes may give rise to similar results; it is difficult to distinguish between them, especially in species in which analysis of hybrids is impractical.

We have reason to believe methionine and alcohol resistance in amebae are genetically determined in an entirely different fashion. Therefore, they can be regarded as two independent characters; for example, we have a strain which, unlike the L, B, and C strains, combines low methionine resistance with intermediate resistance to alcohol (Sopina and Judin, 1965). There exists other evidence as well.

To obtain a heterokaryon, we transplanted a nucleus of one strain into an amebae of another. After a while, the binucleate cell was cut into two mononucleate halves (Figure 3), and a clone was raised from each half. It is difficult to tell which of the nuclei will end in a particular fragment of the bisected cell, but we are sure that one nucleus originates from the first strain and the other from the second because heterokaryons are always bisected before the onset of mitosis. Since the characters chosen as markers are controlled by the nucleus, for each pair of clones grown from the mononucleate halves of a heterokaryon we would expect one clone to resemble one original strain and the second clone, the other original strain. Any deviation from this expectation we would regard as reflecting an interaction between the nuclei in the heterokaryon which had caused heritable changes in the nuclear traits. Such a result would not be ascribable to an effect of the micrurgy, since nothing of that kind is usually observed when ordinary nucleocytoplasmic "hybrids" (nucleus of one strain in enucleate cytoplasm of another) are produced.

What were the actual results of such an experiment?

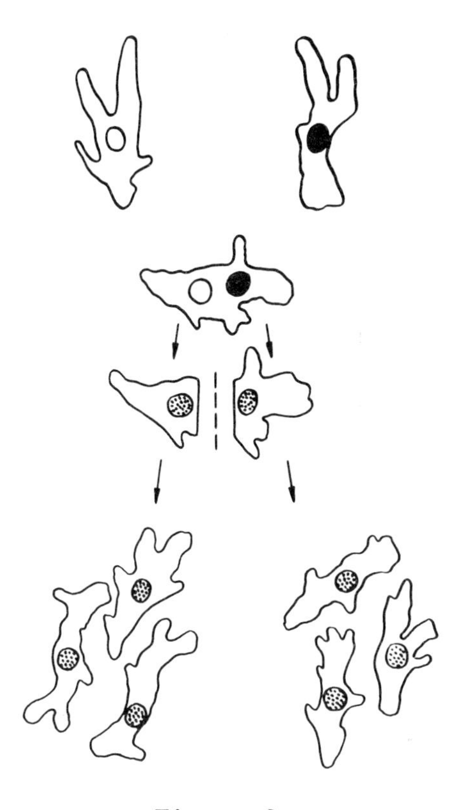

Figure 3

Both clones of a pair originating from one diheterokaryon were found to be similar to one original strain in some experiments and like the other strain in other experiments. In still other tests, they showed intermediate survival values, as is evident in Figure 4 for a pair of clones originating from a diheterokaryon of the $B_nL_nL_c$ type (n is the nucleus and c, the cytoplasm) and tested for resistance to methionine. Thus, both daughter clones, unlike the initial strains, in time displayed _instability_ of phenotype. At any given moment, however, different samples of amebae from the same unstable clone behaved in identical fashion. In general, the situation somewhat resembles the behavior of certain strains of _Paramecium_ that show a very labile differentiation of macronuclei (Sonneborn, 1963).

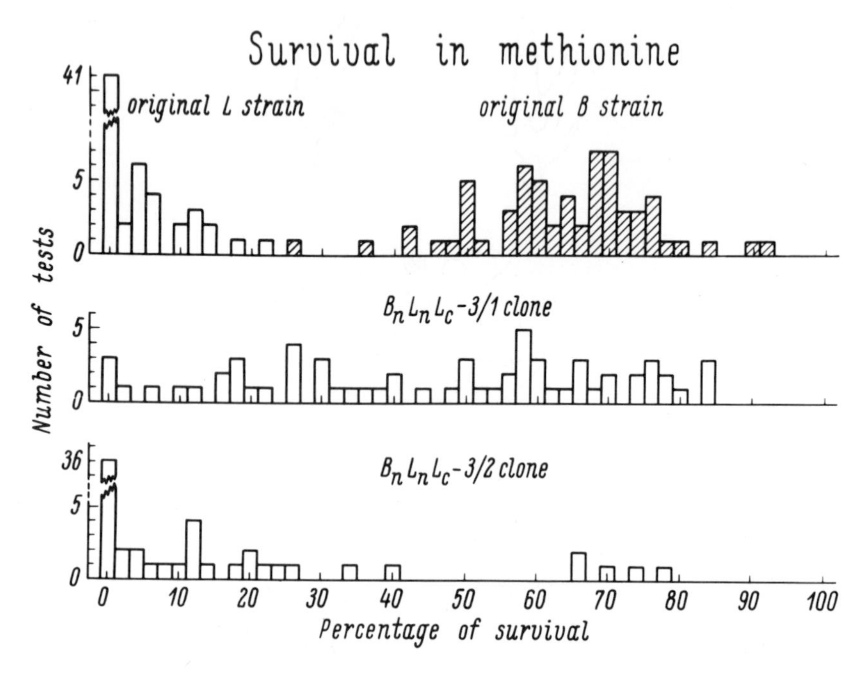

Figure 4

The changes effect both characters - resistance to methionine and resistance to alcohol - randomly selected as markers. Destabilization to alcohol resistance occurs in another pair of clones from a diheterokaryon of the $L_nC_nC_c$ type (Figure 5). The methionine resistance level of unstable clones does not correlate in time with resistance to alcohol.

Changes in phenotype of the cells in a clone occur rather rapidly. Not infrequently, during tests for methionine resistance (which last for about 24 hr), survival rates as high as those typical of the original resistant strain changed, by the following day, to the low survival rates characteristic of the original sensitive strain, and vice versa (Kalinina and Judin, 1964). In some experiments on alcohol resistance, a "switching" from low to high resistance or from high to low was observed even at intervals of from 4 to 5 hr between successive tests on the same clone. Some

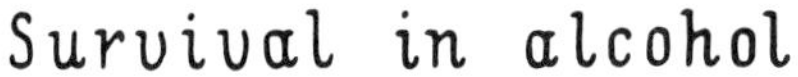

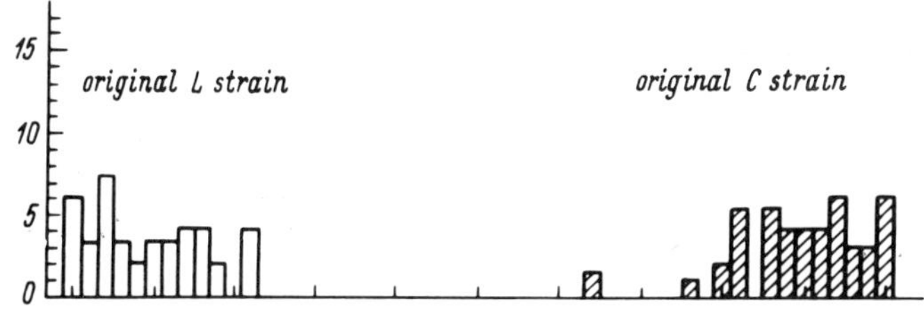

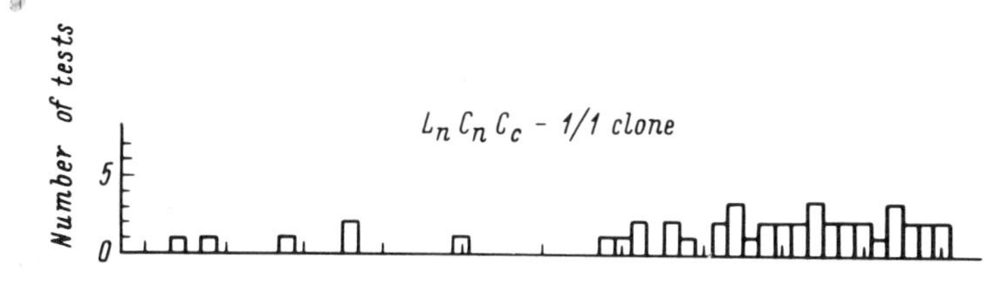

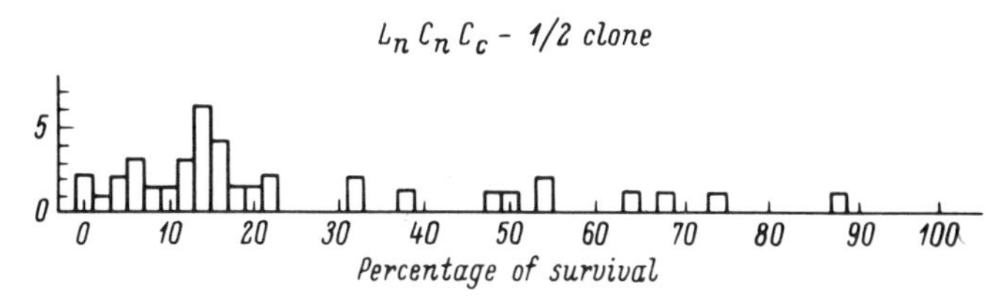

Figure 5

clones, however, can maintain the same resistance level for extended periods of time, indicating that changes in phenotype do not correlate with cell divisions in a growing culture. In fact, we have not been able to discern any regularity in resistance-level alterations. In addition, it is not clear what causes a transition from one state to another or why, in many cases, this transition, whether to high or to low survival values, involves the whole clone simutlaneously.

As already stated, the nuclear changes in question occur in heterokaryons of various genetic combinations. We obtain similar results from heterokaryons of identical genotypes but with differing cytoplasm, evident when we compare heterokaryons of $B_nL_nL_c$ and $L_nB_nB_c$ types (Table 1).

Within each pair of clones originating from one

TABLE 1

Methionine resistance phenotype of clones obtained from diheterokaryons of $B_nL_nL_c$ and $L_nB_nB_c$ types, the nuclei of which had been in the same cytoplasm for four days. (After Kalinina and Judin, 1964.)

No. of original diheterokaryon	Daughter clone	No. of tests	No. of experiments in which survival rate of clones was:		
			Typical for strain L	Intermediate	Typical for strain B
BLL-3	1	63	14	14	35
	2	61	52	4	5
BLL-38	1	23	15	5	3
	2	23	11	2	10
BLL-19	1	17	9	5	3
	2	20	13	3	4
BLL-40	1	18	11	1	6
	2	18	7	1	10
BLL-28	1	15	9	5	1
	2	15	12	2	1
BLL-5	1	11	5	4	2
	2	11	10	-	1
LBB-45	1	32	16	3	13
	2	32	1	5	26
LBB-3	1	30	16	6	8
	2	30	8	4	12
LBB-47	1	29	18	1	10
	2	29	5	-	24
LBB-46	1	21	1	2	18
	2	21	9	4	8
LBB-25	1	13	8	1	4
	2	13	11	-	2
LBB-51	1	11	9	2	-
	2	11	4	2	5

diheterokaryon, frequently, but not always, one of the clones displays mostly the low resistance rate whereas the second displays mostly the high resistance rate. Table 2 illustrates this relationship for alcohol resistance of a group of clones obtained from diheterokaryons of the $L_nC_nC_c$ type. This peculiar behavior of an unstable clone is probably determined by the characteristics of the original nucleus in the initial diheterokaryon.

TABLE 2

Phenotype of clones obtained from diheterokaryons of $L_nC_nC_c$ type, the nuclei of which had been in the same cytoplasm for four days. (From Judin et al., 1966.)

No. of original diheterokaryon	Daughter clone	No. of tests for survival in alcohol	No. of experiments in which survival rate of clones was: Typical for original strain L only	Intermediate	Typical for original strain C only
LCC-1	1	59	5	13	41
	2	53	31	17	5
LCC-3	1	54	2	18	34
	2	60	33	26	1
LCC-8	1	51	27	21	3
	2	54	5	9	40

Our ability to reveal the instability of a given clone depends directly on the number of tests we perform - sometimes a long and arduous procedure. Moreover, if for a particular clone we continue to observe survival values characteristic of both original strains, we can consider that we have definitely proved the instability. But, if with repeated tests the survival rate of the clone remains within the limits typical for only one of the original strains, the degree of stability may be uninterpretable, for possibly destabilization would be revealed after further testing. Hence, the presence of an interaction between nuclei in a heterokaryon may be proved unequivocally, whereas the absence of such an interaction can only be supposed, a supposition which may be more or less significant - depending on the number of tests performed.

Procedure in these experiments requires that the genetic interaction between interphase nuclei must occur through the cytoplasm. This prerequisite suggests that in the heterokaryon there occurs between the nuclei and cytoplasm an exchange of material capable of inducing heritable changes and having a particular affinity for the nucleus. Such migration between nucleus and cytoplasm is characteristic, as autoradiographic data have shown, of certain nuclear proteins of *A. proteus* (Goldstein, 1958, 1963; Byers et al., 1963a, b; Prescott and Bender, 1963). For RNA, the available information regarding migration is contradictory (Goldstein and Plaut, 1955; Iverson, 1962), but nuclear DNA apparently does not migrate in this fashion (Prescott

Strictly speaking, we do not know whether this migrating material responsible for the nuclear instability in heterokaryons also functions in intact mononucleate cells or whether the instability is stimulated by the heterokaryotic state of the cell. We favor the former possibility because of the occurrence of rare unstable clones, along with stable nucleocytoplasmic "hybrids", following ordinary nuclear transplantation (Kalinina and Judin, 1964). In view of these suppositions, the rarity in appearance of instability is surprising; from the time the recipient cell nucleus is removed until the time another nucleus in introduced is only 3 to 5 min, and yet, as a rule the implanted nucleus is not influenced by the one that was removed. It is very possible that the material inducing nuclear instability is extremely unstable in the cytoplasm, losing most of its activity even in such a short time.

After we made these observations, we became interested to know the minimal time for a joint occupancy of the nuclei in common cytoplasm necessary to induce nuclear instability. At first we kept the nuclei together for as long as possible - up to the beginning of division - thus cutting heterokaryons into two parts 4 days after they had been produced. Under such circumstances we found 100% of the clones to be unstable.

Using the $L_nC_nC_c$ heterokaryotic combination, we next tried to determine the minimal exposure necessary to produce instability (Judin et al., 1966). Different sets of such diheterokaryons were bisected 3 hr, 1 hr, 15 min, and 5 min after the introduction of the second nucleus, and the clones derived from the mononucleate cells were tested for alcohol resistance. In each of the four time series, we observed instability of clones with respect to this character in 100% of the cases. We noted a sudden change in the pattern when there was only a 2.5-min exposure before we bisected the diheterokaryon. With an exposure this short, the majority of the clones of the L_nC_c type originating from the heterokaryons $L_nC_nC_c$ were stable with respect to their alcohol resistance - i.e., identical to the original L strain and to ordinary nucleocytoplasmic "hybrids" L_nC_c, L_nB_c, etc. For methionine resistance, almost all clones of the 2.5-min heterokaryons were as unstable as those from the longer exposure series (Nikolayeva, 1966). These data appear in Table 3. In fact, with respect to methionine resistance, we could induce instability by as little as a 1-min exposure. Thus, the time required for destabilization is different for each of the two characters under study.

Only when the time of interaction was reduced to 45 sec or less were we unable to detect instability with respect to alcohol or methionine resistance, even after a comparatively large number of tests. If these results are confirmed, we shall conclude that the minimal effective exposure time is less than 5 min but more than 2.5 min for alcohol resistance and less than 1 min for methionine resistance. Now, however, these data apply only to the specific heterokaryon, $L_nC_nC_c$,

TABLE 3

Phenotype of L_nC_c clones obtained from diheterokaryons of $L_nC_nC_c$ type, the nuclei of which had been in the same cytoplasm for 2.5 min.

No. of clone	Survival in alcohol				Survival in methionine			
	No. of tests	No. of experiments in which survival rate of clones was:			No. of tests	No. of experiments in which survival rate of clones was:		
		Typical for strain L	Intermediate	Typical for strain C		Typical for strain L	Intermediate	Typical for strain C
LC-1	43	43	-	-	35	21	2	12
LC-2	29	29	-	-	23	23	-	-
LC-3	43	43	-	-	33	17	2	14
LC-4	44	44	-	-	36	15	-	21
LC-5	43	-	1	42	35	-	-	35
LC-6	43	43	-	-	36	15	-	21
LC-7	15	12	-	3	12	7	-	5
LC-8	11	11	-	-	8	8	-	-
LC-9	21	21	-	-	18	14	2	2
LC-10	21	21	-	-	18	14	2	2

and only to one of the two kinds of nuclei present.

We can compare the rapidity with which the interactions occur to the data on the migration rate of the so-called cytonucleoproteins in A. proteus. When protein-labeled nuclei are transferred into unlabeled amebae, label appears in the nuclei of host cells as early as 10 min after the operation (Byers et al., 1963b). Brachet (1956) obtained similar values (5 to 10 min) for the rate of penetration of ribonuclease from the external medium into the A. proteus nucleus.

It is difficult to know whether our data reflect the existence of "inducing factors," one kind for each genetic marker, or whether there is only one such factor that requires a slightly different length of time to induce different changes. No doubt other hypotheses can be drawn from these data. In any event, these results provide further evidence in favor of the independent genetic basis for each of the characters investigated, because they show that the traits can change independently of one another. These conclusions support our view - i.e., the supposition that hereditary differences, specifically alcohol and methionine resistance, are due to the presence of intranuclear synbionts, episomes, etc., is most improbable.

L.V. Kalinina (1965), studying some features of the hereditary changes in nuclei arising as a consequence of nuclear-nuclear interactions, showed that the instability can be transferred by transplantation of nuclei of an unstable clone into the enucleated cytoplasm of any original strain. Hence, the inheritance of this property seems to be determined by the nucleus. Moreover, this property can be transferred by the nucleus of any cell of an unstable clone and, thus, the instability is inherent in each cell of the clone. In a diheterokaryon containing a nucleus from an unstable clone and a nucleus of any original strain, the interaction results in the original-strain nucleus also becoming unstable.

When an implanted nucleus has been intentionally damaged so that the recipient cell quickly rejects the graft but retains its own nucleus, the clone arising from such a cell may become destabilized. This observation suggests favorable circumstances for future attempts to obtain similar effects by injecting one ameba with various substances extracted from an ameba of another strain. Such experiments seem feasible because the technique of intracellular injection in amebae is well developed, and because the culture method of Prescott and James (1955), which we use in our laboratory, makes possible obtaining amebae in quantities sufficient for biochemical research.

All the diheterokaryons used in these experiments combined nuclei of strains differing not only in origin but also in the phenotype under investigation. We are now investigating diheterokaryons obtained from ameba strains of different origin but identical or similar phenotype. Preliminary results indicate that some clones derived from such heterokaryons display instability manifested chiefly in the appearance of survival values lower than those of either original strain. Very seldom are these values as low as those of the sensitive L strain - which, however, was not used to obtain these heterokaryons.

Other preliminary data show that the same destabilization is found in clones grown from X-irradiated (150 to 175 kr) cells of the alcohol- and methionine-resistant strain B.

These results raise the possibility of destabilizing nuclei in dihomokaryons. In early stages of our investigation (Kalinina and Judin, 1964), we obtained and tested for their resistance to methionine clones from three dihomokaryons of type $B_nB_nB_c$ and from two dihomokaryons of type $L_nL_nC_n$, after a joint 4-day occupancy of their nuclei in common cytoplasm. Each pair of clones was tested only five times within 6 or 7 days. These showed no changes, although in a parallel series, the same number of tests proved sufficient to establish the instability of many clones derived from heterokaryons. However, the data on homokaryons is insufficient for definitive conclusions, and the question of possibly destabilizing nuclei in homokaryons is not yet settled. This question is obviously important for understanding the interaction between nuclei in heterokaryons and should be studied thoroughly.

Let us briefly conclude with some remarks about the evidence regarding nuclear-nuclear interactions in heterokaryons of amebae. It would be premature if we assigned the effects we have studied to any known category of genetic phenomena. Very important questions must still be answered, and at least three groups of problems exist, the solution of which would help us to understand this apparently new phenomenon.

1. It is important to understand the nature and conditions of nuclear-nuclear interactions and the biochemical nature of the inducing factor(s) which nuclei mutually exchange in heterokaryons.
2. We must investigate the basis of the phenotypic instability of cells in clones derived from heterokaryons after induction has occurred.
3. Problems 1 and 2 are obviously related to the question of the basis of the differences between our original strains, which should also be determined.

Finally, we should determine with certainty whether phenomena akin to the interactions detected in heterokaryons also occur in mononucleate cells, and whether, in the latter case, an inducing factor migrates to and fro between nucleus and cytoplasm. If it does, what is the function of this exchange in the normal cell?

REFERENCES

Apirion, D. 1966. Recessive mutants at unlinked loci which complement in diploids but not in heterokaryons of _Aspergillus nidulans_. Genetics 53: 935-41.

Brachet, J. 1956. Further observations on the action of ribonuclease on living amoebae. Exp. Cell Res. 10: 255-56.

Byers, T.J., D.B. Platt, and L. Goldstein. 1963a. The cytonucleoproteins of amoebae. I. Some chemical properties and intracellular distribution. J. Cell Biol. 19: 453-56.

Byers, T.J., D.B. Platt, and L. Goldstein. 1963b. The cytonucleoproteins of amoebae. II. Some aspects of cytonucleoprotein behavior and synthesis. J. Cell Biol. 19: 467-75.
Comandon, J., and P. de Fonbrune. 1942. Greffes nucléaires croisées entre Amoebae sphaeronucleus et l'une de ses variétés colchiciniques. Compt. Rend. Soc. Biol. 136: 746-47.
Crowe, L. 1961. The exchange of genes between nuclei of a dikaryon. Heredity 15: 397-405.
Garber, E.D., E.G. Wyttenbach, and T.S. Dhillon. 1961. Genetics of phytopathogenic fungi. V. Heterocaryons involving formae of Fusarium oxysporum. Am. J. Botany 48: 325-29.
Goldstein, L. 1958. Localization of nucleus-specific protein as shown by transplantation experiments in Amoeba proteus. Exp. Cell Res. 15: 635-37.
Goldstein, L. 1963. RNA and protein in nucleocytoplasmic interactions. In "Cell Growth and Cell Division," R.J.C. Harris, ed. Academic Press, N.Y. 129-49.
Goldstein, L. 1964. Combined nuclear transplantation and isotope techniques for the study of nuclear activities. Protoplasmatologia 5: 51-71.
Goldstein, L., and W. Plaut. 1955. Direct evidence for nuclear synthesis of cytoplasmic ribose nucleic acid. Proc. Natl. Acad. Sci. U.S. 41: 874-80.
Hämmerling, J. 1963. Nucleo-cytoplasmic interactions in Acetabularia and other cells. Ann. Rev. Plant Physiol. 14: 65-92.
Harris, H. 1965. Behavior of differentiated nuclei in heterokaryons of animal cells from different species. Nature 206: 583-88.
Harris, H. 1966. Hybrid cells from mice and men. Discovery 27: 10-15.
Harris, H., and J.F. Watkins. 1965. Hybrid cells derived from mouse and man: Artificial heterokaryons of mammalian cells from different species. Nature 205: 640-46.
Iverson, R.M. 1962. Passage of material containing uracil-^{14}C between the nucleus and cytoplasm of Amoeba proteus. Exp. Cell Res. 27: 125-31.
Judin, A.L. 1966. The role of nucleus and cytoplasm in the inheritance of some characters in amoebae. In

"Progress in Protozoology." Excerpta Medica Foundation, Amsterdam. 63.

Nanney, D.L. 1963. Cytoplasmic inheritance in Protozoa. In "Methodology in Basic Genetics," W.J. Burdette, ed. Holden-Day, San Francisco, Calif. 355-80.

Parag. Y. 1962. Studies on somatic recombination in dikaryons of Schizophyllum commune. Heredity 17: 305-07.

Pontecorvo, G. 1963. Microbial genetics: Retrospect and prospect. Proc. Roy. Soc. London Ser. B. 158: 1-26.

Prescott, D.M. 1963. RNA and protein replacement in the nucleus during growth and division and the conservation of components in the chromosome. In "Cell Growth and Cell Division," R.J.C. Harris, ed. Academic Press, N.Y. 111-28.

Prescott, D.M., and M.A. Bender. 1963. Synthesis and behavior of nuclear proteins during the cell life cycle. J. Cellular Comp. Physiol. 62, Suppl. I, Part II: 175-94.

Prescott, D.M., and T.W. James. 1955. Culturing of Amoeba proteus on Tetrahymena. Exp. Cell Res. 8: 256-58.

Roberts, C.F. 1964. Complementation in balanced heterokaryons and heterozygous diploids of Aspergillus nidulans. Genet. Res. 5: 211-29.

Sonneborn, T.M. 1963. Bearing of protozoan studies on current theory of genic and cytoplasmic actions. Proc. XVI Intern. Zool. Congr. 3: 197-202.

Weijer, J., and E. Dowding. 1960. Nuclear exchange in a heterokaryon of Neurospora crassa. Can. J. Genet. Cytol. 2: 335-43.

Yaffe, D., and M. Feldman. 1964. The formation of hybrid multinucleated muscle fibers from myoblasts of different genetic origin. Develop. Biol. 11: 300-17.

Калинина Л.В. 1964. Фенотип гетерокарионов, полученных методом трансплантации ядер у амеб. Цитология, 6, 5: 567-576.

Калинина Л.В. 1965а. О генетическом взаимодействии ядер в гетерокарионах у амеб. Цитология, 7, 1 : 66-72.

Калинина Л.В. 1965б. Новые данные о генетическом взаимодействии ядер в гетерокарионах у амеб. Цитология, 7, 3 : 401-404.

Калинина Л.В. и Юдин А.Л. 1964. Генетическое взаимодействие ядер в гетерокарионах у амеб. Цитология, 6, 6 : 695-709.(Перевод: Kalinina L.V. and Yudin A.L. 1965. Genetic interaction of nuclei in heterokaryons of amebas. Feder. Proc., 24, 6, partII (Translation Suppl.):TII35-TII42.)

Николаева Г.В. 1966. Кинетика взаимодействия ядер в гетерокарионах у амеб. Материалы I Научной конф. молодых специалистов Института цитологии АН СССР, М.-Л.:29.

Сопина В.А. и Юдин А.Л. 1965. О наследовании устойчивости к этиловому спирту у амеб. Цитология, 7, 3 : 334-340.

Юдин А.Л. 1961. О роли ядра и цитоплазмы в наследовании некоторых признаков у амеб. Цитология, 3, 5 : 569-576.

Юдин А.Л. 1964. Участие ядра и цитоплазмы в наследовании морфологических различий у амеб. Цитология, 6, I : 52-59.

Юдин А.Л., Калинина Л.В. и Николаева Г.В. 1966. О времени, необходимом для генетического взаимодействия ядер в гетерокарионах у амеб. В сб.: "Клеточная наследственность и злокачественный рост", М.-Л.

Nuclear and Cytoplasmic Protein Synthesis in Various Cell Types from Rats and Mice

Brigitte Schultze and Werner Maurer

Institut für Medizinische Strahlenkunde der Universität Würzburg

The cellular protein metabolism of many cell types has been investigated autoradiographically in the recent past. In these studies, the predominant questions were usually those of special interest for a specific cell type. However, in the studies reported in this paper, emphasis was placed on an overall view of protein metabolism in different cell types from mice and rats. The foremost goal of these studies was the determination of whether and to what extent generally valid patterns exist in protein synthesis, if a wide variety of cells are considered. To this end autoradiographic and biochemical experiments with H^3 and C^{14} labeled amino acids were carried out and evaluated quantitatively by grain counting and activity measurements in liquid-scintillation counters. The purpose of Part I of this report is to show that cellular protein synthesis follows - within certain limits -

a general scheme in the most widely differing cell types. Part II is a description of the relationship between protein metabolism and that of RNA derived from a comparison of autoradiograms with protein and RNA precursors.

PART I

BIOCHEMICAL AND AUTORADIOGRAPHIC EXPERIMENTS WITH H^3 AND C^{14} AMINO ACIDS

Table 1 shows the labeled amino acids used, their kind of label, and their specific acitivty. The H^3 labeled amino acids were synthesized in our laboratory

TABLE 1

Labeled amino acids and their specific activities used in these experiments

Label	Amino acid	Specific activity (mc/mmole)
Tritium	DL-Alanine-(α,β-T_2)	4500
	DL-Arginine-(α,β-T_2)	3000
	DL-Glutamic acid-(β,γ-T_2)	3700
	Glycine-(α-T)	5000
	DL-Leucine-(γ,δ-T_2)	2800
	DL-Lysine-(γ,δ-T_2)	30000
	D-Phenylalanine-(2,4-T_2)	13000
	L-Phenylalanine-(2,4-T_2)	15000
	DL-Proline-(2-T)	2500
	DL-Serine-(α-T)	3000
	DL-Tryptophan-(5-T)	2000
	L-Tyrosine-(3-T)	5100
^{14}C	L-Arginine-(U-^{14}C)	143
	L-Glutamic acid-(U-^{14}C)	120
	L-Leucine-(U ^{14}C)	246
	L-Phenylalanine-(U-^{14}C)	270
	L-Tyrosine-(U-^{14}C)	215

according to methods of Birkofer and Hempel (1). The C^{14}amino acids were supplied by the New England Nuclear Corporation of Boston, Massachusetts.

Biochemical Experiments with H^3 and C^{14} Amino Acids

Mornings, after a 12-hr fasting period, male Wistar rats (150 to 200 g, standard diet) were injected (ip) simultaneously with one H^3 amino acid (1 mc) and one C^{14} amino acid (0.1 mc). One hour later the animals

TABLE 2

Incorporation of labeled amino acids into protein of rat organs, biochemical experiments. (Simultaneous injection of one H^3 and one C^{14} amino acid into one animal. Numbers represent relative incorporation rates; values for liver = 100.)

	I		II		III		IV		V		VI		VII
	^3H-d,l-glutam.	^{14}C-l-glutam.	^3H-d,l-leucine	^{14}C-l-tyrosine	^3H-l-tyrosine	^{14}C-l-leucine	^3H-d,l-lysine	^{14}C-l-arginine	^3H-l-phenyl.	^{14}C-l-arginine	^3H-d,l-glutam.	^{14}C-l-phenyl.	mean
Pancreas	471	501	–	–	549	285	262	488	690	995	757	560	556 ± 156
Small intestine	124	114	127	117	149	71	92	109	98	191	96	76	144 ± 21
Liver	=100	=100	=100	=100	=100	=100	=100	=100	=100	=100	=100	=100	=100
Spleen	101	93	85	85	72	52	70	68	59	111	101	70	80 ± 15
Colon	–	–	–	–	98	82	49	59	64	108	84	67	76 ± 17
Stomach	90	78	70	76	95	74	38	47	87	83	98	76	76 ± 12,5
Serum	36	29	–	–	60	56	44	33	59	51	35	38	44 ± 8,9
Kidney	37	29	53	51	55	22	37	29	54	54	43	43	42 ± 9,6
Bones	–	–	–	–	34	26	–	–	–	–	–	–	30 ± 4
Lung	18	15	22	23	34	22	29	24	23	35	19	21	24 ± 4,6
Skin	–	–	30	33	12	11	–	–	–	–	–	–	22 ± 10
Heart	7	4	24	23	21	26	13	13	19	27	11	17	18 ± 6,2
Testes	32	24	–	–	34	9	8	8	15	22	7	9	17 ± 8,8
Brain	–	–	15	14	12	6	6	5	11	11	4	10	9 ± 3,3
Muscle	–	–	13	13	8	5	7	4	8	12	4	5	8 ± 2,9
Factor ˣ	0,098	0,407	2,84	2,86	2,16	2,77	0,98	3,09	2,69	2,46	0,098	2,72	

ˣMultiplying the values with the factor leads to the absolute activity per gram organ (wet weight) in % of the activity/g body weight applied.

were sacrificed and the protein from their organs was isolated. Then, both the H^3 and the C^{14} activity of the same protein sample were simultaneously measured in a liquid-scintillation counter.

The results from six experiments using different pairs of H^3 and C^{14} amino acids are shown in Table 2. These numbers represent the relative H^3 and C^{14} activity per gram wet weight of the organs. The liver value was taken as 100. Comparison of the individual columns in Table 2 shows that the relative incorporation of the amino-acid pairs used coincided within the different organs. The same is true for the different animals (columns I to VI). Thus, the 12 amino acids used in these experiments have a common incorporation scheme. These studies with pairs of amino acids in one animal have the advantage of eliminating biological fluctuations from animal to animal, which, however, as is evident from Table 2, are relatively small.

Autoradiographic Experiments with H^3 Amino Acids

The biochemical experiments described give only the mean behavior of all cell types from one organ. By comparison, autoradiographic experiments are advantageous, because they give information about individual cell types and individual cells. In this section we shall discuss extensive autoradiographic experiments on mice, rats, and other animals with the H^3 amino acids listed in Table 1.

Mornings, after a 12-hr fasting period an H^3 amino acid (0.02 - 0.01 mc per gram weight) was injected into Copenhagen mice (20 ± 1.0 g) and Wistar rats (160 ± 10 g). Usually the animals were sacrificed after 60 min, but in special series of experiments, after a period of between 5 and 210 min. Tissues were fixed in a mixture of 5% formalin 0.5% TCA and embedded in paraffin. Autoradiograms were prepared from sections 3 µ thick (AR 10, Kodak, London, and G 5 Ilford, London; exposure time, 2 days to 6 weeks).

Figure 1 shows autoradiograms of the stomach of mice and Figure 2, autoradiograms of the choroid plexus - both for different H^3 amino acids. It is

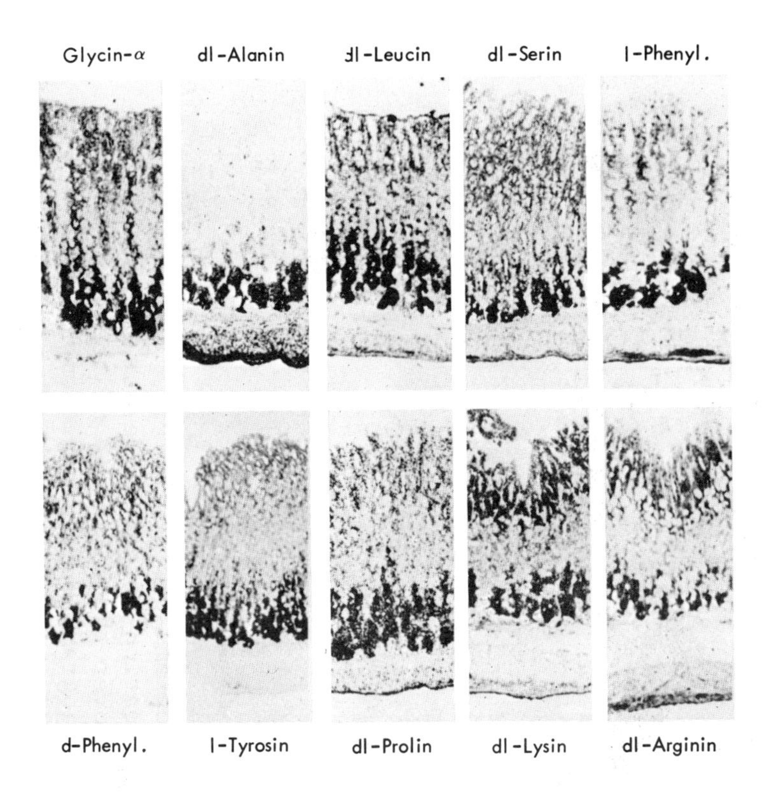

Figure 1. Unstained autoradiograms of the stomach of the mouse 60 min after application of ten different H^3 amino acids. (High grain density over the chief cells, low grain density over parietal cells, submucous membrane and muscle.)

obvious that the different amino acids have a very similar incorporation pattern, which agrees with earlier experiments with S^{35} methionine or S^{35} cystine and C^{14} amino acids. H^3 glycine, serine, and alanine (see Figures 1 and 2) are exceptions from the usual behavior of the other amino acids.

The mean grain number was determined for individual amino acids and for a large number of cell types by grain counting; the value for liver was taken as 100. Apart from a few exceptions, the individual cell types closely corresponded in their relative grain density

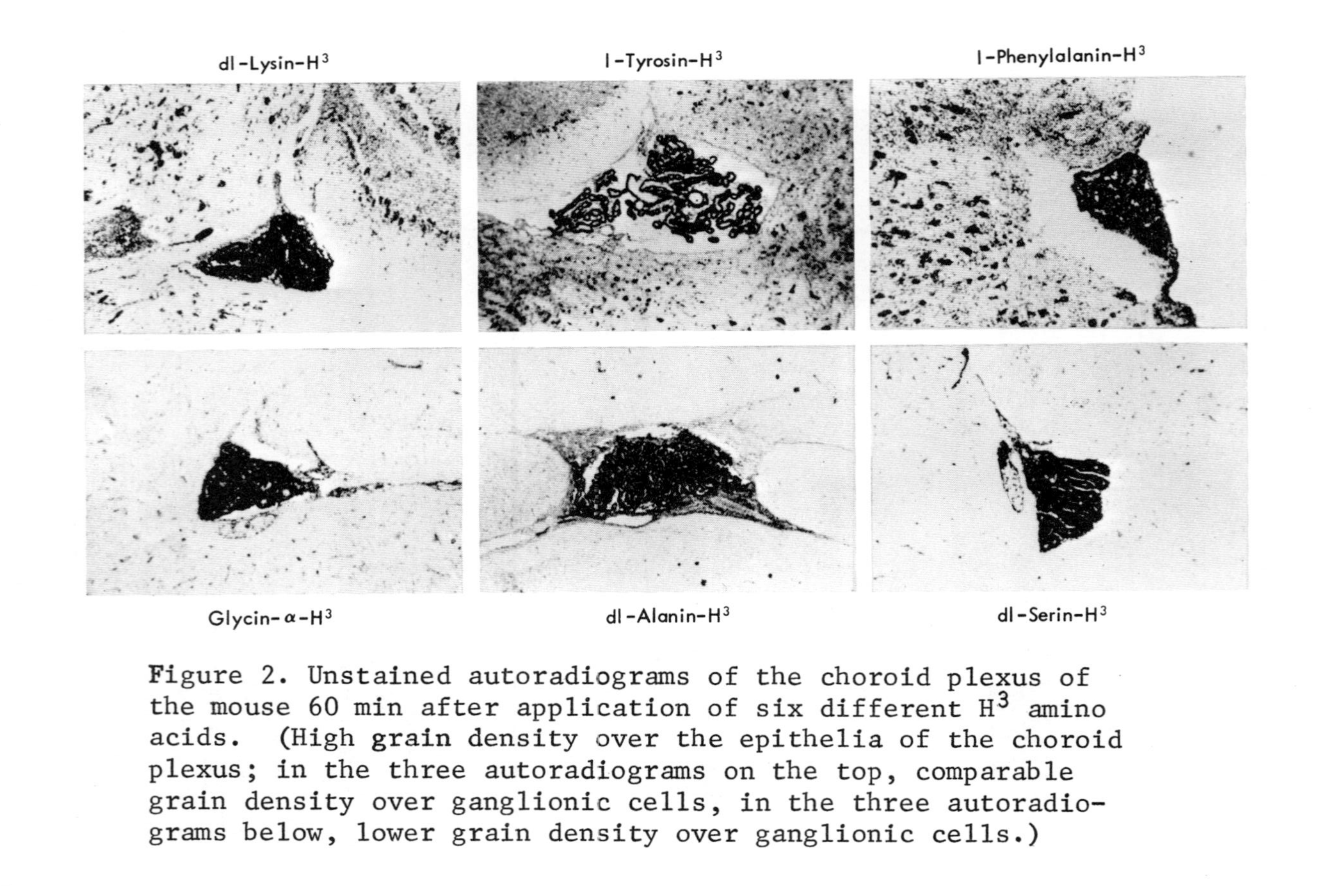

Figure 2. Unstained autoradiograms of the choroid plexus of the mouse 60 min after application of six different H^3 amino acids. (High grain density over the epithelia of the choroid plexus; in the three autoradiograms on the top, comparable grain density over ganglionic cells, in the three autoradiograms below, lower grain density over ganglionic cells.)

for most amino acids. For the exceptions see Citoler et al. (7). Table 3 gives the mean grain density for

TABLE 3

Relative mean grain density over different cell types of the mouse 60 min after application of H^3 labeled amino acids; liver cells = 100. (Numbers are mean values from experiments with H^3 labeled l-tyrosine, l-phenylalanine, d,l-lysine, d,l-arginine and d,l-tryptophan.)

Cell type	Relative mean grain density
1. Cells of the Intestinal Tract	
Chief cells (stomach)	304
Lieberkühn's crypts	294
Pancreas (exocrine)	274
Prestomach, stratified epithelia	219
Colon, mucosa	210
Villus epithelia	151
Tongue (stratum spinosum)	150
Brunner's glands	137
Liver, parenchymal cells	= 100
Salivary glands (serous)	95
Parietal cells (stomach)	70
2. Cells of the Nervous System	
Myenteric plexus	300
Nucleus dentatus	120
Purkinje cells	100
Nucleus olfactorius	80
Glia	12
White matter	9
3. Cells of the Endocrine Glands	
Adrenal cortex (fascicular layer)	117
Epiphysis	110
Pancreus (endocrine)	102
Adenohypophysis	100
Adrenal medulla	88
Neurohypophysis	70
4. Cells of the Urinosexual Tract	
Epididymis epithelia	136
Kidney, cortex (convol. tub)	97
Kidney, cortex (Henle's loops)	94
Spermatogonia	50
Kidney, medulla (collect. tub.)	47
Glomerulum epithelia	37
5. Cells of the Respiratory Tract	
Bronchial epithelia	73
Alveolar epithelia	32
6. Skin, Muscle and Connective Tissue	
Sebaceous glands	60
Smooth muscle	50
Fat cells	41
Skin (stratum basale)	41
Connective tissue (subcutaneous)	34
Heart muscle	29
Tongue muscle	23
Sceletal muscle	12
Cartilage	12
7. Cells of the Inflammatory Infiltration	
Plasmocytes	275
Histiocytes	140
Lymphocytes	37
8. Erythrocytes	~0

different cell types of the mouse averaged for five H^3 amino acids. These numbers represent the mean H^3 incorporation rate per unit volume for the cell types examined.

From the correlation between the relative grain densities for various amino acids, we conclude that the values in Table 3 represent protein synthesis per unit volume in the cell types listed (7). Protein synthesis per unit volume is about 30 to 50 times greater in some cell types - such as the chief cells of the stomach or ganglionic cells - than in others - such as muscle and connective tissue.

Determinations of the grain density for cytoplasm and nucleus separately showed that the large differences in amino acid incorporation rates between individual cell types results almost exclusively from their cytoplasm. Whereas the grain density over cytoplasm in different cell types varied by a factor of more than 30, the grain densities over the nuclei only differed by a factor of 3. If all the grains over cytoplasm were removed, the autoradiograms would have a far more monotonous appearance, because the grain density over the different nuclei is similar. Thus, compared to the great differences in the cytoplasm, grain densities over nuclei can be considered to be approximately equal.

In the following discussion, we shall emphasize three points:

1. nuclear protein synthesis within one cell type;
2. mean nuclear protein synthesis in various cell types;
3. cytoplasmic protein synthesis in different cell types.

Thereafter, we shall derive a general scheme for cellular protein synthesis.

Protein Synthesis in Individual Nuclei within One Cell Type

The number of grains and the size of the cut nuclear area were determined on autoradiograms for individual nuclei of one cell type. Figure 3 illustrates some of the results. A linear relationship exists between the grain number per nucleus and the nuclear area within the limits of statistically predictable fluctuations in the grain number. This linear relationship is represented by the solid line, and the simple statistical plus and minus error in grain number is shown by the dotted lines. On the average, ca. 70% of the points are within the simple statistical error, which indicates that the H^3 activity in individual nuclei increases linearly with the nuclear area without any great fluctuations.

This figure also means the H^3 activity incorporation per unit volume is almost the same in individual nuclei of one cell type. Then the protein synthesis of the whole nucleus is proportional to the size of its volume. In the liver this observation is true predominantly for G_1 nuclei, which are predominant in this tissue, and less valid for S and G_2 nuclei. In intestinal crypts, however, where the duration is the same for S and G_1 phases and, therefore, the number of S and G_1 nuclei is about equal, the linearity holds true for S as well as G_1 nuclei. For the relatively small number of G_2 nuclei, this conclusion is less exact.

Similar grain counting was conducted by Gerbaulet, Maurer and Brückner (9) on intestinal epithelia of the mouse after simultaneous application of H^3 leucine and a small amount of C^{14} thymidine. Thus, the S nuclei were labeled with C^{14}, and in autoradiograms with a thick emulsion layer, they are distinguishable from the G_1 nuclei by their C^{14} tracks. This method gave results similar to those in Figure 3, namely, sequential points on a straight line with the same inclination. It was thus possible to demonstrate the proportionality between the protein synthetic rate and nuclear volume for G_1 and S nuclei separately. Results such as those shown in Figure 3 were obtained from mice, rats, and rabbits for liver parenchymal cells and also for the epithelia of the intestinal villi and crypts, for the prestomach, for the pancreas and smooth muscle, and, as a matter of fact, with various H^3 amino acids. The same results were also found for cell types from animals under pathological conditions (5, 15) as well as for H^3 amino acid incorporation into nucleoli of

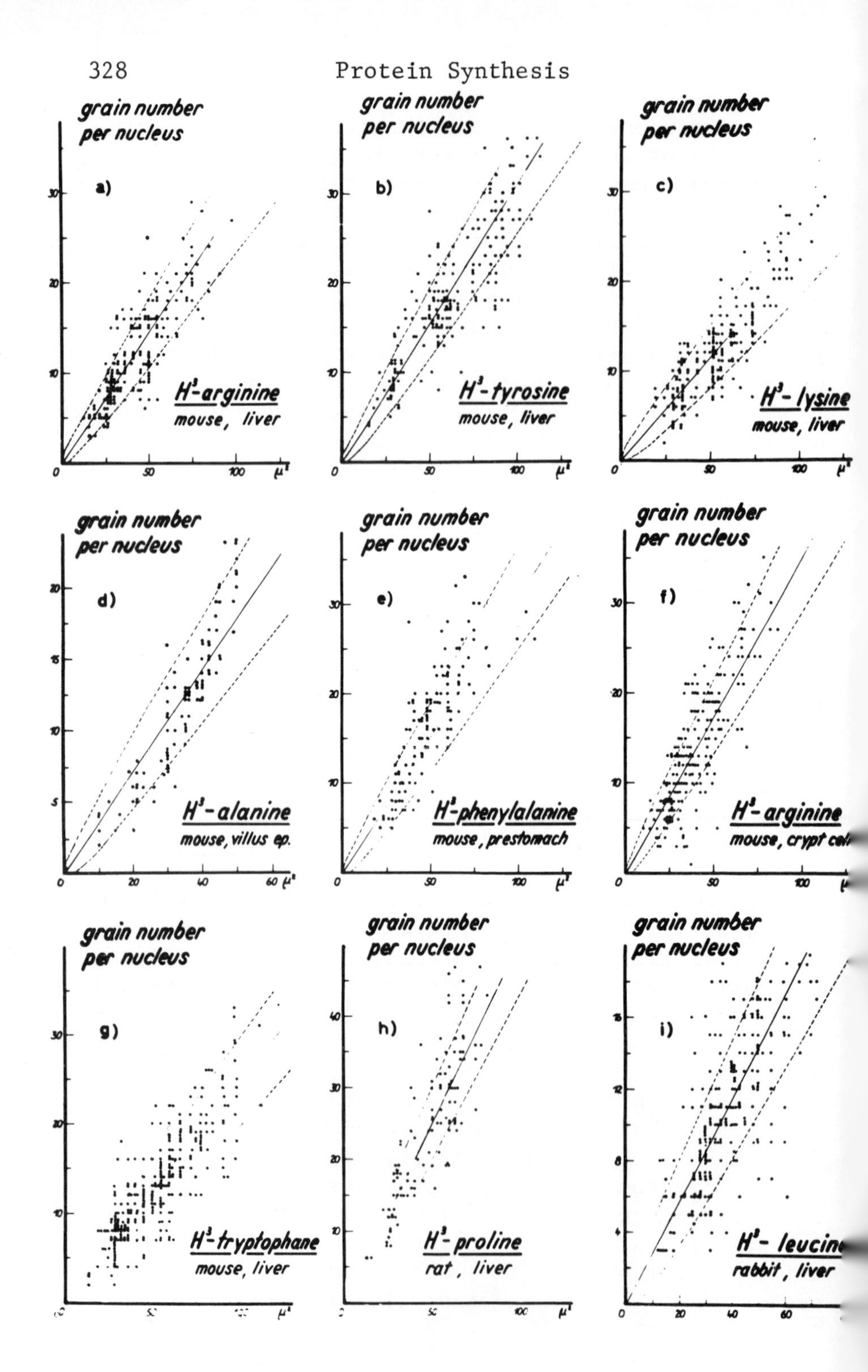
grain number per nucleus
a)
H³-arginine
mouse, liver
b)
H³-tyrosine
mouse, liver
c)
H³-lysine
mouse, liver
d)
H³-alanine
mouse, villus ep.
e)
H³-phenylalanine
mouse, prestomach
f)
H³-arginine
g)
H³-tryptophane
mouse, liver
h)
H³-proline
rat, liver
i)
rabbit, liver
μ²

normal rats and those of rats treated with thioacetamide (TAA) (24). Woodard, Rasch, and Swift (25) also found approximately the same grain density over the nucleolus and nuclear chromatin of meristem cells from Vicia faba after treatment with labeled amino acids, regardless of the cell's position in the cycle.

Since the dry mass per μ^2 in caryoplasm on deparaffinized section 3 μ thick is almost equal to the saturation thickness for H^3 β-radiation, it follows from the linearities of Figure 3 that, in a strict sense, the specific activity of the dry mass is practically equal in all cell nuclei. However, the amount of dry mass should not differ very much from nucleus to nucleus. Killander and Zetterberg (16) and Zetterberg and Killander (26 - 28) examined individual cells from fibroblast cultures simultaneously for their amino acid incorporation autoradiographically and for their dry mass (predominantly protein) interferometrically and cytophotometrically as a function of the cell's position in the cycle. Interestingly these experiments showed a proportionality between protein synthesis and the amount of dry mass, related to either the whole cell or only the cytoplasm.

Comparison of Nuclear Protein Synthetic Rates among Different Cell Types

In the previous section, we showed that all nuclei from one cell type have a common characteristic, i.e., the same rate of protein synthesis per unit volume. Therefore, this value is the most suitable parameter for comparing protein synthesis among different cell types. It is equal to the mean grain density counted for a large number of nuclei.

Figure 3. (Opposite page.) Number of grains over individual nuclei within one cell type as a function of the nuclear area. Each point represents one nucleus. (Dotted lines show simple statistical error of the grain number represented by the solid line.)

Figure 4 shows the mean grain number per nucleus as a function of the mean nuclear area for a great number of cell types. We can see that the protein synthesis rate is high in those cell types with large nuclei (e.g., ganglionic cells) and vice versa. Deviations by individual points from the linearity (solid straight

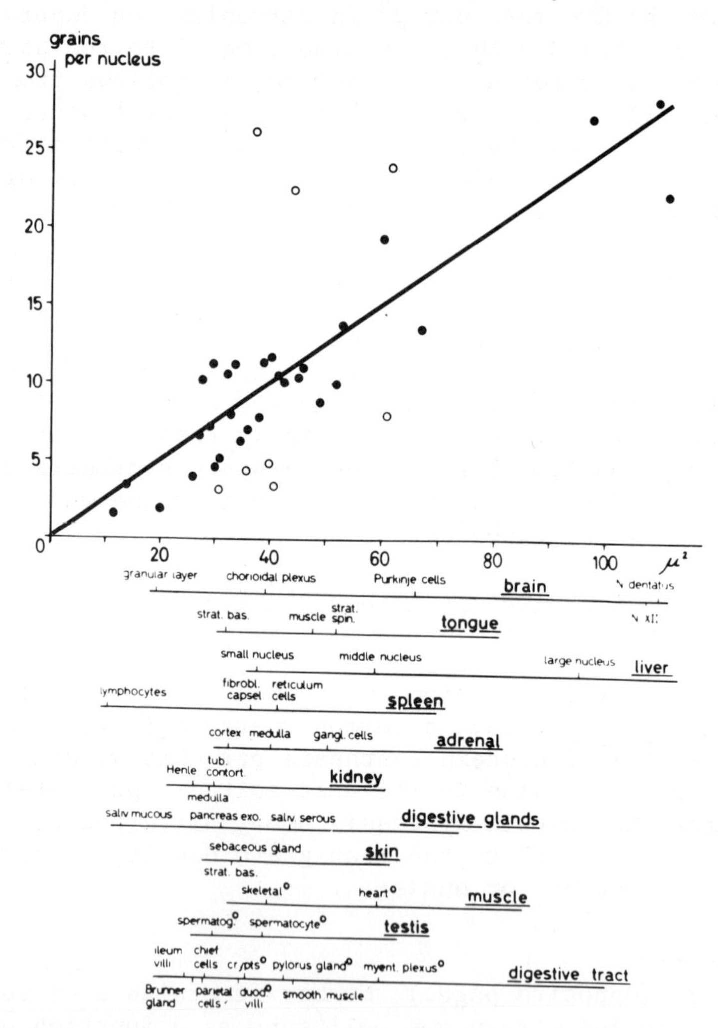

Figure 4. Mean grain number per nucleus as a function of the mean nuclear area for different cell types of the mouse (60 min after application of H^3 1-tyrosine).

line in Figure 4) are in part considerable, as, for instance, by the crypt epithelia in the three sections of the intestine (circles). This observation shows that mean grain densities (grain density/μ^2) over individual types of nuclei are only equal within certain limits. In any case, fluctuations in grain density over the cytoplasm of various cell types are more than ten times greater than those over the nuclei. Compared with the large differences in grain density over the cytoplasm, grain density over the nuclei can be considered relatively constant. It is in this sense that the expression "constant" will be used, i.e. in connection with the nuclear protein synthetic rate per unit volume.

Results similar to those in Figure 4 were obtained for 27 cell types from mice after application of H^3 phenylalanine and from rats after application of H^3 d,l-leucine and C^{14} amino acids in earlier experiments (21).

Since the thickness of the dry mass in caryoplasm on sections 3 μ thick is close to the saturation thickness for H^3 β-radiation, the mean grain density over nuclei is an approximate measure for the specific activity of the dry mass (predominantly protein). However, "equal" specific activity of the nuclear protein in various cell types then means that the mean life span of nuclear protein in all cell types (related to all the nuclear protein) should be the same in the whole organism. In biochemical experiments by Niklas et al. (20) the value for the mean life span of protein (related to all cellular protein) in various cell types of the rat was found to be between less than one day (ganglionic cells) and 30 days (connective tissue). These values were essentially those of the mean life span of the cytoplasmic protein. The mean life span of nuclear protein can be calculated from the ratio of cytoplasmic to nuclear protein synthetic rates determined by autoradiography. The result is approximately 1 day for the mean life span of nuclear protein, which agrees with our previous conclusion.

TABLE 4

Ratios of H^3 amino acid incorporation into all of the cytoplasm of a cell to that into the whole nucleus for different amino acids and different cell types of the mouse

nuclear vol. in % of cell vol.	Cells	Mouse										Rat
		I	II	III	IV	V	VI	VII	VIII	mean	IX	I
		Alan.	Leuc.	Serin	Phen.	Tyros.	Trypt.	Prolin	Lysin	I-VIII	Argin.	Tyros.
30 %	Lieberkühn's crypts		2-3	2,2						= 2,4		
20 %	choroid plexus	5,3	4,8	4,2	4,2	4,5			4,3	= 4,6		4,2
20 %	ganglionic cells (CNS)		5,1 (+)		7,4 (×)	6,9 (•)			6,2 (+)	= 6,4		8,4 (+)
15 %	villi epithelia (small intest.)	5,0	5,4		5,1	5,4	5,1		4,5	= 5 1	3,1	4,6
14 %	pylorus glands	3,1	4,0	4,2	3,8	3,3			3,5 ·	= 3,7	2,2	4,2
14 %	adrenal medulla		7,3	5,7	3,1	3,5	4,3			= 4,9	2,9	4,5
14 %	pancreas endocrine	6,1	5,0	4,9	6,5		4,5			= 5,4		5,0
14 %	salivary gland (serous)	6,9	7,2	7,5		7,2			6,8	= 7,1	6,9	6,0
12 %	Brunner's glands	5,8	5,6	7,3	7,2	5,2			5,4	= 6,1	5,5	5,1
12 %	adrenal cortex	5,3	5,8	6,4	7,2	7,4	6,0		6,1	= 6,3	4,9	5,6
9 %	kidney medulla	5,6		4,5	6,1	4,4	4,2		5,5	= 5,1	3,0	5,4
9 %	liver	7,6	7,9	6,8	8,0	7,7	7,5	7,5	7,1	= 7,5	5,8	7,1
8 %	kidney cortex	6,6		6,4	6,4	6,3	5,7		6,0	= 6,2	4,1	5,2
8 %	kidney (Henle)	6,0	8,5		6,8	6,5	6,8		6,1	= 6,9	3,6	6,8
8 %	pancreas exocrine	13,5	13,4	12,5	17,5	15,8	16,5	13,4		= 14,7	9,6	15,0
5 %	salivary gland (mucous)	6,9	7,1			8,3			6,8	= 7,3	6,9	7,3
4 %	smooth muscle	7,0	7,2	7,1	7,6	6,0	6,4		6,1	= 6,8	3,6	6,0
3 %	heart muscle	6,1	10,5	7,7	6,5	6,7	9,5		6,1	= 7,6	6,6	6,9
1,3 %	skeletal muscle	6,3	7,1	7,1	8,4	9,2	7,1		7,8	= 7,6		6,7

(+) *Nucleus dentatus*
(•) *Nucleus XII*
(×) *Nucleus olfactorius*

Cytoplasmic Protein Synthesis in Various Cell Types

Figures in Tables 4 indicate how much larger is H^3 amino acid incorporation into all the cytoplasm of a cell than into the whole nucleus. The figures were found by counting all the grains over cytoplasm and all the grains over nuclei in large areas on autoradiograms. The quotient from both grain counts then equals the ratio of the cytoplasmic to the nuclear synthetic rate, provided the nuclei are randomly distributed in the tissue. This counting method can also be applied to ganglionic cells. Since grain density over ganglionic cells is 30 to 50 times greater than it is over white matter, practically only ganglionic cells contribute to the grain counts over a whole cranial nerve nucleus.

Table 4 shows that the ratio values obtained for any chosen cell type do not depend on the amino acid used. That arginine regularly gives a smaller value is probably connected with the more intense incorporation of arginine into histones. On the other hand, lysine does not differ from general amino acid behavior. Obviously the contribution of lysine-rich histones to overall H^3 lysine incorporation by the nucleus is relatively small.

That the values in Table 4 are independent of the type of amino acid and the presence of smaller values for arginine suggest that these numbers actually do represent real cellular protein synthetic conditions. In other words, in most cell types, protein synthesis is between five and seven times greater in all the cytoplasm than in the whole nucleus. Grain counts and area measurements of individual cells with well-defined borders showed that ratios similar to those in Table 4 could be obtained also for individual cells, i.e., that the average values in Table 4 very probably correspond to conditions in individual cells.

Determination of grain counts for Table 4 did not consider that β-particle self-absorption is greater in the cytoplasmic dry mass of the sections than in the nuclear. Figure 5 shows that the ratios increase with decreasing thickness of the sections by a factor of approximately 1.3 - (cytoplasmic dry mass/μ^2 : nuclear dry mass/μ^2). After the ratios in Table 4 are corrected for β-particle self-absorption, they all increase by the same factor of about 1.3.

Table 5 contains ratios for cell types from animals under experimentally altered conditions. For example, 2 hr after poisoning with CCl_4, the amino acid incorporation into the centroacinar region of mouse liver is about ten times smaller than the normal amount, and the ratio is 13.2. In contrast, the metabolism in the

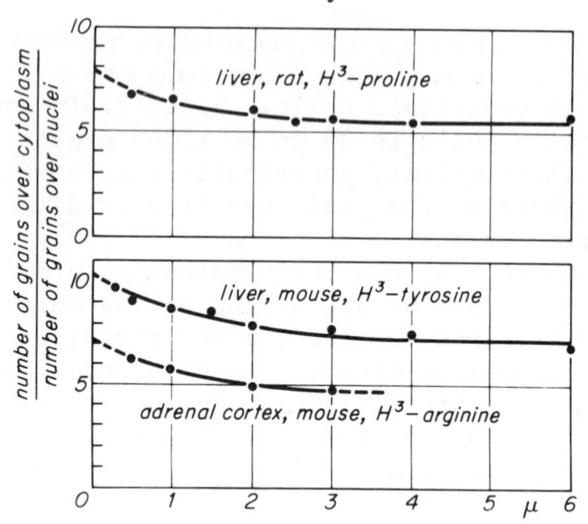

Figure 5. Influence of H^3 β-particle self-absorption on the ratios of H^3 amino acid incorporation into all of the cytoplasm to that into the whole nucleus of a cell.

periphery is slightly raised and has a ratio of 6.6 (normal is 7.5) (6). Similar conditions were found for hepatitis of mice. Furthermore, liver cells regenerating after hepatectomy (2), trained compared with normal heart muscle (18) and fetal compared with maternal heart muscle show reduced ratios. The ratios for carcinoma cells were enormously reduced. These figures suggest that an intensification of metabolism is related to a reduction in the ratio of cytoplasmic to nuclear protein synthesis and vice versa, which also may account for the relatively low value for the crypt cells in Table 4.

Since a migration of protein or peptides from nucleus to cytoplasm is possible, according to the experiments with Amoeba by Goldstein and his group (3, 4, 10, 11), the question can be raised whether migration processes of labeled protein have influenced the ratios in Table 4. We can make three objections against this argument:

TABLE 5

Ratios of H^3 amino acid incorporation into all of the cytoplasm of a cell to that into the whole nucleus for normal and experimentally changed conditions. (- or + means reduced or increased amino acid incorporation compared to normal)

Animal	Organ	–	normal	+	Tumors	
					Adenoma	Carcinoma
Mouse	Liver after CCl_4 (centroacinic-normal-peripheric)	13,2	7,5	6,6		
	Hepatitis (centroacinic-normal-peripheric)	9,1	7,5	7,7		
	Spontaneous Mamma Carcinoma (hypertrophy-adenoma-carcinoma)			3,0	2,1	1,2
Rat	Hepatectomy (control-hepatectomy)		7,5	5,9		
	Heart muscle (control-trained)		7,5	6,1		
	Heart muscle (maternal-fetal)		7,5	5,6		
	Butter yellow carcinoma (DAB liver-adenoma-carcinoma)			6,5	2,4	0,94

1. The ratios show only slight or no changes between 5 and 210 min after application of amino acids. Liver ratios in the examples in Figure 6 only decrease slightly, while the reverse could be true of the adrenal cortex.
2. It is unlikely that the relatively constant ratios in Table 4 result from diffusion equilibrium, since distribution values would have to be completely different between the liver and muscle. for example, because of their different volume ratios for cytoplasm and nucleus.

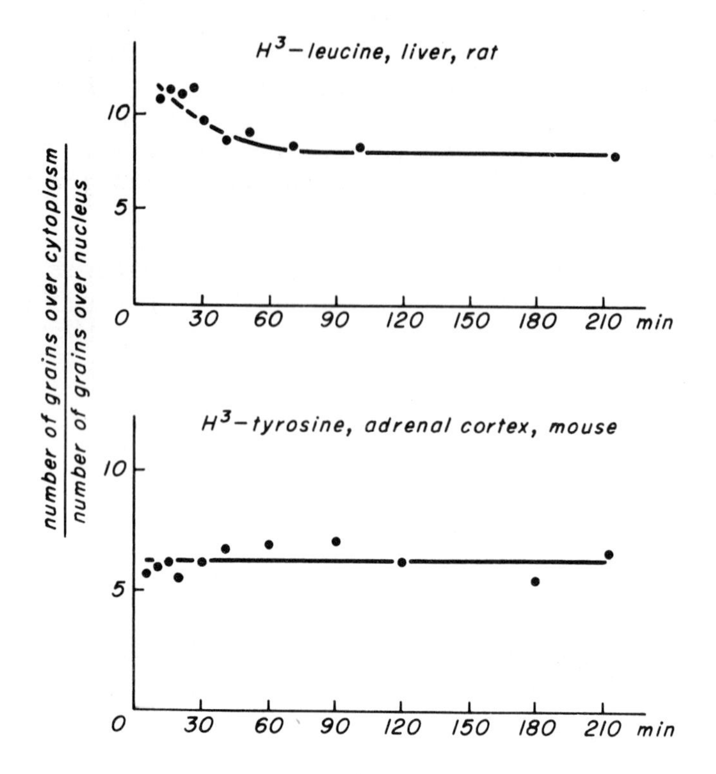

Figure 6. Ratio of H^3 amino acid incorporation into all the cytoplasm of a cell to that into the whole nucleus as a function of experimental time.

3. The constantly lower ratios for arginine do not agree with the assumption that the ratios may result from diffusion equilibrium. Diffusion equilibrium should not, at least in general, depend on the type of label.

Scheme of Cellular Protein Synthesis and its Consequences

Formulation. It follows from the results that protein synthesis in nucleus and cytoplasm in the most different cell types can be understood in terms of a relatively simple scheme, which, aside from those deviations described, has the following idealized form.

1. Nuclear protein synthesis is proportional to nuclear volume (nuclear dry mass).
2. Protein synthesis in all the cytoplasm in a cell is greater by a constant factor than that in the whole nucleus. Thus, cytoplasmic protein synthesis is also proportional to the nuclear volume.

Examples. Two examples - liver and muscle - serve to illustrate how the very great differences in grain density over individual cell types can be understood by this scheme. A relatively large protein synthesis corresponds to the relatively large liver nuclei. It is about nine times larger (β-particle self-absorption considered) in all the cytoplasm. Since the same is also approximately true for the corresponding volumes of the cell structures, the grain density - i.e., amino acid incorporation/unit volume - is approximately equal for the nucleus and cytoplasm, as the autoradiograms of the liver in Figure 7 illustrate.

In muscle the conditions are very different. Because of the smaller volume of muscle nuclei, their total protein synthesis is smaller than that of the liver nuclei. But it is also true of muscle that its cytoplasmic protein synthesis is nine times greater (β-particle self-absorption considered) than its nuclear protein synthesis. This relatively small cytoplasmic protein synthesis is distributed throughout a cytoplasmic volume about ten times greater than that of the liver. Thus, grain density over muscle cytoplasm is extremely small compared to that of liver cells. The autoradiogram for muscle in Figure 7 was exposed much longer than that for liver. Grain density over nuclei would be about the same at identical exposure times; however, almost no grains would then be visible over the cytoplasm.

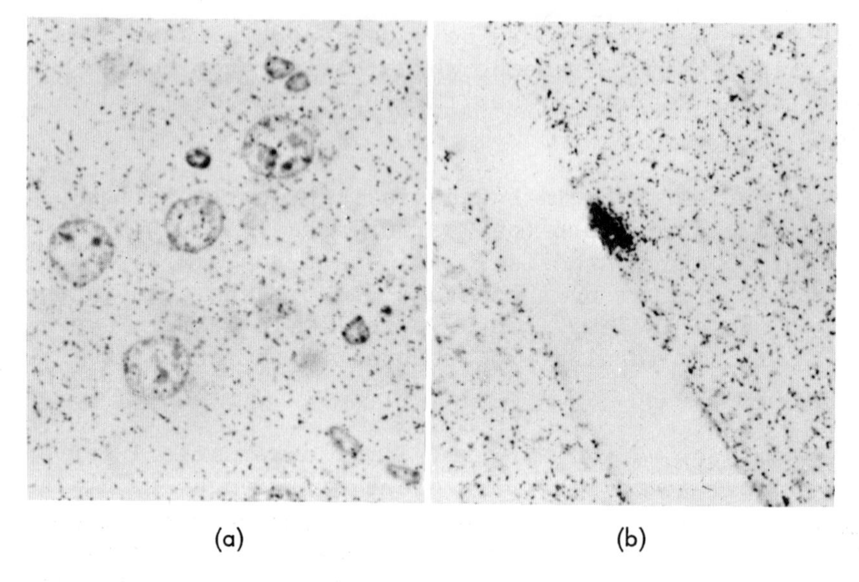

Figure 7. Autoradiogram of the liver (HE-stained) and of the skeletal muscle (unstained) of the mouse 60 min after application of H^3 leucine.

Consequences. An expression for protein synthesis in 1 ml tissue from a certain cell type can be derived from this scheme.

The H^3 activity in all nuclei of 1 ml tissue can be expressed as

$$\text{H}^3 \text{ activity of all nuclei in 1 ml tissue} = \text{nucleus-cell-volume ratio} \cdot c_n \quad (1)$$

The expression on the right equals the volume of all nuclei in 1 ml tissue, and the constant c_n represents the protein synthesis in 1 ml nuclei.

Cytoplasmic protein synthesis can be expressed as

$$\begin{matrix}\text{H}^3 \text{ activity of} \\ \text{cytoplasm in} \\ \text{1 ml tissue}\end{matrix} = \begin{matrix}\text{H}^3 \text{ activity in all nu-} \\ \text{clei in 1 ml tissue}\end{matrix} \cdot F \qquad (2)$$

where F is the ratio of the cytoplasmic to the nuclear protein synthetic rates (Table 4).

The sum gives the protein synthesis in 1 ml tissue

$$\begin{matrix}\text{H}^3 \text{ activity in} \\ \text{1 ml tissue of} \\ \text{a certain cell} \\ \text{type}\end{matrix} = \begin{matrix}\text{nucleus-cell-} \\ \text{volume ratio}\end{matrix} \cdot c_n \cdot (F + 1) \qquad (3)$$

In an idealized situation, where c_n and F are constant, the H^3 activity/ml tissue - i.e., the mean grain density/μ^2 - should be proportional to the nucleus-cell-volume ratio.

In Figure 8, the mean grain density over the different cell types is plotted as a function of the relative nuclear volume (as percent of cellular volume). Apart from a few exceptions, the predictable linear relationship actually does exist to a great extent. Deviations by individual cell types define the limits of the validity for the scheme we have postulated. The volume ratios of the nucleus to cytoplasm alone make it possible to predict the protein synthesis per unit volume in a certain cell type.

It is surprising that such a relatively simple relationship for protein synthesis exists for so many different cell types.

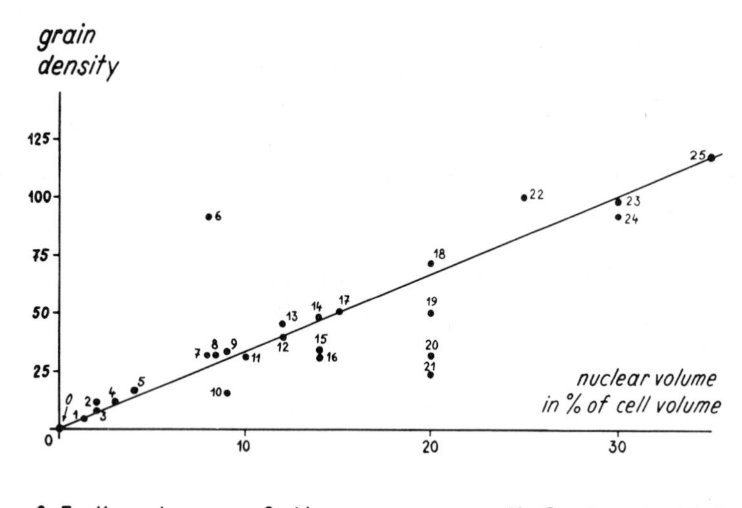

0. Erythrocytes
1. Sceletal muscle
2. Fibroblasts
3. Muscle (tongue)
4. Heart muscle
5. Smooth muscle
6. Pancreas exocrine
7. Kidney cortex
8. Kidney (Henle)
9. Liver
10. Kidney medulla
11. Salivary gland (mucous)
12. Adrenal cortex
13. Brunner's glands
14. Salivary gland (serous)
15. Pancreas endocrine
16. Adrenal medulla
17. Villus epithelia
18. Prestomach epithelia
19. Tongue epithelia
20. Ganglionic cells (CNS)
21. Choroid plexus
22. Chief cells (stomach)
23. Crypt cells (small intestine)
24. Plasmocytes
25. Myenteric plexus

Figure 8. Grain density over different cell types of the mouse as a function of the relative nuclear volume as percent of the cellular volume.

PART II

RELATIONSHIP BETWEEN TURNOVER RATES OF PROTEIN AND RNA

Comparison of Autoradiograms with Protein and RNA Precursors

Experiments similar to those described in Part I for labeled amino acids were also conducted with H^3 uridine and H^3 cytidine. After application of both

RNA precursors to rats and mice, the animals were sacrificed between 10 and 180 min later. Autoradiograms (tissue fixed in neutral formalin, sections of 3 μ, AR 10 stripping film) were prepared from the organs.

Figure 9 shows autoradiograms of mouse intestine

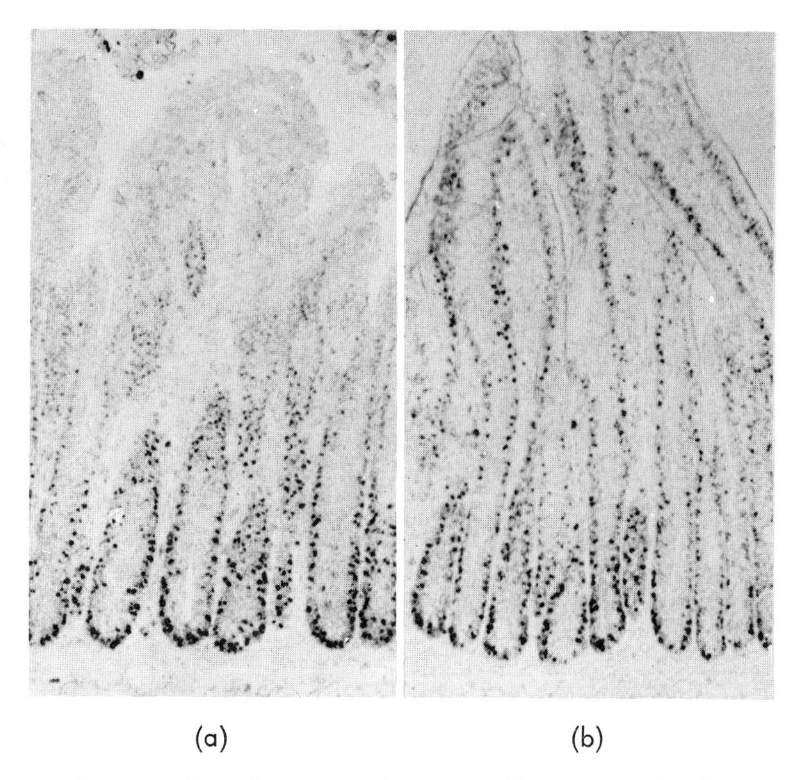

(a) (b)

Figure 9. Unstained autoradiograms of the small intestine of the mouse 60 min after application of H^3 uridine (left) and H^3 cytidine (right).

with H^3 uridine and H^3 cytidine. Aside from the fact that the S phase nuclei have a somewhat greater grain density with H^3 cytidine than do the other nuclei, both autoradiograms are similar with both nucleosides. Crypt epithelia show the greatest grain density. Without exception, comparison of autoradiograms of all other organs showed a comparable correspondence of grain density distribution for the two nucleosides, which can be expected if the autoradiograms actually reveal RNA synthesis. Under comparable conditions there is only one difference between both nucleosides: H^3 uridine causes a grain density five times smaller than that of H^3 cytidine. Biochemical experiments by Hammarsten, Reichard, and Saluste (13, 14) also showed a smaller rate of utilization for uridine. In contrast to cytidine, uridine obviously is catabolized and excreted to a much greater extent.

Comparison of autoradiograms with protein and RNA precursors in Figures 10 and 11 shows that the relative grain density distribution is very similar, provided the mean grain densities are compared - i.e., ignoring the fact that the intracellular distribution of protein- and RNA-precursor incorporation is different. Besides the examples in Figures 10 and 11, similar autoradiograms with the same relative grain density distribution were obtained for esophagus, gut, salivary gland, tongue, spleen, skeletal muscle, plexus, and CNS. Thus, for 25 cell types, a parallelism of mean grain densities was found under comparable conditions for incorporation of protein and RNA precursors, which would indicate that cells with a high RNA turnover rate also have a corresponding high protein turnover rate, and vice versa. This proportionality between both turnover rates was also quantitatively confirmed by counting mean grain densities over the different cell types.

There are only two distinct exceptions from this general proportionality. Protein precursors produced different autoradiograms for the kidney than RNA precursors did. However, it is difficult to determine, especially with respect to protein synthesis, to what extent the different simultaneous processes, such as secretion, resorption, or enzyme production, overlap. Pancreas epithelia are also an exception. Here, amino acid incorporation is greater for all amino acids investigated than we would expect considering nucleoside incorporation. Nucleoside incorporation into ganglionic cells of the CNS is also very small compared to amino acid incorporation. However, this difference

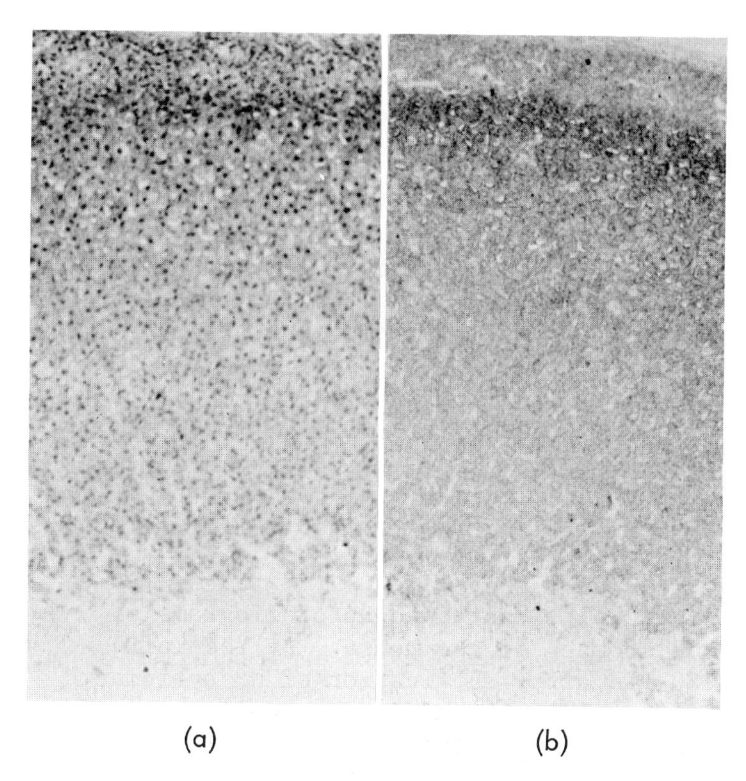

Figure 10. Autoradiograms of the adrenal gland of the mouse 180 min after application of H^3 cytidine (left) and 60 min after application of H^3 leucine (right). (Highest mean grain density over the cortex, especially the outer fascicular layer; lowest grain density over the medulla.)

is not a real deviation from the general proportionality between both synthetic processes. It is rather a result of reduced diffusion of nucleosides, i.e., a blood-brain barrier. This assumption is strengthened by the high nucleoside incorporation rate into peripheric ganglionic cells which is comparable to that of amino acids (23).

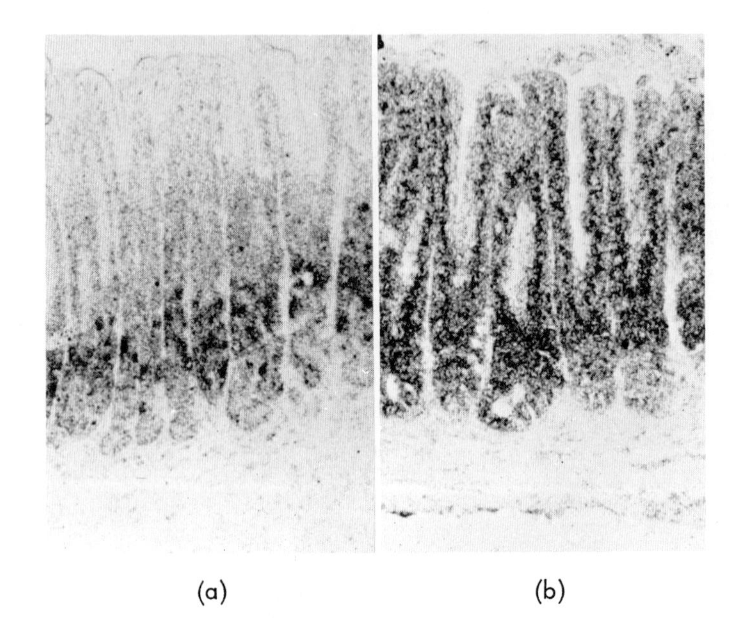

Figure 11. Unstained autoradiograms of the stomach of the mouse. At the left, 180 min after application of H^3 cytidine; at the right, 60 min after application of H^3 leucine. (Highest grain density over the chief cells of the glands; lowest grain density over submucous membrane and muscle.)

Quantitative Comparison of Protein and RNA Turnover Rates in Different Cell Types

The autoradiograms strongly support the assumption that protein turnover is - within certain limits - proportional to RNA turnover (both expressed in g/unit time). The relationship can be expressed as follows:

$$\text{protein turnover rate} = c \cdot \text{RNA turnover rate} \quad (4)$$

The value of the constant c should be as constant for all cells as grain densities are equal.

In earlier experiments with rat liver, a protein synthetic rate of 40 mg/g/day (related to all the liver tissue) (20) and an RNA synthetic rate of 1.7 mg/g/day were measured (8). In both cases, the specific activity of the corresponding precursors (S^{35} methionine or P^{32}, respectively) and the activity of the isolated protein or RNA, respectively, were measured. The synthetic rates were then calculated from these figures.

A value for the constant c follows from these synthetic rates:

$$c = \frac{40 \text{ mg/g/day}}{1.7 \text{ mg/g/day}} = 23 \qquad (5)$$

Related to grams per unit time, the protein turnover rate is about 23 times greater than the RNA turnover rate. Similar conditions should exist for the majority of the cell types.

Table 6 shows the values that result if the two

TABLE 6

Approximate ratios of protein and RNA synthesis in the whole cell and the different cell structures

$$\text{Protein turnover rate} \cong c \cdot \text{RNA turnover rate}$$

$$c \cong \frac{\text{Protein turnover rate}}{\text{RNA turnover rate}}$$

$$c \cong \frac{40 \text{ mg/g} \cdot \text{day}}{1.7 \text{ mg/g} \cdot \text{day}} \quad \text{(for rat liver)}$$

$$c \cong 23$$

	Protein : RNA	Protein : RNA
Cell	23 : 1	
Nucleus	2 : 1	
Caryoplasm	2 : $\frac{1}{3}$	6 : 1
Nucleolus	< $\frac{2}{100}$: $\frac{2}{3}$	< 1 : 30

turnover rates are not related to the whole cell, but to the cytoplasm and nucleus or to the caryoplasm and nucleolus, respectively. According to Table 4, the nuclear protein synthetic rate is about ten times smaller (β-particle self-absorption considered) than that of the whole cell. With respect to the nucleus only, the protein synthetic rate should be about 2.3 times greater than that of the RNA. In this case, all cellular RNA synthesis was considered to be of nuclear origin, as shown by many authors.

Furthermore, grain counts of protein autoradiograms show that only about 1/50 of the nuclear protein synthesis occurs in the nucleolus. On the other hand, 2/3 of all nuclear RNA synthesis takes place in the nucleolus, as was found by Schultze and Maurer (22) (β-particle self-absorption considered). Consequently, the protein turnover in caryoplasm is about six times greater than that of RNA. In the nucleolus, the reverse is true; protein synthesis is about 30 times smaller than RNA synthesis. Conditions should be similar in most of the cell types in the organism (17).

The surprising constant value for the ratio of cytoplasmic to nuclear protein synthesis shown in Table 4 is perhaps connected to the relationship between protein and RNA synthetic rates. Inasmuch as this RNA synthesis is synthesis of messenger RNA, a high RNA synthetic rate could lead to a corresponding high cytoplasmic protein synthetic rate.

Mean Life Span of RNA in Various Cell Types

Caspersson's well known correlation between the RNA content of a cell and its protein metabolism can be expressed in the following way:

$$\frac{\text{protein turnover rate}}{\text{(g/unit time)}} = c' \cdot \text{RNA content} \qquad (6)$$

A comparison of grain densities on protein autoradiograms with RNA contents determined biochemically showed that this relationship is also quantitatively valid (19). Both values are proportional to each other for a series of cell types. Thus, the value for the constant c' should be the same - within certain limits - for many cell types.

Division of Equation 4 into Equation 6 gives the quotient:

$$\frac{\text{RNA content}}{\text{RNA turnover rate}} = \frac{c'}{c} = ML_{RNA} \tag{7}$$

The mean life span (ML) of the RNA related to the whole cellular RNA should, therefore, have approximately the same value for different cell types. Investigations of the specific activity of RNA in different cell types of the mouse by Hammarsten and Hevesy (12), after application of P^{32}, resulted in very similar values. These results also indicate that ML_{RNA} is the same in different cell types. Measurements of the decline of labeled RNA as a function of time further suggests that ML_{RNA} is constant for different cell types.

In earlier biochemical experiments with P^{32} (8), ML_{RNA} of the liver was found to be 5 days. Since the nucleus contains only about 0.1 of the cellular RNA, ML_{RNA}, related to the nuclear RNA only, should be about ten times smaller - i.e., about half a day. This figure correlates very well with the autoradiographically observed migration of labeled RNA from the nucleus into the cytoplasm. The autoradiograms show that the migration throughout the whole cell of labeled RNA synthesized in the nucleus required many hours in all cell types examined.

The scheme for cellular protein synthesis described in Part I of this paper, and the relationship between protein and RNA synthesis discussed in Part II, are, of course, only of limited precision. However, they show that the individual cell types are very much more similar with respect to their protein and RNA synthesis than we could expect from the great differences in their morphology and function.

REFERENCES

1. Birkofer, L., and K. Hempel. 1963. Chem. Ber. 96: 1373.
2. Busanny-Caspari, W., and M. Deimel. 1963. Ges. Exp. Med. 136: 456.
3. Byers, T.J., D.B. Platt, and L. Goldstein. 1963a. J. Cell. Biol. 19: 453.

4. Byers, T.J., D.B. Platt, and L. Goldstein. 1963b. J. Cell Biol. 19: 467.
5. Citoler, P., and W. Maurer. 1963a. Beitr. Pathol. Anat. Allgem. Pathol. 128: 359.
6. Citoler, P., and W. Maurer. 1963b. Beitr. Pathol. Anat. Allgem. Pathol. 129: 73.
7. Citoler, P., K. Citoler, K. Hempel, B. Schultze, and W. Maurer. 1966. Z. Zellforsch. 70: 419.
8. Ernst, H. Dissertation presented in Cologne, May, 14, 1956.
9. Gerbaulet, K., W. Maurer, and J. Brückner. 1963. Biochim. Biophys. Acta 68: 462.
10. Goldstein, L. 1958. Exp. Cell Res. 15: 635.
11. Goldstein, L. 1965. Symp. Intern. Soc. Cell Biol. 4: 79.
12. Hammarsten, E., and G. Hevesy. 1946. Acta Physiol. Scand. 11: 335.
13. Hammarsten, E., P. Reichard, and E. Saluste. 1949. Acta Chem. Scand. 3: 433.
14. Hammarsten, E., P. Reichard, and E. Saluste. 1950. J. Biol. Chem. 183: 105.
15. Hempel, K., K.-J. Lennartz, and W. Maurer. 1962. Beitr. Pathol. Anat. Allgem. Pathol. 126: 381.
16. Killander, D., and A. Zetterberg. 1965. Exp. Cell Res. 38: 272.
17. Leblond, C.P., and M. Amano. 1962. J. Histochem. Cytochem. 10: 162.
18. Müller, D., and W. Maurer. 1966. In preparation.
19. Niklas, A., and W. Oehlert. 1956. Beitr. Pathol. Anat. Allgem. Pathol. 116: 92.
20. Niklas, A., E. Quincke, W. Maurer, and H. Neyen. 1958. Biochem. Z. 330: 1.
21. Oehlert, W., and B. Schultze. 1960. Beitr. Pathol. Anat. Allgem. Pathol. 123: 101.
22. Schultze, B., and W. Maurer. 1963. Z. Zellforsch. 60: 387.
23. Schultze, B., W. Oehlert, and W. Maurer. 1961. Biochim. Biophys. Acta 49: 35.
24. Stöcker, E. 1963. Z. Zellforsch. 58: 790.
25. Woodard, J., E. Rasch, and H. Swift. 1961. J. Biophys. Biochem. Cytol. 9: 445.

26. Zetterberg, A. 1966. Exp. Cell Res. 42: 500.
27. Zetterberg. A., and D. Killander. 1965a. Exp. Cell Res. 39: 22.
28. Zetterberg, A., and D. Killander. 1965b. Exp. Cell Res. 40: 1.

Section IV

The Control of Gene Expression

*Nuclear Transplantation Studies of Nucleocytoplasmic Interactions in Amphibian Hybrids**

Sally Hennen

Department of Zoology
Indiana University

Early work in experimental embryology established that, in general, each egg type has a characteristic distribution of cytoplasmic materials which determines the pattern for the main organ-forming areas of the embryo (Wilson, 1904; Conklin, 1905; Spemann, 1901; and others). However, these cytoplasmic regions cannot, by themselves, initiate the series of inductive interactions necessary for normal differentiation. These events require the presence of nuclei containing a balanced genome (Boveri, 1902; Fankhauser, 1934). Following this early work, evidence from a variety of experiments pointed to the conclusion that normal differentiation involves specific and precise nucleocytoplasmic interactions (see review by Briggs and

*This investigation was supported by Grant GM 05850-08 from the Research Grants Division, U.S. Public Health Service.

King, 1959). It is now generally accepted that the regional differences in egg cytoplasm must be responsible for the differential behavior of an initial population of genetically identical nuclei. Thus, a crucial problem in embryonic differentiation is the manner and extent to which the components of the egg cytoplasm control the expression of the genetic information carried by the nuclei.

One of several experimental approaches to this problem has been the study of nucleocytoplasmic interactions in amphibian hybrids exhibiting clear-cut deviations from the normal pattern of development. I shall not attempt to review the extensive literature on this subject (see, e.g., J.A. Moore, 1955; Barth and Barth, 1966). Rather, I shall limit the work considered in this paper to studies of nucleocytoplasmic interactions by means of nuclear transplantation.

TRANSPLANTATION OF NUCLEI BETWEEN *RANA PIPIENS* AND *RANA SYLVATICA*

Among the numerous amphibian hybrids are several whose development ends abruptly during late cleavage or early gastrulation. Since the lethal effect of hybridization takes place before or shortly after the onset of morphogenesis, such hybrids are of special interest for studies of nucleocytoplasmic interactions during early development. Lethal hybrids of this type are obtained from crosses between *Rana pipiens* and *Rana sylvatica*. The diploid hybrids are arrested early in gastrulation (J.A. Moore, 1941, 1946). The androgenetic haploid hybrids (produced by removing the egg nucleus after fertilization by sperm from the other species) do not develop beyond a late blastula stage (Moore and Moore, 1953).

In 1958, J.A. Moore described an experiment in which he transplanted nuclei from diploid *R. pipiens* blastulae into enucleated *R. sylvatica* eggs. The resulting nucleocytoplasmic hybrids, if allowed to develop, behaved in the same way as did their corresponding androgenetic haploid hybrids, i.e., they were arrested as late blastulae.* Prior to their arrest, some nucleocytoplasmic hybrids were sacrificed for transfers of their nuclei back into enucleated *R. pipiens* eggs. If the *R. pipiens* nuclei had remained unchanged during replication in *R. sylvatica* cytoplasm, the back-transfer embryos should have developed normally; however, they did not develop beyond an early gastrula stage (Moore, 1958). This remarkable result indicated that a genetic change of some sort had occurred in *R. pipiens* nuclei during their division in *R. sylvatica* cytoplasm - a change which prevented the nuclei from promoting normal development in their own type of egg cytoplasm. Similar experiments with two species of *Xenopus* have been carried out by Gurdon who showed, as did Moore in subsequent studies, that these nuclear changes are irreversible (Gurdon, 1962; J.A. Moore, 1960).

Concurrent with these experiments, work of another nature, also involving nuclear transplantation, revealed that abnormal development of nuclear transplant embryos was often accompanied by cytologically detectable alterations in the chromosome complements (Briggs et al., 1961). It therefore seemed logical that the next step in analyzing the nature of the cytoplasmically induced nuclear changes in lethal hybrid systems should be examination of the back-transfer embryos' chromosome complements.

Experiments similar to those of J.A. Moore were carried out with the following results (Hennen, 1963). Diploid nuclei from *R. pipiens* blastulae were transplanted into enucleated *R. sylvatica* eggs. After about 10 to 20 divisions in the foreign cytoplasm, the nuclei were back-transferred into enucleated *R. pipiens* eggs. Of 62 back-transfer embryos so obtained, all but one developed abnormally and were arrested at various stages ranging from late blastulae to young tadpoles. Analysis of the metaphase plates in squash preparations revealed that all abnormal back-transfer embryos studied did, in fact, contain abnormal numbers

*This was actually shown in later experiments (Hennen, 1963).

and types of chromosomes. The chromosomal abnormalities were most severe in back-transfer embryos dying in early stages and less pronounced in embryos developing to late tailbud stages and beyond. These results demonstrate that the cytoplasmically induced nuclear changes are actually alterations in the number and gross structure of the chromosomes. The occurrence of such karyotypic abnormalities can explain why the nuclei are unable to promote normal development in the back-transfer embryos and why this phenomenon is irreversible.

The significance of these results for studies of the nature of nucleocytoplasmic interactions in development depends upon the manner in which the chromosomal abnormalities arise and whether any consistent pattern is discernible in their occurrence. Unfortunately, because of the highly variable and complex nature of the chromosomal abnormalities, we know little about either of these points. Apparently the chromosomal changes arise during early cleavage stages when *R. pipiens* nuclei are dividing in *R. sylvatica* cytoplasm. The changes are extensive and lead to variations in chromosome number and the production of abnormal types of chromosomes, many of which are unstable and undergo further rearrangement (Hennen, 1963; Hennen, unpublished observations). This type of chromosomal behavior is difficult to analyze and, while no consistent pattern of abnormalities has been found, such a consistency would be hard to demonstrate because of the complexity of the changes.

Consequently, it is impractical to draw any conclusions, other than those already stated, about the developmental significance of the cytoplasmically induced chromosomal changes in nucleocytoplasmic hybrids between *Rana pipiens* and *Rana sylvatica*. For this reason it is uncertain whether further studies with this lethal hybrid combination will provide meaningful clues concerning the nature of nucleocytoplasmic interactions that normally occur in development. Furthermore, the same complications created by the presence of highly variable chromosome complements may also exist in ordinary hybrids between these two species as well as in other lethal hybrids. Unless we find some way to make sense out of these complex chromosomal abnormalities, such complications will remain and make it very difficult to interpret experiments involving lethal hybrid combinations.

TRANSPLANTATION OF *RANA PIPIENS* NUCLEI INTO EGGS OF *RANA PALUSTRIS*

In view of the complications in analysis and interpretation posed by the variable chromosomal alterations in the lethal hybrid system, it seemed desirable to examine nucleocytoplasmic interactions between more closely related species. The two selected, *Rana pipiens* and *Rana palustris*, are morphologically distinct frogs whose diploid hybrids develop normally through metamorphosis (J.A. Moore, 1941). That the nuclei and cytoplasm of these two species are not completely compatible is indicated by the following observations. Although ordinary haploids of either species develop to tadpole stages in a manner typical for frog haploids (Porter, 1939), the androgenetic haploid hybrids, in contrast, rarely develop beyond neurula stages (Figure 1) (A.B.C. Moore, 1950). The poorer development of the haploid hybrids suggested that a nucleocytoplasmic incompatibility between these two species is expressed when nuclei containing chromosomes of only one species are present in the cytoplasm of the other.

Since haploidy by itself is a lethal condition, a valid test of this hypothesis required the analysis of embryos containing diploid nuclei of one species in the cytoplasm of the other - so-called nucleocytoplasmic hybrids. Such an investigation was carried out with the following results (Hennen, 1965). When diploid nuclei from *R. pipiens* blastulae were transplanted into enucleated *R. palustris* eggs, the majority of the recipients formed normal blastulae. The post-blastula development of all these nucleocytoplasmic hybrids was abnormal with a consistent pattern of deficiencies occurring in the anterior axial structures.

The development of the nucleocytoplasmic hybrids will be described in more detail later; the fact that they developed abnormally established that there is a genuine

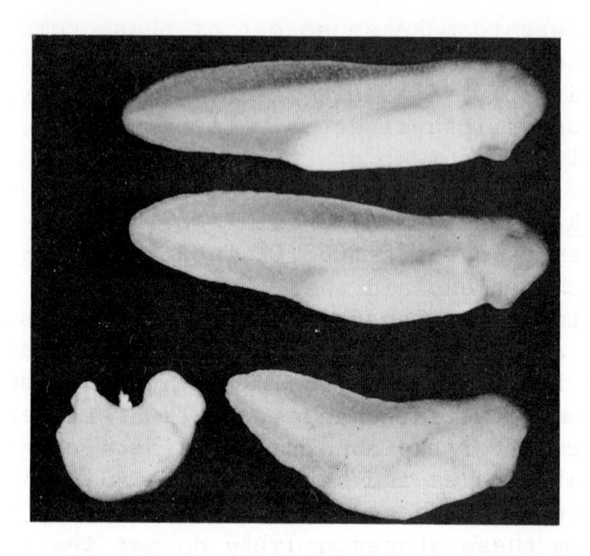

Figure 1. From top to bottom: (a) diploid, R. palustris ♀ × R. palustris ♂; (b) diploid hybrid, R. palustris ♀ × R. pipiens ♂; (c) androgenetic haploid, (R. palustris ♀) × R. palustris ♂, bottom right; (d) androgenetic haploid hybrid (R. palustris ♀) × R. pipiens ♂, bottom left. The parentheses denote removal of female chromosomes. Magnification is approximately 8 X.

nucleocytoplasmic incompatibility between these two species. It was important to determine if this incompatibility was associated with stable changes in the nuclei. Accordingly, nucleocytoplasmic hybrids were sacrificed at mid-blastula stages and their nuclei (containing R. pipiens chromosomes) were transplanted back into enucleated R. pipiens eggs. Almost all (91%) the back-transfer embryos developed normally. Serial transplantation of R. pipiens nuclei into enucleated R. palustris eggs for two and three successive blastula generations before back-transfer into R. pipiens eggs gave a similar result; the large majority of the back-transfer embryos developed normally. Analysis of metaphase plates from a random sample of the back-transfer embryos and their nucleocytoplasmic hybrid donors revealed the presence of normal diploid complements of 26 chromosomes.

In the experiments just described, the nuclei were back-transferred before the incompatibility of the nucleocytoplasmic hybrids was expressed. Therefore, the normal development of the back-transfer embryos shows only that _R. pipiens_ nuclei can replicate normally in _R. palustris_ cytoplasm and that at mid-blastula stages no cytoplasmically induced nuclear changes occur which can explain the later appearance of abnormalities in the nucleocytoplasmic hybrids. In order to obtain a true test of whether the incompatibility expressed in the nucleocytoplasmic hybrids actually causes stable nuclear changes, the nuclei should be transferred after the abnormalities appear - i.e., at mid-gastrula stages and beyond. Such an experiment has complications, because, in intrapsecific transfers, nuclei from these stages usually do not promote the normal development of recipient eggs (Briggs and King, 1957; and others). Nevertheless, a few attempts have been made to back-transfer, into enucleated _R. pipiens_ eggs, nuclei from endoderm cells of nucleocytoplasmic hybrids in late gastrula or early neurula stages. The results obtained thus far have not differed from those obtained in control transfers of _R. pipiens_ nuclei from similar stages in development into enucleated _R. pipiens_ eggs (Hennen, unpublished observations). In both cases most of the recipient eggs developed abnormally. No differences were found in the types of abnormalities expressed by the two groups.

These experiments provided no evidence that _R. pipiens_ nuclei undergo stable changes during division in _R. palustris_ cytoplasm affecting their capacity to promote normal development in cytoplasm of their own type. However, another aspect of the species incompatibility is of special interest to the problem of nucleocytoplasmic interactions during development. This is the development of the nucleocytoplasmic hybrids (_R. pipiens_ nuclei in _R. palustris_ cytoplasm) mentioned briefly in the beginning of this section. Over 100 of these embryos have now been analyzed. Their development deviates from the normal pattern in characteristic and highly consistent ways. The embryos invariably lack a ventral lip of the blastopore during gastrulation and form a short, narrow, neural plate before invagination of the endoderm is completed. As a result of these and other abnormalities during gastrulation and neurulation, the nucleocytoplasmic hybrids develop with small, poorly differentiated heads and associated structures of which the suckers are especially defective (Figure 2). In addition to these

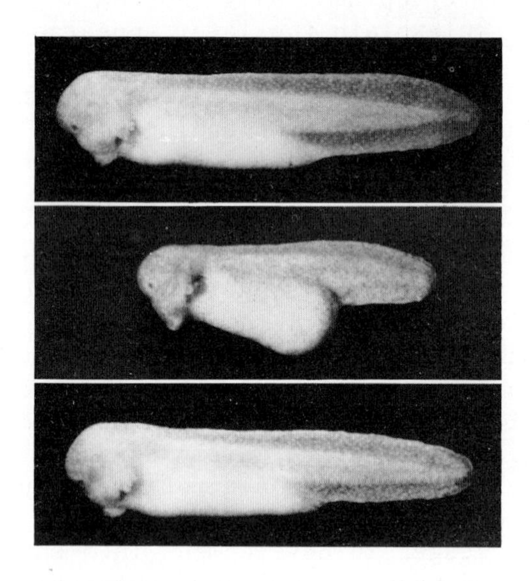

Figure 2. From top to bottom: (a) diploid control, _R_. _palustris_ ♀ × _R_. _pipiens_ ♂; (b) nucleocytoplasmic hybrid, _R_. _pipiens_ → (_R_. _palustris_); (c) triploid hybrid, _R_. _pipiens_ → _R_. _palustris_. The parentheses denote removal of female chromosomes; the arrow denotes nuclear transplantation. Magnification is approximately 8 X.

striking deficiencies in the anterior axial organs, the embryos are abnormally short with posteriorly displaced endoderm. (See Hennen, 1965, for a more detailed description of development.) The majority of the nucleocytoplasmic hybrids develop to post-neurula stages when, after a period of immobility, they die without feeding.

These results show that the abnormal interactions

between *R. pipiens* nuclei and *R. palustris* cytoplasm affect the main events of early morphogenesis, namely gastrulation and primary induction. Before attempting to characterize further these abnormal interactions, it was necessary to determine if the karyotypes of the nucleocytoplasmic hybrids remained normal throughout development. Although the nucleocytoplasmic hybrids were known to have normal chromosomes at mid-blastula stages, it was still possible that karyotypic abnormalities might arise later in development and contribute to the deficiencies in differentiation. This proved not to be the case. Practically all the nucleocytoplasmic hybrids analyzed after their development had ceased had normal chromosome complements (Hennen, 1965). Thus, the abnormal behavior of the nucleocytoplasmic hybrids is not associated with a loss or change in genetic activity caused by cytologically detectable alterations in karyotype.

The results of the chromosome studies indicated that the strucutural integrity of the *R. pipiens* genome is maintained in *R. palustris* cytoplasm and that the abnormal development of the nucleocytoplasmic hybrids results from the inability of the *R. pipiens* genes to function normally in the foreign cytoplasm. Because *R. pipiens* genes are capable of normal expression in the ordinary diploid hybrids, it seemed reasonable to suppose that the abnormal development of the nucleocytoplasmic hybrids might be corrected by the addition of a haploid set of *R. palustris* chromosomes. This addition was easily accomplished by transplanting *R. pipiens* nuclei into nucleated rather than enucleated *R. palustris* eggs (Hennen, 1964). The donor and host nuclei fused to give triploid hybrids with completely normal development (Figure 2). Several of the triploids were reared through metamorphosis into young frogs whose spotting pattern was more characteristic of *R. pipiens* than of *R. palustris*.

It is evident from this account of the nucleocytoplasmic hybrids that *R. pipiens* nuclei and *R. palustris* cytoplasm interact in abnormal ways which affect the normal expression of *R. pipiens* genes during early development. The consistency with which the nucleocytoplasmic hybrids showed deficiencies in their anterior axial structures indicated that these nucleoctyoplasmic interactions are highly specific, and this, in turn, suggested that the type of abnormalities expressed might depend on the particular combination of nuclei and cytoplasm involved. To test this point, experiments have been carried out recently with the reciprocal combination, a preliminary account of which follows.

TRANSPLANTATION OF *RANA PALUSTRIS* NUCLEI INTO EGGS OF *RANA PIPIENS*

The experiments to be described were performed in a manner similar to that previously reported (Hennen, 1963, 1965).

Nucleocytoplasmic Hybrids

When diploid nuclei from *R. palustris* blastulae were transplanted into enucleated *R. pipiens* eggs, the majority of the recipients formed normally cleaved blastulae. The subsequent development of these nucleocytoplasmic hybrids, like that of the reciprocal combination, was always abnormal. The abnormalities were however, significantly different. Both lips of the blastopore appeared during gastrulation, but invagination was greatly retarded. Approximately 25% of the embryos did not develop beyond gastrulation. Neurulation in the remaining embryos was also delayed and the anterior portion of the neural plate was abnormally wide. Approximately 50% of the nucleoctyoplasmic hybrids died during neurulation. The remaining 25% formed abnormal early post-neurulae with very large heads and suckers (Figure 3). In addition to pronounced macrocephaly, these embryos had severe defects in the lateral and ventral mesoderm causing the ectoderm to lose its integrity where it had direct contact with the endoderm (see Townes and Holtfreter, 1955). As a result, most of the post-neurulae disintegrated before developing functional musculature, hearts, or ciliated ectoderm. Thus, these nucleocytoplasmic hybrids, when compared with the reciprocal combination, show a poorer development with opposite abnormalities

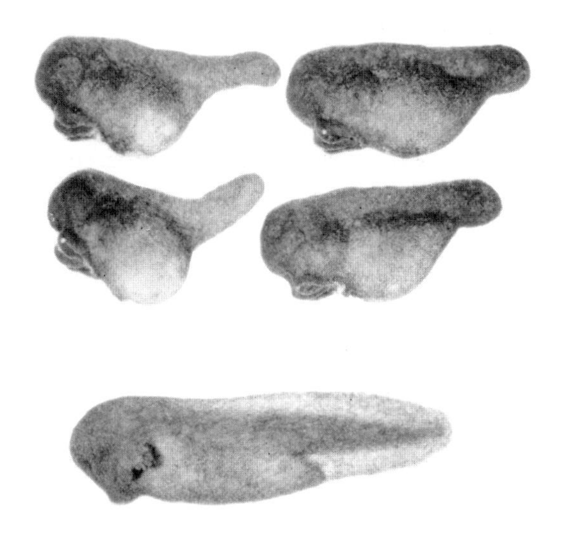

Figure 3. Four nucleocytoplasmic hybrids containing diploid *R. palustris* nuclei in *R. pipiens* cytoplasm. Diploid *R. pipiens* control is at bottom. Magnification is approximately 8 X.

occurring during gastrulation and neurulation.

Back-transfer Embryos

The above evidence shows that nucleocytoplasmic interactions in the two combinations of nucleocytoplasmic hybrids have different consequences for development. It therefore seemed worthwhile to investigate the possibility that, during division in *R. pipiens* cytoplasm, *R. palustris* nuclei might undergo changes affecting their ability to promote normal development in cytoplasm of their own type, even though it had been established that this was not true for the reciprocal combination.

This point was tested in the usual way by transplanting blastula nuclei (containing *R. palustris* chromosomes) from nucleocytoplasmic hybrids, sacrificed for the occasion, into enucleated *R. palustris* eggs. More than 100 such transfers were performed. Seventy percent of the recipients cleaved normally; of these, 78% developed into normal tadpoles. In control transfers of R. palustris balstula nuclei into enucleated R. palustris eggs, 68% of the recipients formed normal blastulae of which 83% developed normally. Analysis of metaphase plates from a random sample of normal

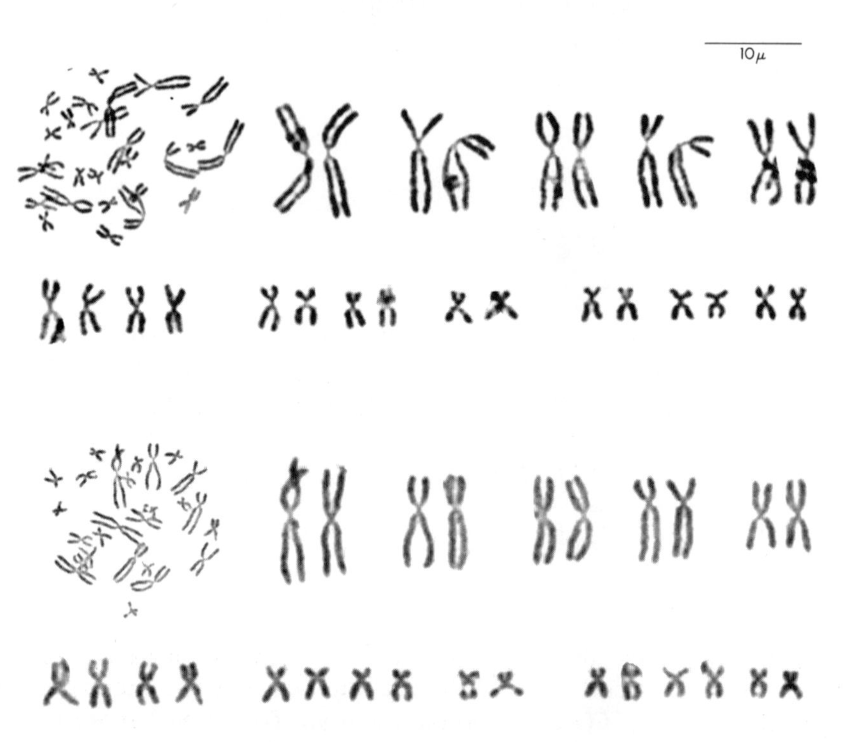

Figure 4. Karyotypes of R. palustris chromosomes from a back-transfer embryo (top) and a diploid R. palustris control (bottom). Chromosomes are tentatively arranged in order of decreasing length. The diploid R. palustris complement contains 26 chromosomes (Parmenter, 1933), of which 5 pairs are conspicuously larger than the other 8. Slight variations between homologues result from differences in condensation. There appear to be no significant differences between the two karyotypes.

back-transfer embryos showed them to contain the normal diploid R. palustris complement of 26 chromosomes (Figure 4). Therefore, no stable changes in the developmental capacity of R. palustris nuclei had occurred after approximately 12 divisions in R. pipiens cytoplasm. Back-transfer of the nuclei from later stages in the development of these nucleocytoplasmic hybrids has not yet been attempted.

Triploid Hybrids

In the experiments described in the preceding para-

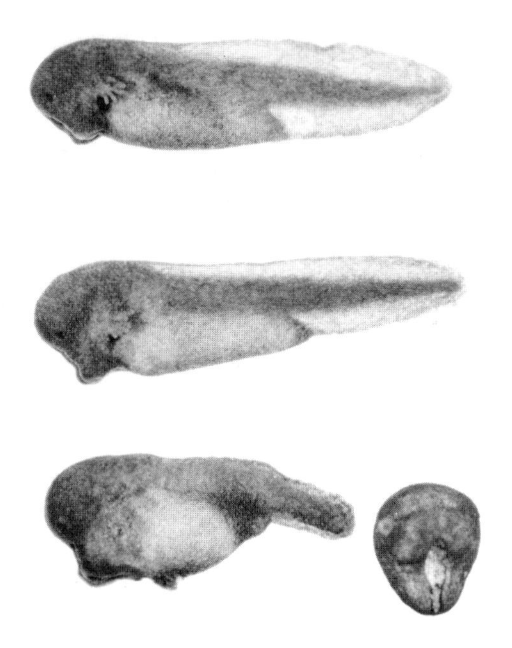

Figure 5. From top to bottom: (a) diploid control, R. pipiens ♀ × R. pipiens ♂; (b) triploid hybrid, R. palustris → R. pipiens; (c) nucleocytoplasmic hybrid, R. palustris → (R. pipiens), bottom left; (d) androgenetic haploid hybrid, (R. pipiens ♀) × R. palustris ♂, bottom right. The parentheses denote removal of female chromosomes; the arrow denotes nuclear transplantation. Magnification is approximately 8 X.

graphs, the same R. palustris donors sacrificed for nuclear transplantation into enucleated R. pipiens eggs also provided nuclei for transfers into nucleated R. pipiens eggs. For the most part, the host and donor nuclei fused to give triploids consisting of one set of R. pipiens chromosomes and two sets of R. palustris chromosomes in R. pipiens egg cytoplasm. The early development of these triploid hybrids was slightly abnormal. Gastrulation was slightly retarded and the anterior portion of the neural plate was abnormally wide. Once the neural folds had fused, it was obvious that the triploid hybrids had unusually large heads and suckers (Figure 5). Macrocephaly and sucker enlargement began to be less obvious after gill circulation was well established. By the time the triploid hybrids had completed embryonic development, they could be distinguished from their triploid R. pipiens controls only by their lighter pigmentation, a characteristic of R. palustris. Several of the triploid hybrids were reared through metamorphosis. Thus,

---

Figure 6. (Opposite page.) (a) Metaphase plate from a nucleocytoplasmic hybrid containing two sets of R. palustris chromosomes in R. pipiens cytoplasm. The normal diploid complement of 26 chromosomes is present. The two chromosomes at the upper left were actually located farther away from the rest of the chromosomes in the metaphase plate. Small black dots are pigment granules. Magnification is approximately 2000 X. (b) Metaphase plate from a triploid hybrid obtained by transplanting a diploid R. palustris nucleus into a nucleated R. pipiens egg. There are 39 chromosomes present, the expected triploid number. Preliminary studies indicate that there are slight differences between the karyotypes of R. pipiens and R. palustris, making it possible to identify, with respect to species, the origin of certain chromosomes. Thus, we have a cytological basis for demonstrating that these hybrids actually contain one set of R. pipiens chromosomes and two sets of R. palustris chromosomes. Magnification is approximately 2000 X.

the addition of a haploid R. palustris chromosome set eventually corrects the nucleocytoplasmic hybrid abnormalities despite slight irregularities present during neurulation.

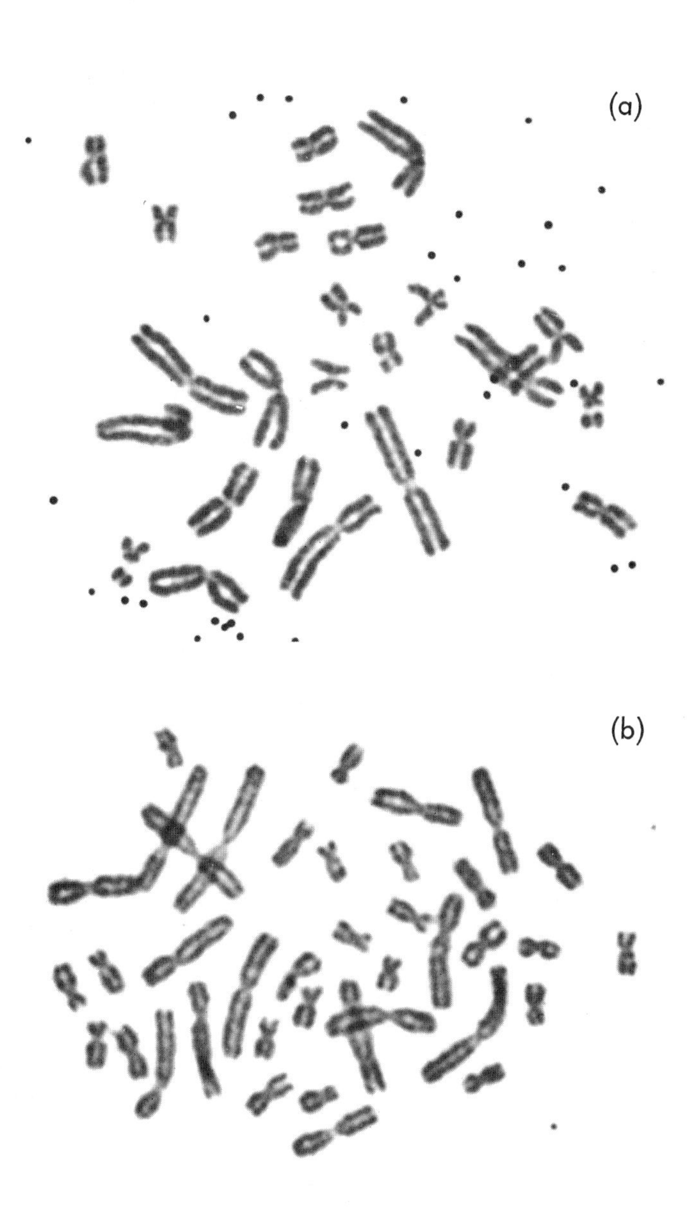

Chromosome Studies

Previous studies with the reciprocal combination indicated that the karyotypes of the nucleocytoplasmic hybrids remained normal throughout development. The same appears to be true for nucleocytoplasmic hybrids containing *R. palustris* chromosomes in *R. pipiens* cytoplasm. As many as 20 analyzable metaphases per embryo have been recorded. So far, counts on over 400 metaphase plates from the nucleocytoplasmic hybrids and their corresponding triploid hybrids show the majority to contain normal chromosome numbers (26 in nucleocytoplasmic hybrids, Figure 6a; 39 in triploid hybrids, Figure 6b). Current studies indicate the karyotypes are normal.

NATURE OF THE NUCLEOCYTOPLASMIC INTERACTIONS

From the results presented in the preceding sections we may conclude that egg cytoplasm contains components which interact with foreign nuclei in specific ways to alter the genetic events required for normal gastrulation and the inductive processes involved in the formation of axial organs. We now turn to a brief consideration of the origin and nature of these cytoplasmic components.

An interesting observation related to the origin of the cytoplasmic materials was reported a few years ago by Huff (1962). He injected *R. pipiens* blastulae with the contents of germinal vesicles from *R. pipiens* oocytes and found that there occurred in the recipients a striking enlargement of the head structures plus defects in the lateral plate mesoderm. This effect was species specific and indicated that the nonchromosomal material contributed to the egg cytoplasm by the germinal vesicle plays an important role in gastrulation and primary induction. Such a role, as suggested by Huff, might be to activate the genes controlling these early events in morphogenesis. If so, abnormally high amounts of germinal vesicle material could cause an abnormally high degree of genetic activity during early development.

The development of *R. pipiens* blastulae injected with *R. pipiens* germinal vesicle material and of *R. pipiens* eggs injected with *R. palustris* nuclei is remarkably similar, if not identical. It is also unusual since abnormal amphibian embryos ordinarily show reductions rather than increases in the size of head structures. This circumstantial evidence strongly suggests that the cytoplasmic components which affect the behavior of the foreign nuclei in the nucleocytoplasmic hybrids are derived from the germinal vesicle. Apparently the amount of this material normally present in *R. pipiens* eggs exceeds the requirement of *R. palustris* nuclei for controlled genetic expression during early morphogenesis.

We know little as yet concerning the nature of the cytoplasmic materials that control the expression of foreign genes; however, some additional indirect evidence suggests that the abnormal development of the nucleocytoplasmic hybrids may be related, in some way, to the number of DNA templates available for transcription just prior to, and during, early morphogenesis. This evidence is from observations of the effect of polyehtylene sulfonate on amphibian development.

Polyethylene sulfonate (PES) is a polyanion of high molecular weight which, when added to isolated calf thymus chromatin, causes a marked increase in RNA synthesis (Frenster, 1965). In this capacity, PES is thought to act as a derepressor of DNA-dependent RNA synthesis. Recently it has been shown that when *R. pipiens* eggs are placed in high concentrations of PES for 4 to 6 hr shortly after fertilization, their subsequent development is characterized by slight enlargement of the anterior axial organs and a decrease in the thickness of the lateral plate mesoderm (Figure 7) (Hennen, 1966). In other words, PES-treated eggs show, although to a lesser degree, some of the same developmental abnormalities found in nucleocytoplasmic hybrids containing *R. palustris* nuclei in *R. pipiens* cytoplasm. If the enlargement of head structures in these nucleocytoplasmic hybrids is related to an abnormally high rate of genetic transcription, it should be

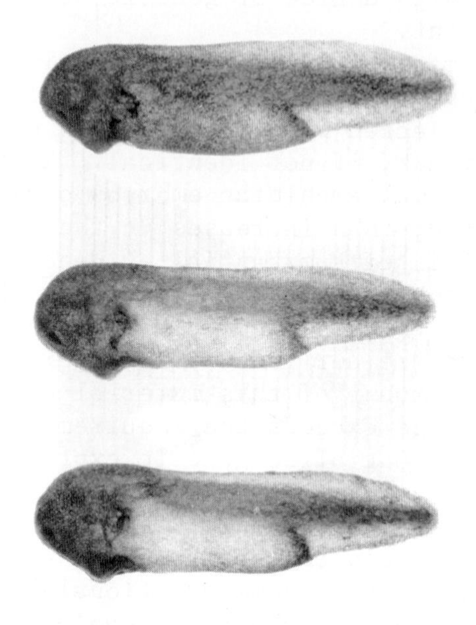

Figure 7. Embryo at the top is a diploid R. pipiens control. The two embryos pictured below the control were placed in polyethylene sulfonate (1 mg/ml) for 6 hr at 19°C shortly after fertilization. See text for description. Magnification is approximately 8 X.

possible to correct, at least partially, the condition of microcephaly in nucleocytoplasmic hybrids of the reciprocal combination by exposing them to PES. Observations of a most preliminary nature indicate that such a partial correction occurs (Figure 8).

While these tentative results support the interpretation that the abnormal development of the nucleocytoplasmic hybrids may result from unbalanced genetic transcription, other mechanisms, perhaps operating at the level of genetic translation, may also be involved.

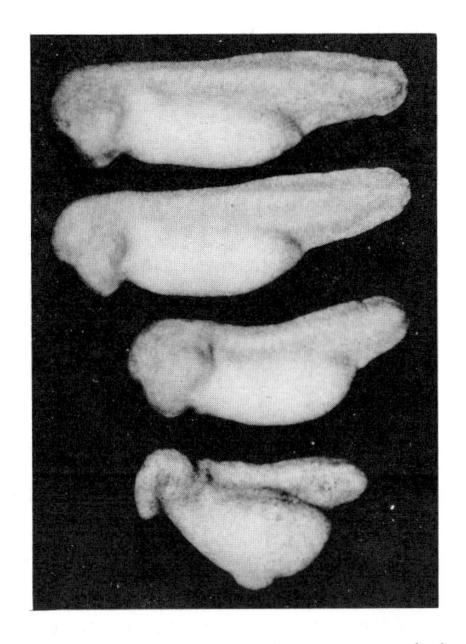

Figure 8. From top to bottom: (a) diploid hybrid, *R. palustris* ♀ × *R. pipiens* ♂; (b) triploid hybrid, *R. pipiens* → *R. palustris*; (c) nucleocytoplasmic hybrid, *R. pipiens* → (*R. palustris*) treated with polyethylene sulfonate (1 mg/ml) for 7 hr after nuclear transplantation; (d) nucleocytoplasmic hybrid not exposed to polyethylene sulfonate shows particularly deficient development, typical in this experiment. The parentheses denote removal of female chromosomes; the arrow denotes nuclear transplantation. Magnification is approximately 8 X.

SUMMARY

Nuclear transplantation studies with the lethal hybrid combination, *Rana pipiens* and *Rana sylvatica*, have shown that during replication in *R. sylvatica* egg cytoplasm, *R. pipiens* nuclei undergo changes affecting their capacity to promote normal development in cytoplasm of their own type (J.A. Moore, 1958, 1960; Hennen, 1963). These cytoplasmically induced nuclear changes are actually extensive and highly variable changes in the number and gross structure of the chromosomes (Hennen, 1963). The significance of these complex karyotypic changes for an understanding of nucleocytoplasmic interactions in early development is uncertain, and, unless a pattern to the chromosomal abnormalities is found, it is doubtful whether this lethal hybrid system can be further exploited for this purpose.

Nuclear transplantation studies which appear to provide more meaningful information concerning the nature of nucleocytoplasmic interactions during development have recently been carried out with more closely related species, *Rana palustris* and *Rana pipiens*. Nucleocytoplasmic hybrids between *R. pipiens* and *R. palustris*, obtained by transplanting blastula nuclei from one species into enucleated eggs of the other, develop in characteristically abnormal ways with the most striking effects occurring in the anterior axial structures. The specific pattern of abnormalities expressed depends on the particular combination of nuclei and cytoplasm involved. Thus, nucleocytoplasmic hybrids containing diploid *R. pipiens* nuclei in *R. palustris* cytoplasm form abnormal post-neurulae with small heads, and rudimentary suckers. Nucleocytoplasmic hybrids of the reciprocal combination develop as abnormal neurulae or early post-neurulae with enormous heads and suckers.

The abnormal development of nucleocytoplasmic hybrids between *R. pipiens* and *R. palustris* is not associated with a change in genetic activity caused by alterations in chromosome number and type because the majority of these embryos have normal chromosome complements throughout development. Nor is it preceded by stable changes in the capacity of the nuclei to promote normal development in egg cytoplasm of their own type after 12 or so divisions in the foreign cytoplasm. It apparently stems from the failure of genetically competent nuclei to provide the orderly set of instructions required for normal morphogenesis when placed in egg cytoplasm the initial components of which are the gene products of another species. This failure occurs only when the nuclei lack a set of chromosomes of the same type as the egg cytoplasm. Addition of such a haploid set of chromosomes to the nucleocytoplasmic hybrids corrects the abnormal development, although the haploid set alone is incapable of promoting normal differentiation.

The occurrence of a predictable set of abnormalities affecting gastrulation and primary induction in embryos whose nuclei contain normal chromosomes and are known, under defined conditions, to be genetically competent, makes this hybrid system especially favorable for studying the genetic and biochemical control of these important phases of early morphogenesis. Of the several possible mechanisms which might account for the abnormalities observed in the nucleocytoplasmic hybrids, a deficiency in the regulation of genetic transcription is consistent with the data so far obtained. Other mechanisms, however, cannot be excluded.

ACKNOWLEDGMENTS

I wish to thank Dr. Robert Briggs for a critical reading of the manuscript and Mrs. Carolyn Huffman for assistance in photographic printing.

REFERENCES

Barth, L.J., and L.G. Barth. 1966. Differentiation and competence of cells from hybrid embryos. Develop. Biol. 13: 95-111.

Boveri, T. 1902. Über mehrpolige Mitosen als Mittel zur Analyse des Zellkerns. Verh. d. phys. med. Ges. Wurzburg N.F. 35: 67-90.

Briggs, R., and T.J. King. 1957. Changes in the nuclei of differentiating endoderm cells as revealed by nuclear transplantation. J. Morphol. 100: 269-312.

Briggs, R., and T.J. King. 1959. Nucleocytoplasmic interactions in eggs and embryos. In "The Cell," J. Brachet and A. Mirsky, eds. Academic Press, N.Y. I: 537-617.

Briggs, R., T.J. King, and M. Di Berardino. 1961. Development of nuclear transplant embryos of known chromosome complement following parabiosis with normal embryos. In "Symposium on the Germ Cells and Earliest Stages of Development," Fondazione A. Baselli, Milano. 441-77.

Conklin, E.B. 1905. Mosaic development in ascidian eggs. J. Exp. Zool. 2: 145-223.

Fankhauser, G. 1934. Cytological studies on egg fragments of the salamander _Triton_. V. Chromosome number and chromosome individuality in the cleavage mitoses of merogonic fragments. J. Exp. Zool. 68: 1-57.

Frenster, J.H. 1965. Nuclear polyanions as de-repressors of synthesis of ribonucleic acid. Nature 206: 680-83.

Gurdon, J.B. 1962. The transplantation of nuclei between two species of _Xenopus_. Develop. Biol. 5: 68-83.

Hennen, A. 1963. Chromosomal and embryological analyses of nuclear changes occurring in embryos derived from transfers of nuclei between _Rana pipiens_ and _Rana sylvatica_. Develop. Biol. 6: 133-183.

Hennen, S. 1964. The transfer of diploid nuclei from _Rana pipiens_ blastulae into non-enucleated eggs of _Rana palustris_. Am. Zoologist 4: 288. (Abstract.)

Hennen, S. 1965. Nucleocytoplasmic hybrids between _Rana pipiens_ and _Rana palustris_. I. Analysis of the developmental properties of the nuclei by means of nuclear transplantation. Develop. Biol. 11: 243-67.

Hennen, S. 1966. Effect of the polyanion, polyethylene sulfonate, on the development of _Rana pipiens_ eggs. Am. Zoologist 6: 355. (Abstract.)

Huff, R.E. 1962. The developmental role of material derived from the nucleus (germinal vesicle) of mature ovarian eggs. Develop. Biol. 4: 398-422.

Moore, A.B.C. 1950. The development of reciprocal androgenetic frog hybrids. Biol. Bull. 99: 88-111.

Moore, J.A. 1941. Developmental rate of hybrid frogs. J. Exp. Zool. 86: 405-22.

Moore, J.A. 1946. Studies in the development of frog hybrids. I. Embryonic development in the cross _Rana pipiens_ ♀ × _Rana sylvatica_ ♂. J. Exp. Zool. 101:

173-220.
Moore, J.A. 1955. Abnormal combinations of nuclear and cytoplasmic systems in frogs and toads. Advan. Genet. 7: 139-82.
Moore, J.A. 1958. Transplantation of nuclei between _Rana pipiens_ and _Rana sylvatica_. Exp. Cell Res. 14. 532-40.
Moore, J.A. 1960. Serial back-transfers of nuclei in experiments involving two species of frogs. Develop. Biol. 2: 535-50.
Moore, J.A., and B.C. Moore. 1953. Studies in the development of frog hybrids. IV. Competence of gastrula ectoderm in androgenetic hybrids. Biol. Bull. 104: 68-74.
Parmenter, C.L. 1933. Haploid, diploid, triploid, and tetraploid chromosome numbers, and their origin in parthenogenetically developed larvae and frogs of _Rana pipiens_ and _R. palustris_. J. Exp. Zool. 66: 409-53.
Porter, K.R. 1939. Androgenetic development of the egg of _Rana pipiens_. Biol. Bull. 77: 233-57.
Spemann, H. 1901. Entwicklungsphysiologische Studien am Tritonei I. Arch. Entwicklungs mech. Organ. 12: 224-264. Cited by H. Spemann, 1938, in "Embryonic Development and Induction." Yale University Press, New Haven Conn., Chap. I.
Townes, P.L., and J. Holtfreter. 1955. Directed movements and selective adhesion of embryonic amphibian cells. J. Exp. Zool. 128: 53-120.
Wilson, E.B. 1904. Experimental studies on germinal localization. I. The germ-regions in the egg of _Dentalium_. J. Exp. Zool. 1: 1-72.

The Control of Antigenic Type in Paramecium[*]

Irving Finger
Biology Department
Haverford College

The evolution, or, more properly, the revolution during the 1950's and 60's in our knowledge of differentiation has let in air, and occasionally light, on a hundred problems. Particularly significant is that we no longer think genes are triggered to act by a positive action; rather we assume a negative, repressive bar to activity must be removed. The normal state of many genes is inertness. Unless repressors are continuously restrained from binding to an operator or a ribosome or from destroying s-RNAs (Stent, 1964), a cistron will behave as though it has lapsed into its natural cryptic condition.

Coincident with the formulation of this model of regulation is the renewed emphasis on two aspects of

*Supported by Grant C-3793 from the National Science Foundation and Grant GM-12017 from the National Institutes of Health.

the control of phenotype expression:

1. the distinction between determination, the choice of the final route taken by a cell, and differentiation, the actual acquisition of the new function;
2. the role played by small molecules in controlling the function and synthesis of macromolecules.

Most evidence adduced in favor of particular explanations and many of the best-known examples describing the sequence of steps between gene and character have been gathered either from bacteria, fungi, and viruses, or from the fruit fly, maize, amphibia, and man. I would like to direct attention to an organism tiny enough to be cultured readily by the barrel, large enough to be handled singly with ease, and possessing the forced versatility of unicellularity and the uniqueness of separate germinal and somatic nuclei. The system studied is not concerned with the formation of an enzyme or of a structure but with the production of a neutral large protein, the apparent function of which is to be a nonenzymic part of the cell surface. The organism is _Paramecium aurelia_ and the system is the ciliary antigenic types or serotypes.

In 1905, Rössle showed that paramecia bear on the cilia an antigen or antigens responsible for cell immobilization by serum prepared against the entire organism. Not all paramecia were affected by the same serum. Resistant paramecia could be used to elicit antibodies against their own ciliary antigen. It was soon shown that strains of paramecium could make at least one dozen immobilization antigens. Intensive study, primarily by Sonneborn and Beale, resulted in the following description of the serotypes (Sonneborn, 1950; Beale, 1954, 1957).

Each genetically homogeneous clone can potentially manufacture many ciliary antigens. A cell can give rise to a clone with the same serotype as its own if the environment is carefully controlled. This serotype can be maintained for many hundreds of generations but it can often be transformed readily to another serotype in one or two generations (or possibly without cell division) by altering the environment. This long-lasting but reversible differentiation was shown by a series of straightforward experiments to be controlled by three factors: environment, cytoplasm, and nucleus. The environment controlled the expression of a particular gene by inducing in the cytoplasm a state that selected which locus would have its information utilized (Sonneborn and LeSuer, 1948). Even though a cell acquired no selective advantage through the possession of a particular antigen, only one antigen was made at one time - except during the actual process of transformation. These two curious and potentially significant aspects of serotype inheritance - mutual exclusion of antigenic types and reversibility of differentiated serotypes - have attracted theorists (Delbrück, 1949; Jacob and Monod, 1961; Nanney, 1963; and Kimball, 1964); these aspects are the major concern of this paper.

CHEMISTRY OF THE ANTIGENS

The number of cistrons specifying the structure of discrete ciliary antigens exceeds 12 and no linkage between cistrons has been discerned among the serotypes examined; nevertheless, the antigens are remarkably similar in their molecular weights and amino acid compositions (Steers, 1963, 1965; Jones, 1965a). The same purification procedure (saline-alcohol extraction followed by acidification and salting-out of the neutralized supernatant) serves for antigens with widely differing serological specificities (Preer, 1959). Only the percentage of ammonium sulfate need be varied to discriminate among the various types.

Three aspects of antigen structure are of particular interest.

1. They are large molecules (ca. 250- to 310,000 in molecular weight) probably composed on nine subunits and evidently arranged in sets of three identical trimers (Steers, 1965). In heterozygotes, hybrid antigens are made. These are molecules in which reassortment of subunits is possible, apparently according to a scheme inter-

mediate between the completely random reassortment in the LDH isozymes and the restricted reassortment in the hemoglobins (Finger and Heller, 1963; Jones, 1965b).

2. On tryptic digestion and fingerprinting, as many as 90 to 100 peptide spots can be developed by ninhydrin (as much as 45% of the antigen remains as undigested core) (Steers, 1962, 1965; Jones, 1965a). Crossreacting antigens have a proportionately larger number of peptides located in the same chromatographic position than do noncrossreacting antigens. Allelic antigens possess patterns with the greatest similarities. Among noncrossreacting antigens, as many as 80 to 90% of the spots distinguish any two antigens, with only about 20 peptides appearing as shared (Figure 1) (Steers, 1962, 1963).

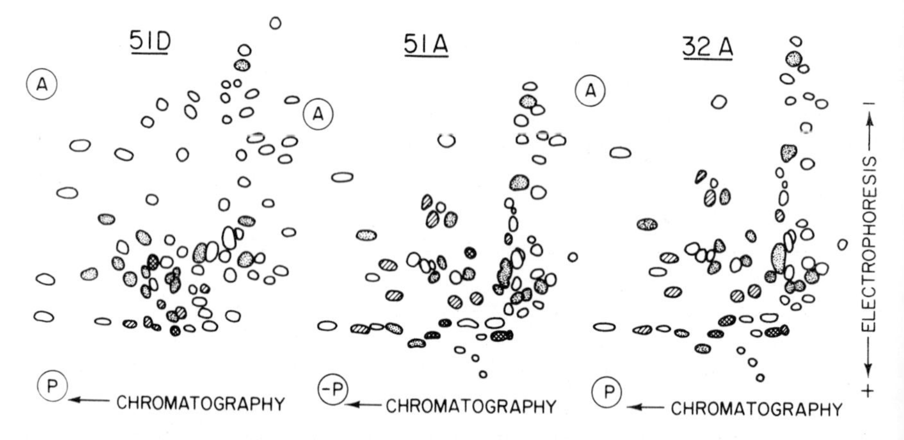

Figure 1. Fingerprints of three purified ciliary antigens: 51A and 32A are specified by A alleles in different stocks; 51D is specified by a different locus (Steers, 1963).

3. Cystine accounts for about 5% of the amino acid content of the antigen, a large proportion compared with most other proteins. The individual subunits of 35,000 molecular weight are held together by the disulfide bonds formed between

cysteine residues (Steers, 1965).

From this brief discussion of antigen structure, we shall simply refer, without further elaboration, to the questions raised by these data.

1. What is the evolutionary significance of multiple loci for the antigens? The presence of so much genetic information is particularly puzzling when we realize that the antigens differ from each other by many peptides, as though there are considerable lengths of regions that can be altered without apparently altering their function. In other words, why so much redundance?
2. What is the physiological role of the antigens? Its importance is indicated both by the phenomenon of mutual exclusion - the fact that a cell cannot exist without some one of the ciliary antigens - and by the redundance.
3. Is the essential portion of the antigen restricted to the sequences represented by the common peptides shared among the antigens determined by different loci as well as among allelic antigens?
4. Can the ciliary antigens serve as a model for antibody biosynthesis? Both are proteins consisting of subunits joined by S-S bridges; both can assume considerable variation in composition; etc. As we shall discuss, some parallels in genetic control also exist.

CYTOPLASMIC STATES AND REGULATION OF GENE EXPRESSION

With the unraveling of the pathway from gene to polypeptide, came the accompanying dogma and discovery of the roles played by assorted RNAs and cytoplasmic organelles in translating nuclear information into amino acid sequence. Most significant was the knowledge that in many cases the transcribed messenger RNA was the only information the cell needed to begin to synthesize a protein. The same biochemical machinery was used repeatedly to make all proteins.

Antedating this era, one viable view of transformation held that the various antigens had identical amino acid sequences, and that conversion of one serotype to another somehow involved reversible changes in configuration. Both dogma as to the role played by different cistrons and the data on the chemical differences among the antigens speaks strongly against this suggestion.

Similarly, the idea first proposed by Delbrück (1949) - i.e., mutual exclusion originates when an enzyme in the pathway leading to one antigen is inhibited by the other antigens - had to be recast in new terms. In general terms this model suggested that once an antigen is made, it tends to perpetuate itself and to perpetuate simultaneously the repression of all the other antigens. From the new knowledge of protein synthesis it seemed unlikely that, within an individual cell, what distinguishes the mechanism of synthesis of one protein from that of another is the kinds of enzymes (such as amino acid activating enzymes, RNA polymerases, etc.) involved in the process from information for amino acid sequence to finished protein.

Although Delbrück's notion in its narrowest interpretation is very probably erroneous, he did make a significant contribution by influencing the direction of thought regarding epigenetic systems (for a detailed critique of Delbrück's hypothesis see Beale, 1954). Within the framework of steady states Delbrück placed maintenance of differences in phenotypes which, though inherited, are reversible, involving changes in differentiation without changes in genetic information.

In the years since Delbrück's work, Jacob and Monod (1961) have proposed numerous models to explain various systems of differentiation, concerning themselves predominantly with regulation of enzyme synthesis. However, the emphasis now generally placed on small molecules acting either as inducers of m-RNA synthesis, inhibitors of transcription or translation, or repressors of enzyme function via allosteric effects, probably does not pertain to the paramecium antigens. The control of the synthesis of a macromolecule with no known enzymatic function by the macromolecule itself therefore presents fascinating new problems in regulation. We shall return to this question of antigen expression regulation shortly. The majority of experiments we shall describe were, in fact, designed to answer many of the questions regarding regulation in paramecium raised by the phenomena of mutual exclusion and the reversibility of antigenic type.

When we examine the genetics of antigenic inheritance, we find that nothing especially unique has been discovered. Genes determine the specificity of the antigens, with one gene specifying one protein (as far as can be detected). Whether a particular antigen can be made by a cell - i.e., the cell's capability - is also controlled by Mendelian genes. That cytoplasmic states control the expression of the antigens, although exciting when first discovered, is no longer a novel phenomenon. Indeed, the data presented by Jacob and Monod show that repression of gene activity in bacteria results from the action of cytoplasmic substances; however, the precise nature of the cytoplasmic state - a definition in molecular terms - has yet to be elucidated.

ALLELE REPRESSION

The perpetuation of cytoplasmic states in vegetatively reproducing cells, elegantly demonstrated by Beale (1952), has now been joined by a related phenomenon. True, the previous cytoplasmic condition of a cell's forebears will determine which locus will be expressed in the cell; but a cell can also inherit information beyond this. In some cases, the instruction is so exact that different alleles at a particular locus can be discriminated (Finger and Heller, 1964).

In the variety we have studied, syngen 2, matings may be made in two ways: either both parents express antigens specified by a single locus, or they express antigens determined by two different loci. The genes exchanged by the partners at conjugation are, of course, identical in both crosses. If we suppose that the two kinds of crosses are carried out and the progeny are reared at a temperature promoting the expression of only one of the loci, surprisingly enough the

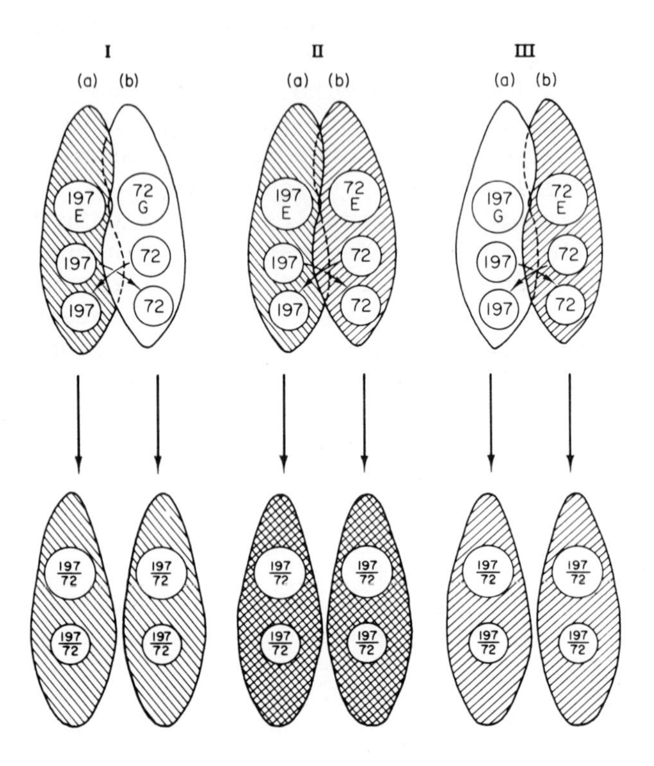

Figure 2. Diagram of the results of crosses between stocks 72 and 197 when both parents are expressing E (II), and when only one parent is expressing E (I and III). For clarity, only one micronucleus is depicted in the F_1 cell. In the conjugants, the two micronuclei shown are haploid gametic nuclei before exchange and fertilization. The serotypes of the parents are indicated by the macronucleus and the hatching. The E serotypes of the F_1 are represented only by the hatching.

matings yield different results (Figure 2, Table 1). When both parents expressed their alleles, so did their progeny (cross II); when only one of the alleles had been expressed prior to mating, it predominated in the heterozygotes (crosses I and III).

TABLE 1

Influence of specific E serotypes of parents on phenotype of F_1 clones*

Crosses	Number of clones of each serotype among progeny		
	72E	Mixed	197E
72E × 197E	92	291	31
72E × 197 non-E	356	33	2
72 non-E × 197E	24	149	70

*Finger and Heller, 1964.

Each of the two micronuclei of P. aurelia is a diploid nucleus prior to meiosis. During fertilization, a cell receives a haploid gamete micronucleus from its mate; the cytoplasms of the two mates are generally kept quite separate. The gene in the gametic nucleus has either been expressed (or, more cautiously stated, has been in a cell expressing its information), or has been inert (originating in a cell with some other locus turned on). If we assume the gene has been expressed, its fate in a recipient expressing another serotype is one of three (in order of decreasing probability).

1. It will continue to be expressed but its allele will not.
2. Both it and its allele will contribute to the formation of a hybrid phenotype.
3. It will not be expressed at all.

Two points are significant: the new macronucleus formed by an exconjugant is at least 100 ploid and is descended from a diploid fertilization nucleus, with half its genes provided by the incoming micronucleus. Although the single newly arrived gene (e^{197} in exconjugant b of cross I, e^{72} in exconjugant a of cross III) is very much a "tiny minority" housed in a cytoplasm originally inhospitable to its serotype, it determines the phenotype of the cell. The cytoplasm, however, may not be a passive participant in the proceeding. Replicate matings yield different proportions of the two parental serotypes and of the hybrid serotype among the offspring (Table 2). Because variation in gene

TABLE 2

Examples of variations in influence of parental serotype on progeny serotype*

Serotypes of conjugants	Number of clones of each serotype among progeny		
	72E	Mixed	197E
Set I crosses			
72E × 197E	4	34	0
72E × 197 non-E	26	4	0
72 non-E × 197E	1	44	2
Set IV crosses			
72E × 197E	0	39	46
72E × 197 non-E	0	15	2
72 non-E × 197E	0	0	21

*Finger and Heller, 1964.

dosage is not involved - only haploid nuclei are exchanged - the cytoplasm of the recipients and/or the donor must differ in their abilities to support the expression of the two alleles.

If we follow this reasoning one step further, we discover that if repressors are invoked, they must be allele specific. We therefore have here an example of an amplified effect of a single gene that, possibly, from the time of its entrance into a cell, determines a cytoplasmic condition which, in turn, differentiates a developing macronucleus.

The same mechanism in a converse situation may operate in the other mate (exconjugant a in cross I, exconjugant b in cross III). Here, the cell expressing the E serotype receives an E "inactive" micronucleus. Descendants of this nucleus continue to be inert, even though there is nowhere about a cytoplasm favorable to the expression of the non-E (e.g., G) serotype it once determined. Instead, it is now in an E-favoring cytoplasm, and it again appears that some cytoplasmic substance can discriminate between alleles.

Other examples are known of the determination of future gene function by its history. One relevant to our study deals with the control of the flagellar antigens of Salmonella. A phenomenon analogous to that of mutual exclusion has been analyzed by Lederberg and Iino (1956). Only two loci (H_1 and H_2) are involved, rather than one dozen, with several alleles at each locus. Both loci are not expressed by a single bacterium. Transduction experiments have demonstrated that the expression of one phase (H_2) appears to be dominant to the other. A cell expressing H_1 that receives an actively expressed H_2 has its H_1 locus turned off. The important difference between this situation and that of the E serotypes in paramecium, of course, is that H_1 and H_2 are not alleles, while e^{72} and e^{197} are.

Probably the best-known example of differential allelic activity is that of the differential functioning of the X-chromosome in the mouse. Lyon (1962), combining evidence from genetics and cytology, has gathered considerable support from cases of humans with various diseases for his hypothesis that in heterozygotes both alleles at a sex-linked locus need not be simultaneously active. In some cells, one X chromosome will be inactivated, and in other cells, its homologue will be inactivated. In mammals, X-chromosome differentiation is determined early in development. Henceforth, all the progeny of such a cell will have the same alleles suppressed.

Current concern focuses on the sequence of events leading to immunoglobulin synthesis. In animals heterozygous for at least one locus determining a particular allotype (an antigenic specificity localized on a small region of one of the polypeptide chains of gamma globulin), only one kind of gamma globulin is made by a cell, although the total serum contains molecules of both specificities (Dray, Young, and Nisonoff, 1963). Hybrid molecules have not been observed but can be readily formed in vitro by reassociation of separated chains. Inside a cell, only one allele is active, and thus a homozygous molecule is made (Pernis, et al., 1965). Different alleles may function in neighboring cells.

Mage and Dray also studying gamma globulins (1965) found that female rabbits of an allotype determined by the b^4 allele at the b locus produce heterozygotes (b^4b^5), after an appropriate mating, which may express predominantly the b^4 allele when the mother is first immunized with b^5 globulins. When the mother is of the b^4b^5genotype and immunized with b^4 globulins, the offspring's b^4 genes are suppressed. Here, then, is an example in a mammal of a gene being influenced in its expression by its past environment - i.e., this inactive state persisted in the daughter genes (within the globulin-producing cell of the heterozygous progeny).

The most extreme example of differential gene expression is that of another protozoan, Tetrahymena. In four systems - serotypes, mating types, phosphatases, and esterases (Nanney, 1963; Allen, 1965) - heterozygotes, after showing that both alleles at a locus are present and functioning, ultimately produce cells that manifest, for an indefinite number of generations, the phenotype characteristic of only one allele. Different progeny clones express, as a consequence of "allelic repression", either one or the other of the two alleles.

Thus there really may be two kinds of regulation at the gene level - one that selects a particular cistron and another (possibly the same) that selects a particular sequence of nucleotides within that cistron. Both kinds of regulation would seem to require a feedback mechanism to ensure continued production of one kind of message after the environment initiates the first messages.

REGULATION BY END-PRODUCT ADDITION

Translation of operationally defined terms such as "cytoplasmic state," "allelic repression," "mutual exclusion," and "repression" into chemical concreteness is the key to progress beyond mere description. Even if this goal is considered one of degree rather than kind, the problems in making the transition are far from trivial. Presumably the first steps are those leading to an in vitro system. Even the most highly refined systems, such as those worked out for DNA and polypeptide syntheses, are feeble imitations of the cell in terms of efficiency. On occasion, even their validity as representatives of in situ cellular systems has been doubted. A major factor in accounting for differences between cellular and test-tube systems, however, is the necessary loss of organization in preparing the latter. Furthermore, in the preparation of the macromolecular components of an in vitro system, it is often difficult to avoid denaturation, contaminants, etc. And, lastly, many of the molecules, such as repressors, supposedly work in such low concentrations that their assay and purification becomes exceptionally forbidding, especially when the specific molecule may be one of a large number of related molecules with differing specificity but similar composition and structure.

Despite these difficulties, we have attempted to define in more precise terms the phenomena already described and to test directly some of the hypotheses. The paramecium system of serotype inheritance, while of immediate complexity, offers certain advantages that bacterial and viral systems and differentiated cells do not. The antigens may be purified by a relatively simple procedure to yield homogeneous preparations of native protein. The antigens retain their serological and physical characteristics under a variety of conditions and can be handled readily at room temperature. Although the paramecium's cytoplasm is bound by a highly structured cortical layer, the usual restriction placed on the organism by a cell membrane is partially sidestepped by its mouth, through which particles and large molecules can enter the cell. (Boundaries of the food vacuoles, however, may still form the counterpart of the cell membrane.) Finally, the possession of a particular serotype offers no selective advantage; therefore, each serotype may be considered a neutral character (although, apparently, a cell deprived of all antigens cannot survive).

Our first experiment was determination whether a modofied version of Delbrück's steady-state scheme might account for mutual exclusion. Rather than search for the effect of a hypothetical enzyme responsible for the synthesis of a particular antigen, we studied the effect of adding the end-product itself, the ciliary antigen. Regardless of the exact way in which the end-product may exert an effect, if it has any influence it should be expected to enhance its own synthesis either directly or by suppression of all other antigens.

Purified C and G antigens, when added separately to cells exclusively of one serotype, generally had little effect. The control set of paramecia grown in culture fluid retained their starting type as did also the treated set of subclones. However, a few recipient clones were affected by the antigen introduced with the anticipated results: animals of the C serotype were unaffected by C antigen, but were induced to transform to G serotype by G antigen. Analogous results were obtained with treated G clones.

Interestingly, clones susceptible to antigen treatment were also slightly unstable in culture fluid alone; therefore, to facilitate our experiments, we exposed clones to puromycin prior to, or coincident with, treatment with antigen. It was thought, through the use of this inhibitor of protein synthesis, that cells would be induced to become unstable. At the same time, any pool of endogenous antigens might somehow be depleted, thereby allowing externally added antigen to act. Antigens administered after puromycin pretreatment and subsequent washing were perceptibly more effective in directing transformation towards the serotype from which the antigen was isolated.

Several other efforts to enhance the antigen influence also yielded consistent results. Cells were exposed to dilute homologous antiserum (known to induce random transformation) and, then treated with puromycin and antigen. In another series of experiments, the antigen was fed in the form of antigen-antibody precipitate in the hope of protecting the antigen from digestion during its journey into the interior proper. In the last experiment, following pretreatment with puromycin, we introduced the antigen-antibody precipitate into the culture fluid.

All of these experiments strongly supported the notion that the antigen influences its own synthesis via some sort of positive feedback (Table 3). It also seemed likely that the antigen does not initiate synthesis but only contributes to determining the path transformation will take once the cell becomes unstable. However, extended experiments with highly unstable clones and clones which, when treatment began, were less than 95% of one serotype established that, in these cases, random and directed synthesis under antigen influence were equally likely to occur.

TABLE 3

Direction of transformation by addition of end-product*

	Puromycin, antigen	Puromycin, serum, antigen	Puromycin, serum-antigen precipitate	Serum-antigen precipitate
Directed	9	8	4	4
No effect	14	3	2	5
Reversal	3	0	0	0
Total	26	11	6	9

*Finger and Onorato, in preparation.

SEROTYPE TRANSFORMATION BY CELL PRODUCTS

No readily testable proposition appeared to explain the discrepancies between the responses of relatively stable and highly unstable clones. Without detailed knowledge of the causes and meaning of instability, we deferred further analysis of end-product control of antigen synthesis. The following experiments resulted from studies of the nature of stability (Finger and Heller, 1965).

Paramecia cultured under conditions of high-population density seemed to be more similar in serotype than a few comparable cells kept in a relatively large volume of culture medium, suggesting that cells may secrete a substance which, in sufficient concentration, might somehow modify other cells. Out first experiments confirmed our suspicions: cells do release substances into their culture fluid. (For the protocol for these experiments, see Figure 3.) Returning this medium (generally exhausted of the bacteria used as food by the paramecia) from which the paramecia had been removed to the tube containing the original paramecia is not the same as replacing this medium with either fresh culture fluid or with another exhausted medium. The changes observed with these substituents for the original medium follow a pattern.

1. Fresh culture fluid either may have a stabilizing influence (i.e., inhibit transformation) or it may stimulate transformation. Which effect it exerts depends on the recipient clones. If these clones tend to lose their original serotype even in their own growth medium, the fresh medium will prevent this spontaneous transformation. On the other hand, clones only moderately unstable, that tend to retain their original serotypes, will generally become more unstable when transferred to fresh culture fluid (Figure 4). Clones which retain 95 to 100% of the same serotype in either fresh culture fluid or their own fluid may be considered very stable. They are

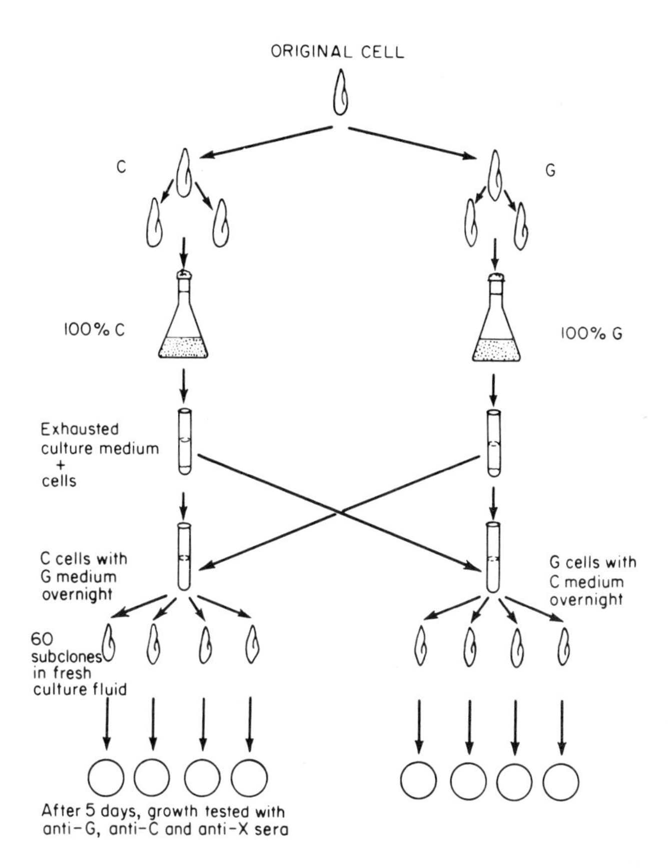

Figure 3. Protocol for experiments on the effect of conditioned medium. After growth into mass cultures (flasks), the medium is separated from the cells by centrifugation, and mixtures of cells and different media are made. The following day, 60 subclones are isolated from each mixture and allowed to grow up in fresh culture fluid. After 5 days, samples are tested with anti-G, anti-C, and anti-X sera.

generally unaffected by the addition of any conditioned medium.

2. Exhausted culture fluid in which other paramecia have been grown also may either inhibit or stimulate transformation. Here, the determining fac-

tor is the donor of the conditioned medium. Does it originate from a clone of the same serotype as the recipient (homologous fluid) or from one of a different serotype (heterologous fluid)? Homologous mixtures tend to stabilize the initial serotype of the recipient; heterologous mixtures encourage transformation (Figure 5, Table 4).

Let us return briefly to the notion that the ciliary antigen stimulates its own continued synthesis. Perhaps the significant substance released into the medium is excess antigen produced by the donor cells, antigen which is ingested in turn by the recipient cells. If so, then at least two expectations should be fulfilled: antigen should be present in reasonable amounts in exhausted culture fluid, and the kind of antigen found should parallel the pattern of transformation. Fluid that induces G transformation should possess G antigen, C-inducing medium, C antigen, etc.

Gel diffusion assay for the anticipated antigens

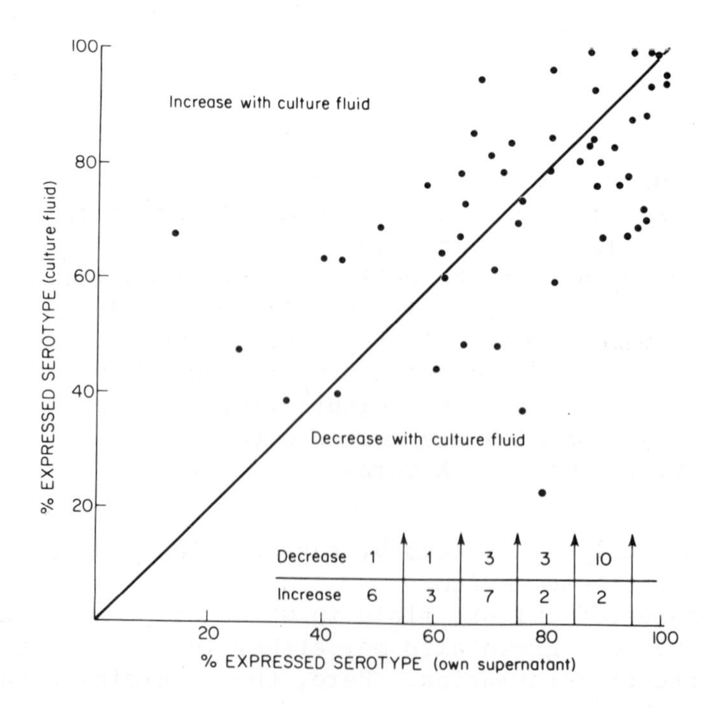

proved negative on both counts. Medium capable of markedly altering the serotypes of recipients was often devoid of detectable antigen, and when antigen could be isolated, the specific type often had little or no relationship to the serotypes assumed by the recipients. Thus, although externally added antigen apparently can affect the synthesis of new antigen, it is not the agent responsible for conditioning the medium.

Is it proper to consider the influence of heterologous medium as a form of induction? In operational terms, we are asking whether a particular conditioned culture fluid will elicit in all recipients the same response. Will transformation, when it occurs, proceed along the same pathway? The answer appears to be yes if we consider only the fluid from stable donors, and no when we include data from experiments with unstable donors (Table 4).

Figure 4. (Opposite page.) Effect of fresh culture fluid on clones of different degrees of stability. Each point represents an individual recipient clone from which 60 subclones had been isolated. On the abscissa is noted the percentage of those subclones tested in which any cells of the original serotype were observed. These tests were made after the cells has been maintained in a culture tube in their own medium for 18 hr prior to isolation of the subclones in depression slides and growth for 5 days in fresh culture fluid. The ordinate represents a similar number of subclones taken from the same initial clone, but with the omission of the 18 hr exposure to the clone's own medium. If treatment with this medium has no effect, all the points fall on a line passing through the origin. The box in the lower part of the figure summarizes the results with those 38 clones in which the two conditions yielded different results. The more stable a clone - i.e., the more subclones that have retained the original serotype - the greater the tendency for growth in fresh culture fluid alone to induce transformation to a new serotype (Finger, Heller, and Larkin, in preparation).

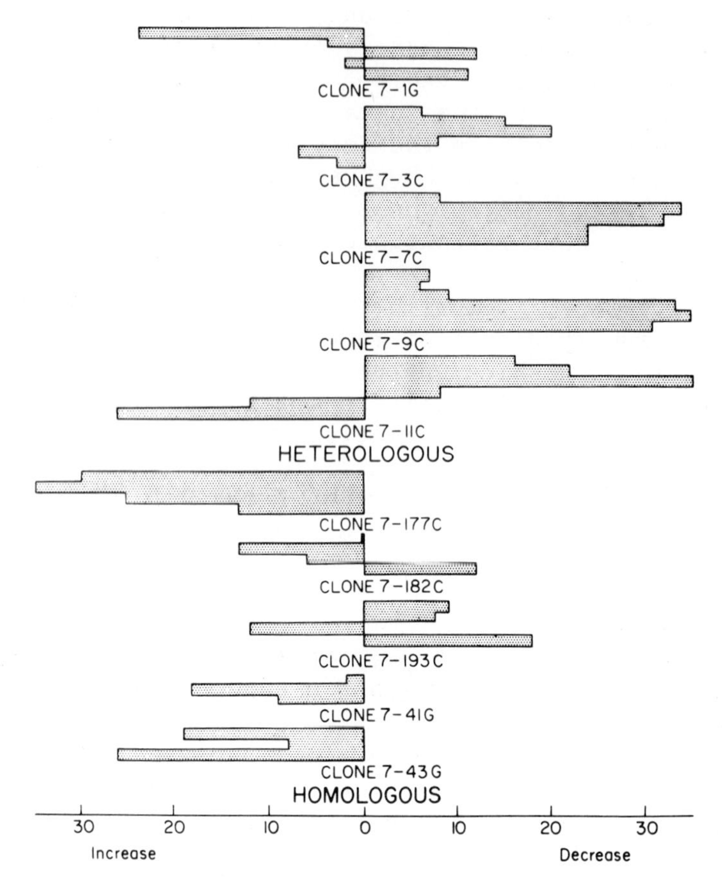

Figure 5. Comparison of homologous and heterologous culture fluid effects (Finger, Heller, and Larkin, in preparation). Each horizontal bar represents an individual mixture of a supernatant with the recipient clone listed below. The length of a bar equals the percentage of increase or decrease in expressed serotype (the original serotype) compared with the same cells mixed with their own medium, represented as 0.

TABLE 4

Directed transformation by conditioned medium from stable and unstable heterologous donors*

Effect of added medium	Stable clones	Unstable clones
Decrease in expressed serotype	12	13
Increase in expressed serotype	2	4
No change	3	14
$\chi^2 = 9.76$, $0.01 > P > 0.001$		
"Directed" transformation	14	7
Random transformation	2	8
No change	5	14
$\chi^2 = 9.20$, $0.05 > P > 0.01$		

*A "clone" represents one treatment from which 60 subclones are isolated, of which about 40 are tested (Finger, Heller, and Larkin, in preparation).

A CULTURE MEDIUM AS A COLLECTION OF REPRESSORS

One interpretation of these results, that has at least the virtue of leading to several predictions, follows. Stable cells release into their medium repressors for all serotypes not expressed. Unstable cells liberate also some repressors for the antigenic type currently expressed. From the standpoint of the recipients, stable clones are immune to the action of supernatants because, in addition to being fully repressed for all unexpressed antigens, they are making sufficient amounts of a single antigen (or another product) to inactivate, bind, or destroy any added repressor concerned with the synthesis of this antigen. Unstable recipients, however, are susceptible to almost any repressor because the synthesizing system for no individual antigen is operating at full capacity.

According to this scheme, heterologous media transform recipients by increasing the concentration of repressors directed against the then expressed serotype. What new antigen will be synthesized is not a function exclusively of the donor, but will also be determined by the internal and external environments of the recipient. Stable donors tend to induce transformation toward their own serotype because their media contain a relatively high concentration of all repressors but that specific for the donor's own type.

We can view the homologous culture fluid's predilection to stabilize the recipient's serotype in similar terms. This fluid should contain repressors for only the unexpressed types when the fluid is derived from a stable donor. An unstable donor's medium may increase, decrease, or have the same effect as the recipient's own medium, depending on the comparative degrees of instability of the recipient and donor. We would therefore expect the net result of the experiments with homologous media to yield an excess of stabilized recipients.

The differential effect of fresh culture fluid also becomes understandable. For a rather stable clone, fresh culture fluid acts as though it were diluting the repressors for the unexpressed serotypes, thereby allowing one of these to have an increased probability of coming to expression. In the case of unstable clones, repressors for the serotype manifested may be among those removed by the fresh medium. An increase in cells with the initial serotype would follow.

The idea that conditioned medium consists, in part, of a collection of specific repressors leads to certain predictions and to new kinds of experiments. We would anticipate that each recipient clone would be nearly unique in its pattern of responses to a battery of media from different donors. Just as each heterologous fluid can be described in terms of relative quantities of certain repressors, with certain media rich in G repressors, others in C repressors, etc., so should each recipient be capable of definition in terms of its own unique limited responses. In other words, not only should an individual recipient clone be capable of being transformed, but its future serotype should also be independent of the donor, limited in the possible kinds of serotypes it can assume only by the kinds of repressors present in the added fluid. For example, a particular C recipient clone, when C serotype is repressed by any of several donors, will spontaneously transform to, say, G. A second C recipient clone, exposed to the same group of media, will regularly be converted primarily to X.

Experiments again substantiated our expectations. Table 5 lists the responses of two clones to several

TABLE 5

Transformation of paramecia serotypes by addition of cell-free medium*

Recipient clone no. and serotype	Medium added	Number of subclones tested	Percent of all subclones with cells of serotype		
			C	G	X
2-G	culture fluid	32	6	94	16
	own medium	33	6	70	27
	3-C	74	23	46	14
	4-C	47	0	70	38
	5-Z	48	4	92	17
4-C	culture fluid	20	30	80	15
	own medium	20	55	60	30
	2-G	53	75	28	43
	5-Z	50	66	58	42

*Percentages may total greater than 100 when a subclone is classified under more than one heading - for example, when a subclone consists of more than one serotype. Percentages totaling less than 100 result from the presence of subclones that are neither C, G, nor X. The clone numbers (2, 3, 4, 5) are arbitrary designations. All clones are descendants of a single stock 7 cell. (Finger, Heller, and Larkin, in preparation.)

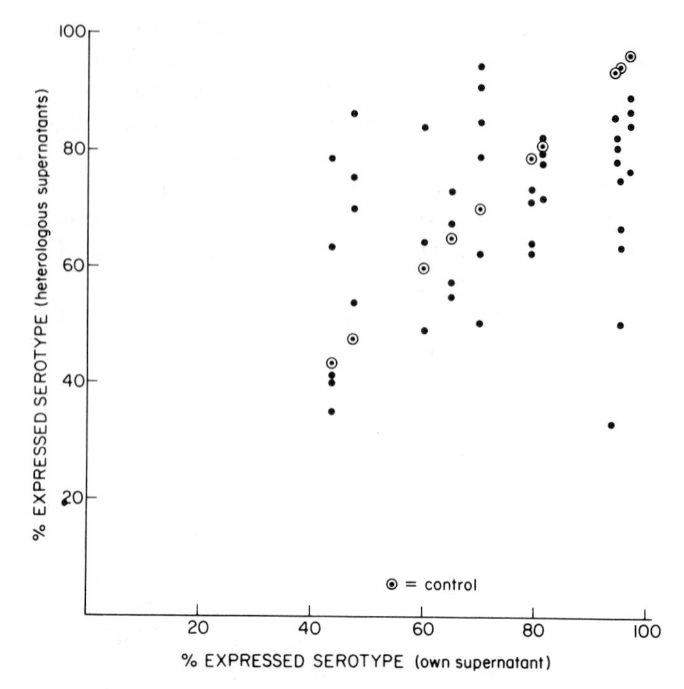

Figure 6. A clone's own medium as limits on the effects of heterologous media. Each vertical column of dots represents the results of a single experiment. The circled dot indicates the percent of subclones that continued to express the serotype initially expressed by the parental clone after these subclones had been removed from their own medium and cultured in fresh culture fluid. The dots below and above a circled dot represent the effect of exposing other samples of the same parental clone to media in which clones of different, heterologous antigenic types had grown. Such media tended to induce transformation (indicated by the points falling below the circled dot) when the initial clone was fairly stable in its own medium. (Finger, Heller, and Larkin, in preparation.)

conditioned media, each with a somewhat different repressor composition. Clone 2 (an unstable G) manifests a proclivity for transforming to X rather than to C (except when 3-C medium - rich in G and X repressors - is added). Clone 4 (an unstable C) tends to stabilize to C when conditioned medium is added, rather than to transform to X or G. Thus, it is the repression that is medium-dependent, not the direction the transformed cells will follow.

We would also predict that the response of a recipient, when resuspended in its own medium, should serve as a limit to what influence a heterologous medium will exert. In the case of a relatively stable recipient, its own fluid should cause it to be more stable than added foreign fluids, which we might expect to possess repressor for the recipient's own serotype. However, should the recipient be an unstable clone, added heterologous fluids might actually tend to prevent spontaneous transformation, because they may contain repressors to the very serotypes toward which an undisturbed recipient might tend. Thus, with unstable clones, the recipient's own fluid may serve as a lower limit for transformability by any medium; the fluid of stable clones, in similar circumstances, would provide an upper limit. Again, as Figure 6 illustrates, experiments have fulfilled our predictions.

ANTIREPRESSORS

Encouraged by these results, we looked for an in vitro assay for the supposed repressors. Because of the difficulties inherent in the strictly in vivo studies - i.e., a very small number of molecules could have a very marked effect (assuming they operate as repressors at the transcription level); several populations of repressors may be present concurrently; using a negative character (decrease in synthesis) imposes limitations - we began to search for specific antirepressors. The immunological approach is most likely to yield such molecules. Antibodies directed against repressors should be able to turn on specific genes (i.e., induce the expression of specific genes) and provide an in vitro assay system.

Rabbits were immunized with ammonium sulfate fractions of conditioned medium free of ciliary antigens. Partially purified gamma globulins from antisera were tested for antirepressors. If several kinds of repressors were present in the immunizing medium, then cells exposed to serum with antibodies against these repressors should be induced to express several serotypes. In other words, two or more antigenic types may appear with increased frequency and others will be suppressed. Superficially, the response to antirepressor is similar to the effects of certain media we have viewed as containing repressors; a serotype is repressed and others appear to take its place. How, then, can the effect of a collection of repressors be distinguished from the effect of antirepressors? In both instances, some serotypes are stimulated and others are inhibited.

First, we can take advantage of sera prepared against immobilization antigen. Such sera would reasonably be expected to have marked repressive activity against their homologous antigen when it is expressed by cells; this is indeed the case. Sera prepared against ciliary antigen have a pronounced and fairly specific effect on the course of transformation. For example, an anti-C serum tends specifically to repress C production, an anti-G serum, G production, etc. Thus, the response of clones to such sera known to behave by inhibiting specific antigen expression can be used to determine whether other sera, without antibodies to immobilization antigen, will specifically and regularly stimulate the expression of a limited number of serotypes.

Table 6 lists the antirepressor titer assigned to five antimedia sera based on the stimulatory effects of these sera on 21 recipient clones. Taken together, half these recipient clones tended spontaneously to transform to X, one-quarter to C, and one-quarter to G. In many instances, a clone would transform to more than one serotype, but the overall distribution was as indicated. Nevertheless, the different antimedium sera induced the same clones to transform in different directions (Table 7). For example, recipient 4, initially of the C serotype, is induced to transform to X

TABLE 6

Antirepressor content of sera from rabbits immunized with conditioned medium

Antimedium serum	Antirepressors		
	G	C	X
1074	+±	±	+±
1075	++±	±	±
1076	±	-	++±
1077	++±	-	±
1080	++	±	++

The number of +'s indicates the relative concentrations of antibodies directed against a particular serotype repressor. +++ indicates the maximum concentration, ++± the next most concentrated, etc.

by four of the sera and to G by two sera. The two most effective sera differentially stimulated G and X serotype expression: 1076 favored X markedly; 1077 favored G (see recipients 4, 5, and 6 in Table 7). (The reactions of the sera are listed twice: once as if they were repressorlike in their action, and once as if they stimulated - i.e., were antirepressorlike.)

A second criterion for distinguishing antirepressors from the inhibitory action of sera is examination of the spectrum of serotypes formed by individual recipient clones. A particular clone shows basically the same pattern - except in degree - with all repressive (i.e., homologous) immobilization antisera; one type is turned off, and generally only one new type will be induced (Table 8). We cannot predict which serotype will come into expression, but it will be the same one regardless of the immobilization serum applied. In this instance, the preferred new serotype is X. With antirepressors, however, all susceptible recipients will not have the same serotype expressed. The new serotypes are predictable, and the same clone will generally transform to several serotypes, because

TABLE 7

Responses of four recipient clones to antimedium sera*

Recipients	Repressors			Antirepressors		
	G	C	X	G	C	X
Recipient 3 (G)						
1074	-	-	±	-	±	-
1075	-	-	+	++	+	-
1076	+++	-	+	-	-	-
1077	-	-	++	+	-	-
1080	-	-	+	+	-	-
Recipient 4 (C)						
1074	-	+	±	+	-	++
1075	-	+	-	-	-	++
1076	-	++	-	-	-	++
1077	-	++	-	+++	-	+
1080	-	-	-	-	-	-
Recipient 5 (C)						
1074	-	-	-	-	-	-
1075	-	++	-	++	-	-
1076	-	-	-	-	-	-
1077	-	+	-	++	-	-
1080	±	-	-	-	-	±
Recipient 6 (G)						
1074	-	-	+	+	-	-
1075	-	-	-	-	-	-
1076	++	-	-	-	-	+
1077	-	-	++±	++±	-	-
1080	-	-	++	++	-	-

*The effect of each antiserum has been listed twice: once when considered in terms of inhibiting the expression of a particular serotype (the columns under the "Repressors" heading) and again viewed as acting by inactivating repressors of specific serotypes.

TABLE 8

Effects of immobilization and medium antisera on serotype G cells

A. Effect of homologous antisera (Recipient 7-128)

	Percent of subclones with cells of serotype		
	G	C	X
Culture fluid control	64	8	72
23 (anti-G)	24	2	94
24 (anti-G)	23	4	86
25 (anti-G)	41	4	78

B. Effect of conditioned medium antisera (Recipient 7-137)

	Percent of subclones with cells of serotype		
	G	C	X
Culture fluid control	87	17	9
1074	92	27	20
1075	95	24	18
1076	88	4	15
1077	96	5	7
1080	96	30	15

different antimedium sera have different antirepressors (Table 8).

If we mix the two kinds of sera, one with and one without immobilization antibodies, the effects of each should be greatly enhanced. The effect of the immobilization antibodies binding homologous antigen, reinforced by the coincident stimulation of a new serotype by the serum containing antirepressors, should markedly reduce the original expressed serotype. This serum would reduce further the expressed type, as a consequence of the self-adjustment of the antigens, to a nearly constant level. Table 9 shows that this is exactly what occurs. Thus, with the G recipient, the anti-X repressor activity of serum 1074 is enhanced. With a C recipient, the G and X antirepressor activities of 1077 are greatly increased.

TABLE 9

Enhancement of antirepressor effect by mixing with anticiliary antigen serum (repressor)*

Serum	Recipient	Percent of all subclones with cells of serotype		
		G	C	X
None	G	66	3	87
24 (anti-G antigen)	G	40	0	75
1074 (anti-medium)	G	49	6	75
24 mixed with 1074	G	13	4	87
None	C	2	85	24
1071 (anti-C antigen)	C	7	74	28
1077 (anti-medium)	C	13	58	52
1071 mixed with 1077	C	36	2	68

*Percentages may total greater than 100 when a subclone is classified under more than one heading - for example, when a subclone consists of more than one serotype. All four G recipients were taken from the same G culture and all C recipients from the same C culture.

We may summarize by saying the evidence adduced in favor of the view that repressors are released into culture medium is of several kinds.

1. The effects of various media in stimulating antigenic transformation are best explained as a consequence of repression rather than of direct induction. Only within this frame of reference can we infer a reasonably consistent pattern of behavior for each donor's medium.
2. The dependence of the effects of fresh culture fluid and heterologous culture fluid on the stability characteristics of donor and recipient are predicted from this hypothesis.
3. Antiserum prepared against conditioned medium induces the expression of specific genes.

CONCLUSIONS

The potential byproducts of these investigations into the influence of one cell upon another are intriguing. For example, it is possible that the repressors can be isolated and characterized chemically. Also, the increase and wane in concentration of repressors under shifting environments can perhaps be followed. But rather than continue to list the many possibilities inviting conjecture (it can hardly be claimed that we have proven we are dealing with repressors), it may be more profitable to return to our original questions. Our Current answers follow.

There exists a regulatory mechanism in paramecium that assures a minimum level of a certain class of surface proteins. When the synthesis of one of these antigenic proteins is suppressed, other antigens are made to take its place. A cell apparently continues to manufacture a particular antigen because it has already made it. Cells already induced by the environment to cease synthesizing an antigen are especially susceptible to further repression or to direction of new synthesis. Substances can be passed from cell to cell to alter the serotype and set a new inheritance pattern.

The following are among the problems that have resisted study or have yet to be examined:

1. the immediate molecular responses to such diverse environmental stimuli as temperature, serum, proteolytic enzymes, nucleases, and pH - all of which apparently initiate or enhance transformation;
2. the function of the antigens, if any, apart from their presumed role as structural elements proper of the pellicle and cilium;
3. the genetic and functional basis for differences observed between stocks with regard to stability of individual serotypes and exceptions to the rule of mutual exclusion.

These problems have been with us for several decades, but others have arisen recently.

1. Does the control exerted by an antigen over its own synthesis come about by the binding of the repressor governing this synthesis or through the simultaneous shutting off of all other antigens? The latter suggestion accounts for mutual exclusion but raises the new question of how the antigen distinguishes its own effector from the effectors specific for each of the other antigens. On the other hand, if the antigen acts to inactivate its own repressor, then the mechanism of mutual exclusion is divorced from this synthetic feedback mechanism.
2. Are the cytoplasmic states allele-specific in some cases, as the results with unexpressed alleles would suggest? And, if the state is really a collection of repressors, does this imply that repressors can distinguish alleles, a proposition that would differentiate these repressors from those operating at the transcription level in such cases as the bacterial β-galactosidase system.

As is the usual paradoxical measure of true progress, we have raised more questions than we have answered. The questions, however, seem to be moving from the realm of one kind of description, which at one time was mere naming, to a realm approaching mechanism.

REFERENCES

Allen, S.L. 1965. Genetic control of enzymes in _Tetrahymena_. In "Genetic Control of Differentiation." Brookhaven Symp. Biol. 18: 27-54.

Beale, G.H. 1952. Antigenic variation in _Paramecium aurelia_, variety 4. Genetics 37: 62-74.

Beale, G.H. 1954. "The Genetics of _Paramecium aurelia_." Cambridge Univ. Press, Cambridge, England.

Beale, G.H. 1957. The antigen system of _Paramecium aurelia_. Intern. Rev. Cytol. 6: 1-23.

Delbrück, M. 1949. In "Unités Biologiques Douées de Continuité Génétique." Colloq. Intern. Centre Natl. Rech. Sci. Paris 8: 33.

Dray, S., G.O. Young, and A. Nisonoff. 1963. Distribution of allotypic specificities among rabbit γ-globulin molecules genetically defined at two loci. Nature 199: 52-55.

Finger, I., and C. Heller. 1963. Immunogenetic analysis of proteins of _Paramecium_. IV. Evidence for the presence of hybrid antigens in heterozygotes. J. Mol. Biol. 6: 190-202.

Finger, I., and C. Heller. 1964. Cytoplasmic control of gene expression in _Paramecium_. I. Preferential expression of a single allele in heterozygotes. Genetics 49: 485-98.

Finger, I., and C. Heller. 1965. Induction of gene expression in _Paramecium_ by cell-free culture fluid. Am. Zool. 5: 649. (Abstract.)

Jacob, F., and J. Monod. 1961. On the regulation of gene activity. Cold Spring Harbor Symp. Quant. Biol. 26: 193-209.

Jones, I.G. 1965a. Studies on the characterization and structure of the immobilization antigens of _Paramecium aurelia_. Biochem. J. 96: 17-23.

Jones, I.G. 1965b. Immobilization antigen in heterozygous clones of _Paramecium aurelia_. Nature 207: 769.

Kimball, R.F. 1964. Physiological genetics of the ciliates. In "Biochemistry and Physiology of Protozoa," S.H. Hutner, ed. Academic Press, N.Y. III: 243-75.

Lederberg, J., and T. Iino. 1956. Phase variation in

Salmonella. Genetics 41: 743-57.

Lyon, M.F. 1962. Sex chromatin and gene action in the mammalian X-chromosome. Am. J. Human Genet. 14: 135-48.

Mage, R., and S. Dray. 1965. Persistent altered phenotype expression of allelic γG-immunoglobulin allotypes in heterozygous rabbits exposed to isoantibodies in fetal and neofetal life. J. Immunol. 95: 525-35.

Nanney, D.L. 1963. Aspects of mutual exclusion in *Tetrahymena*. In "Biological Organization at Cellular and Supercellular Levels," R.J.C. Harris, ed. Academic Press, N.Y. 91-109.

Nanney, D.L. 1964. Macronuclear differentiation and subnuclear assortment in Ciliates. In "The Role of Chromosomes in Development," 23rd Symp. Soc. Study Develop. Growth, M. Locke, ed. Academic Press, N.Y. 253-73.

Pernis, B., G. Chiappino, A.S. Kelus, and P.G.H. Gell. 1965. Cellular localization of immunoglobulins with different allotypic specificities in rabbit lymphoid tissues. J. Exp. Med. 122: 853-76.

Preer, J.R., Jr. 1959. Studies on the immobilization antigens of *Paramecium*. IV. Properties of the different antigens. Genetics 44: 803-14.

Rössle, R. 1905. Spezifische Sera gegen Infusorien. Arch. Hyg. Berl. 54: 1-31.

Sonneborn, T.M. 1950. Cellular transformations. Harvey Lectures 44: 145-64.

Sonneborn, T.M., and A. LeSuer. 1948. Antigenic characters in *P. aurelia* (variety 4): Determination, inheritance and induced mutations. Am. Naturalist 82: 69-78.

Steers, E., Jr. 1962. A comparison of the tryptic peptides obtained from immobilization antigens of *Paramecium aurelia*. Proc. Natl. Acad. Sci. U.S. 48: 867-74.

Steers, E., Jr. 1963. A biochemical study of immobilization antigens of *Paramecium aurelia*. (Ph.D. Dissertation, Univ. of Pennsylvania.)

Steers, E., Jr. 1965. Amino acid composition and quaternary structure of an immobilization antigen from *Paramecium aurelia*. Biochemistry 4: 1896-1901.

Stent, G.S. 1964. The operon on its third anniversary. Science 144: 816.

Molecular Nature of Hereditary Cytoplasmic Factors Controlling Gene Expression in Mitochondria

J. C. Mounolou, H. Jakob, and P. P. Slonimski

Laboratoire de Génétique Physiologique du C.N.R.S.
Gif-sur-Yvette

Yeast affords a complete system, genetically and physiologically, for the study of the molecular nature and function of mitochondrial hereditary cytoplasmic factors. Indeed, aerobically grown yeast cells contain fully developed and well characterized mitochondria and many of their respiratory enzymes have been carefully studied (1, 2).

Moreover, the existence of stable haploid and diploid phases and the ability to perform tetrad analysis have permitted the identification of many chromosomal genes affecting the mitochondrial system. These genes can be classified into several groups according to the physiological and biochemical characteristics of the phenotype they affect:

1. Genes belonging to the first class and called pl_1, pl_2, ... pl_6, lead to an increased efficacy of the respiratory chain enzymes. Recessive

mutations are known to occur at six unlinked chromosomal loci, and cells bearing one of these mutations more efficiently respire nonfermentable C and energy sources - e.g., lactate or ethanol (3, 4).

2. Another group are genes affecting the synthesis of cytochrome c. Cytochrome c has a low molecular weight and is the easiest protein of the respiratory chain to study chemically. Haploid yeast contains at least two iso-cytochromes c that differ by their amino-acid sequence (5). The cy_1/CY_1 chromosomal locus is the structural locus coding for the iso-1-cytochrome c (5, 6). Several unlinked chromosomal loci are known to control increased production of iso-2-cytochrome c, to influence its amino acid composition, and to exert regulatory action on the synthesis of iso-1-cytochrome c. Therefore, they share both structural and regulatory properties (7, 8). Mutations at other loci appear to decrease to a variable extent the production of both iso-cytochromes c (9).
3. The last class is probably the most heterogenous and was the first one studied. It covers chromosomal mutations that render cells unable to grow on nonfermentable substrates - such as lactate, ethanol or glycerol. Most of the loci known at the present time (abbreviated $p_{number}/\underline{P}$) affect cytochrome oxidase synthesis and often cytochrome b as well. The mutated p alleles lead to the lack of cytochromes a and a_3 and consequently to the absence of respiration. Cells containing only one of those mutated alleles will grow, but the required energy is furnished only by fermentation. The p genes are all chromosomal and segregate in Mendelian fashion during meiosis. They are independent and some of them have been localized on the chromosomes. We now know at least 10 loci for p genes. A mutation in only one of them will lead to the lack of cytochromes a and a_3 and is recessive (10 - 13). Two major questions which are interdependent are raised by the existence of p genes.

By what mechanism does a single mutation in any one of many unlinked genes lead to the deficiency of cytochrome oxidase? By what mechanism does a single mutation lead to a multienzymatic deficiency? These questions certainly reflect the high degree of integration in the formation, structure, and function of the mitochondrion (see discussion in 12).

But the expression of all chromosomal genes depends upon the presence in the cytoplasm of a hereditary determinant which in the wild-type form is called ρ+. This hereditary factor does not segregate in a Mendelian fashion during meiosis (15), is transmitted through the cytoplasm in heterokaryons (16), and is necessary for the synthesis of cytochrome oxidase, cytochromes a, a_3, b, and therefore for respiration (17). A mutation of the ρ+ determinnant is irreversible and can be induced by acriflavine (18). The mutated cell forms mitochondria which are not only functionally deficient (17), but also morphologically aberrant (19).

That cytochrome oxidase formation requires simultaneous presence of the cytoplasmic factor ρ+ and of the wild-type chromosomal genes, permits the construction of various respiratory deficient mutants, called "petites," phenotypically alike and genotypically distinct. The following examples involving three gene loci summarize some of the possible combinations.

$\underline{P}_1$ $\underline{P}_5$ $\underline{P}_7$ ρ+ : "grande," wild type
p_1 $\underline{P}_5$ $\underline{P}_7$ ρ+ : chromosomal "petite", absence of cytochrome oxidase
$\underline{P}_1$ p_5 $\underline{P}_7$ ρ+ : chromosomal "petite", absence of cytochrome oxidase
$\underline{P}_1$ $\underline{P}_5$ $\underline{P}_7$ ρ- : cytoplasmic "petite", absence of cytochrome oxidase
p_1 $\underline{P}_5$ $\underline{P}_7$ ρ- : double "petite", absence of cytochrome oxidase

In the following discussion, all wild-type chromosomal alleles will be universally abbreviated as $\underline{P}$ and only the mutated alleles (p_{number}) will be specifically indicated.

With these various genotypes at hand we can study the effect on mitochondrial function of the normal and mutated cytoplasmic factor in association with various chromosomal genes. These interactions are most easily followed at the level of respiration; the experimental system used is the crossing of two complementing petites (20).

Let us consider a cross between a haploid chromosomal

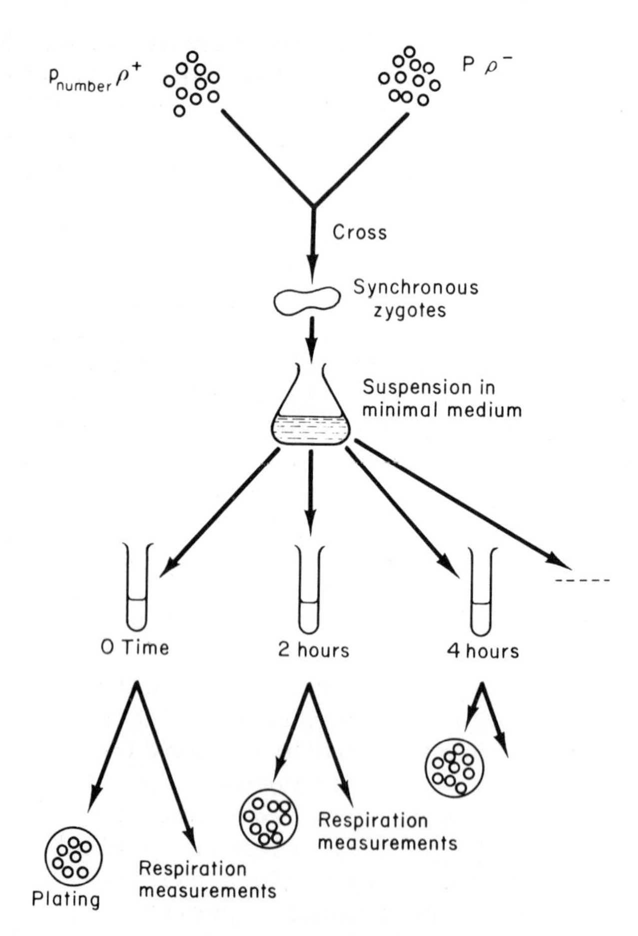

Figure 1. Design of a typical experiment. The cross is made between two petites, haploid, auxotrophic and able to complement. Only prototrophic grande diploid zygotes will grow on minimal medium according to (20), modified.

petite p_5 ρ+, and a haploid cytoplasmic petite, P ρ-. Neither respires, but the zygote and its diploid progeny will develop a functional respiratory system.

Cross:	p_5 ρ+	×	P ρ-
Zygote:	p_5/P		ρ+/ρ-

The design of the experiment appears in Figure 1 and consists mainly in measuring the respiratory capacity at various times after the cross. Synchronous prototrophic zygotes must be obtained or all measurements will be meaningless (20).

Results show that the diploid zygotes formed in the cross do not respire immediately; some time must elapse before a measurable rate of respiration is observed. This lag time is specific for the p_{number} mutation in the cross (Figure 2 and Table 1). We can therefore

TABLE 1

Lag time between zygote formation and the onset of respiration in various combinations of chromosomal genes with hereditary cytoplasmic factors

Cross	Lag time (hr)
$p_5\ \rho^+ \times$ P ρ^-	0.5
$p_7\ \rho^+ \times$ P ρ^-	5
$p_1\ \rho^+ \times$ P ρ^-	10
$p_1\ \rho^- \times$ P ρ^-	∞
$p_5\ \rho^+ \times p_7\ \rho^+$	0.5
$p_5\ \rho^- \times p_7\ \rho^+$	5
$p_5\ \rho^+ \times p_7\ \rho^-$	0.5

classify different genes with respect to the brevity of the lag period between zygote formation and the onset of respiration: $p_5 < p_7 < p_1$. In other words, the expression of active genes can be ordered in time after they enter the permissive cytoplasm.

We should now take up how a zygote formed by a cross between nonallelic complementary chromosomal

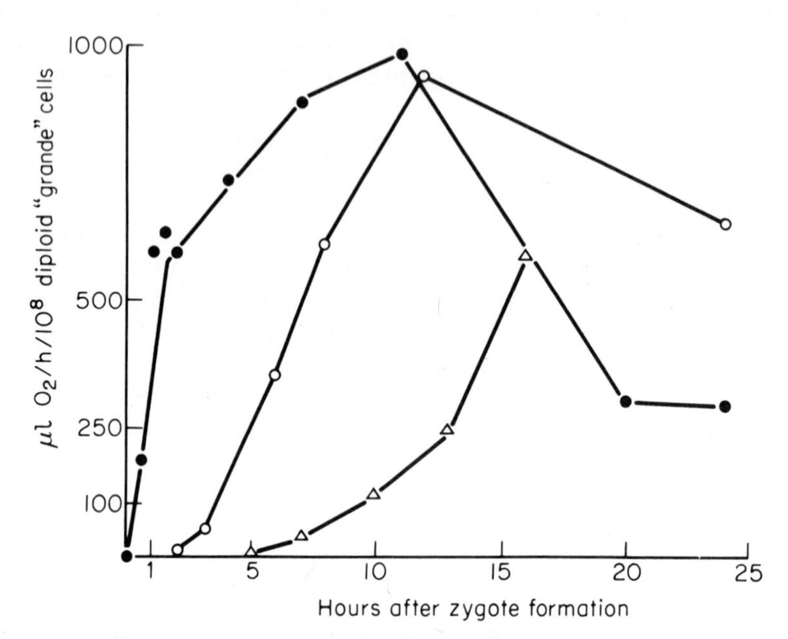

Figure 2. Evolution of respiration in diploid cells issued from crosses between complementing petites. Respiration rates measured on ethanol at various times after zygote formation (20, modified). Crosses:

$p_5\ \rho+ \times \underline{P}\ \rho-$ ●—●
$p_7\ \rho+ \times \underline{P}\ \rho-$ o—o
$p_1\ \rho+ \times \underline{P}\ \rho-$ Δ—Δ

petites will develop a normal respiratory function.

Cross: $p_5\ \rho+ \times p_7\ \rho+$
Zygote: $p_5/\underline{P}\ \ p_7/\underline{P}\ \ \rho+/\rho+$

We could imagine that the lag time observed in the zygote should correspond to the longest one - i.e., 5 hr - found in the preceding cross involving the same chromosomal gene, p_7. Table 1 shows that this is not the case and that the short lag period is epistatic on the long one in all cases studied, with no intermediate time periods.

In this experiment, both p genes were previously

associated with the wild-type ρ+ factor. We can now ask what will happen if one of the p genes is associated with the ρ- mutated factor. Two reciprocal crosses are compared:

Crosses: p_5 ρ+ × p_7 ρ- and p_5 ρ- × p_7 ρ+
Zygotes in both cases: p_5/P p_7/P ρ+/ρ-

If the active ρ+ factor or the inactive ρ- factor does not affect the expression of the p genes, the two crosses should lead to the same result and the lag time should be 0.5 hr, corresponding to that observed when both p genes are associated with the ρ+ determinant. Table 1 shows that the observed lag period is not the same in the two reciprocal crosses, but depends on which mutated chromosomal gene was previously associated with the active cytoplasmic factor.

We can draw two conclusions from these experiments:

1. In a normal ρ+ cytoplasm, we can rank the mutant p genes in a linear order. The earliest one expressed is epistatic, if mutated, on the others.
2. Previous association with the normal ρ+ factor is a fundamental condition for the early expression of any chromosomal gene.

The easiest way to interpret these results is to postulate that events leading to the onset of respiration in a diploid zygote take place in sequence, each particular step requiring a constant period of time, with the first reaction under the control of the hereditary cytoplasmic factor and each gene acting on a product of the preceding one. This interpretation is, of course, methodologically and conceptually analogous to the ordering of biochemical steps in a linear metabolic pathway, as in the classical experiments of Beadle and Tatum. The exact biochemical nature of blocks in mitochondrial development is not known. It could directly concern the biosynthesis of cytochrome oxidase itself or, more probably, the sequential integration of enzymes into morphological structures. In this respect, it is pertinent that precisely these enzymes which are the most strongly bound to mitochondrial membranes are the most easily affected by cytoplasmic and genic mutations. Figure 3 illustrates in

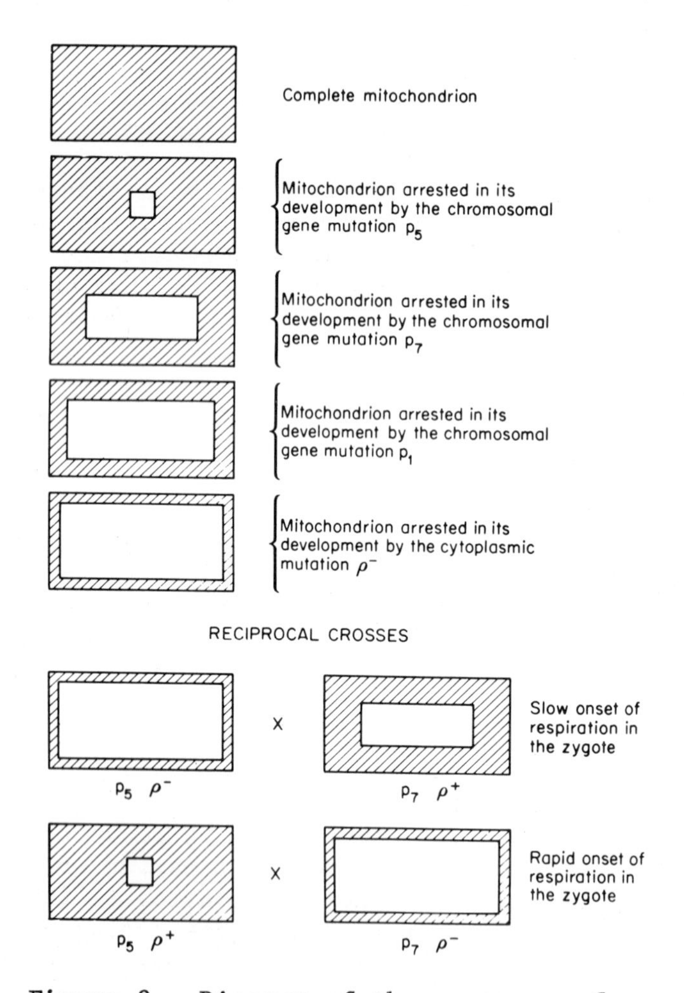

Figure 3. Diagram of the sequence of blocks in the development of mitochondria (according to 20, modified).

a naive way the deduced order of events in the formation of mitochondria and permits a visualization of the experimentally observed difference between two reciprocal crosses. Although the genotypes of both zygotes ($p_5/\underline{P}$ $\underline{P}/p_7$ $\rho+/\rho-$) are identical, the original gaps to be filled to obtain functional mitochondria are not the same.

Let us examine the possible molecular nature of the cytoplasmic hereditary information. It has been shown recently for yeast cells that mitochondria contain DNA associated with their membranes (22 - 29). Thus, we can ask whether this DNA can be the carrier of cytoplasmic information. To answer, we have isolated and studied mitochondrial DNA (24). Aerobically grown cells are suspended in a high osmotic medium (0.44 M sucrose) and ground in a Nossal shaker in the presence of EDTA (30). The intact cells and debris are eliminated by a low-speed centrifugation (1000 g), and a mitochondria-rich fraction is then collected by a high-speed centrifugation (25,000 g). DNA from this fraction, as well as from intact cells, is isolated by lysis in 1% duponol for 4 hr. A sequence of deproteinizations, ribonuclease (pancreatic and T_1) and pronase treatments, is then necessary to eliminate the majority of RNA and proteins. Further purification is obtained by ethanol and isopropanol treatments according to Smith and Halvorson (31). Extraction by the phenol technique (32) is also possible with the same results. DNA is then analyzed by CsCl density gradient centrifugation (33) to determine its buoyant density.

Figure 4 shows the pattern of DNA extracted from whole cells of a grande P ρ+. Three components are present: a major band, 1.701 g/cm^3; a lighter band, 1.687 g/cm^3; and a heavier band, 1.705 g/cm^3. DNA isolated from mitochondria-rich fractions of the same strain shows two peaks, but the quantitatively major one corresponds to the light satellite (1.687 g/cm^3) of whole-cell DNA. This material has a typical absorption spectrum of nucleic acid, and the CsCl bands disappear after deoxyribonuclease treatment; thus we can identify it as mitochondrial DNA.

With this information, we can compare mitochondrial DNA in cells of various genotypes - namely, the chromosomal petites and the cytoplasmic petites. The question whether mitochondrial DNA is present or absent in cytoplasmic ρ- petites is of paramount importance because the features of "mutation" of the ρ factor are very special:

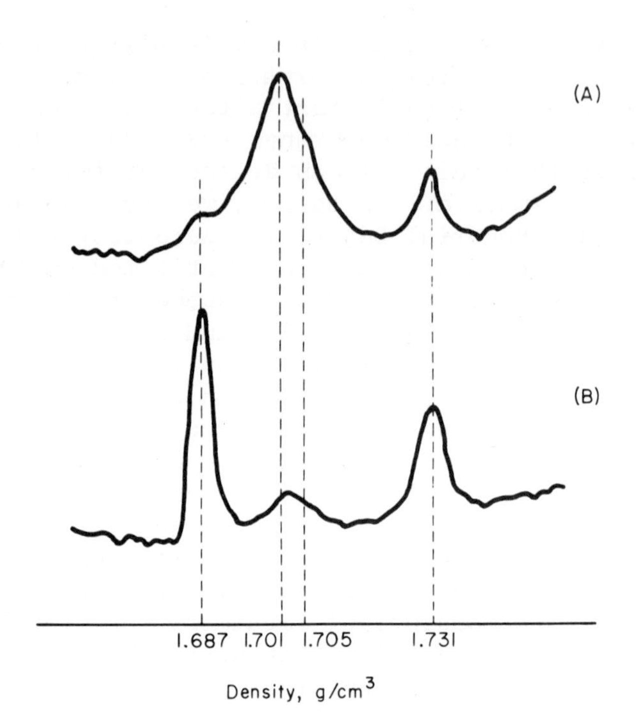

Figure 4. A - Microdensitometer tracing of bulk DNA from P ρ+ cells in CsCl density gradient. B - Microdensitometer tracing of mitochondrial DNA from the same cells. DNA from Micrococcus lysodeikticus (1.731 g/cm^3) is used as density marker in both cases (24).

1. A reversion to the wild type has never been observed in cells carrying the mutated ρ- cytoplasmic determinant, although the ρ+ cells have an enormous selective advantage. The ρ- mutation is therefore irreversible.
2. The rate of spontaneous mutation to ρ- is much higher than that for a normal chromosomal gene. It even is possible to obtain, with acridines (18) and with 5-fluorouracil (40, 41) 100% of petite daughter cells from a culture of wild-type yeast in one generation. This kind of mutation does not affect nuclear genes.

However, before discussing the relation of mitochondrial DNA to cytoplasmic mutation, we have to return to the genetics of ρ- petites. We know of at least two classes of ρ- mutants (34 - 36, 14):

1. In all the experiments described thus far, "neutral" cytoplasmic petites, ρ^-_n, have been used, signifying that in the following cross, all the zygotes and their diploid progeny can synthesize cytochrome a, a_3, and b, do respire, and develop normal mitochondria:

   Cross: $\underline{P}$ ρ^-_n × $\underline{P}$ ρ+
   Zygote: $\underline{P}/\underline{P}$ ρ^-_n/ρ+

   All the diploid cells are grande. By definition, such a cytoplasmic petite is said to be "neutral" (the ρ^-_n factor behaves like a recessive one).
2. However, in some cytoplasmic petites, which we call "suppressive" (^-_s), a high proportion (up to 95%) of the diploid progeny of the zygotes $\underline{P}/\underline{P}$ ρ^-_s/ρ+ lack cytochrome oxidase and is of petite type, although a small proportion (5%) of the zygotes gives rise to grande progeny. By definition, such a cytoplasmic petite is said to be highly suppressive. The property of the ρ^-_s factor is stable and hereditary. In other ρ- mutants, we can find various degrees of suppressiveness - e.g., 50% petite diploid progeny.

We must deal with the problem of the biochemical nature and function of the cytoplasmic factor ρ in terms of all these different situations.

If we face this question in terms of mitochondrial DNA, the necessity for grande-petite comparison is obvious, but that between a P_{number} ρ+ and a P_{number} ρ- is also fundamental inasmuch as they have the same phenotype. Indeed, mitochondrial development is greatly influenced by the respiration and the fermentation of a cell (2, 21, 38, 39) and such conditions could completely modify the amount of mitochondrial DNA and, therefore, the results of the experiment. The amount and the molecular properties of this DNA have to be determined in a set of four cellular genotypes - $\underline{P}$ ρ+, P_{number} ρ+, P_{number} ρ-, and $\underline{P}$ ρ- - which should be as closely identical as possible. We can do so by comparing a P_{number} ρ+ mutant to its back mutant, $\underline{P}$ ρ+, and to cytoplasmic petites derived from them. We can make several predictions based on the results, two of which are especially meaningful:

1. If we find one kind of mitochondrial DNA, let us say A, in the first genotype and different kinds or drastically different amounts, say B, in the other three, it would mean that this difference reflects changes in respiratory metabolism and not in cytoplasmic genome.
2. On the other hand, if we find the same mitochondrial DNA, A, in the first two genotypes, and a different one, B, in the two others, the difference cannot be attributable to changes in respiratory metabolism but rather to changes in cytoplasmic genome. This alternative is summarized in Table 2.

TABLE 2

Genotypes		$\underline{P}$ ρ+	P_{number} ρ+	P_{number} ρ-	$\underline{P}$ ρ-
Respiratory phenotype		(+)	(-)	(-)	(-)
Two predictions for mit. DNA	1	A	B	B	B
	or 2	A	A	B	B

Table 3 provides the answer.

From this information, we can make several points:

1. Both chromosomal and cytoplasmic petites contain mitochondrial DNA in amounts similar to the grande. Cytoplasmic mutation, therefore, does not result from a loss of mitochondrial DNA.
2. Mitochondrial DNA exhibits the same buoyant density in $\underline{P}$ ρ+ and P_{number} ρ+ cells but shows a different density in P_{number} ρ-, whereas bulk DNA has the same density in all cases. These changes are clearly specific to cytoplasmic mu-

TABLE 3

Main features of nuclear and mitochondrial DNAs prepared from chromosomal and cytoplasmic mutants affecting respiratory chain enzymes

Strains*	Nature of genetic determinants		Q_{O_2}	Cytochromes			DNA			No. runs	No. cult.
	Chromo-somal	Cyto-plasmic		$(a + a_3)$	(b)	(c)	Nuclear density	Mitochondrial density	Mitochondrial % total		
Normal grande P $\rho+$	normal	normal	100	+	+	+	1.701 ±0.002	1.687 ±0.002	14	8	3
Chromo-somal petite p_7 $\rho+$	mutated reces-sive gene	normal	0	-	-	+	1.701 ±0.002	1.687 ±0.002	10	8	3
Neutral petite p_7 ρ^-_n	mutated reces-sive gene	mutated "reces-sive"	0	-	-	+	1.701 ±0.002	1.683 ±0.002	14	6	2
Suppres-sive petite p_7 ρ^-_s	mutated reces-sive gene	mutated "domi-nant"	0	-	-	+	1.702 ±0.001	1.695 ±0.001	10	6	3

*All strains are isogenic except for specified differences. Every culture corresponds to an independent chemostat (glucose limited, mean generation time 6 hr, cells harvested after at least 8 divisions (24)).

tations and do not reflect chromosomal mutations or the effect of respiratory metabolism.

3. Moreover, mitochondrial DNA shows remarkable differences according to the cytoplasmic genome: it is lighter than normal in a neutral cytoplasmic petite (1.683 g/cm^3) and heavier in a highly suppressive petite (1.695 g/cm^3).

Is the difference noted between the densities of mitochondrial DNA from a ρ+ grande strain and a neutral cytoplasmic petite $\rho^-_{\underline{n}}$ significant? We tested this by making an artificial mixture of the two DNAs in similar amounts and performing a CsCl centrifugation. Figure 5 shows that this mixture has been resolved into the two different components of the original types.

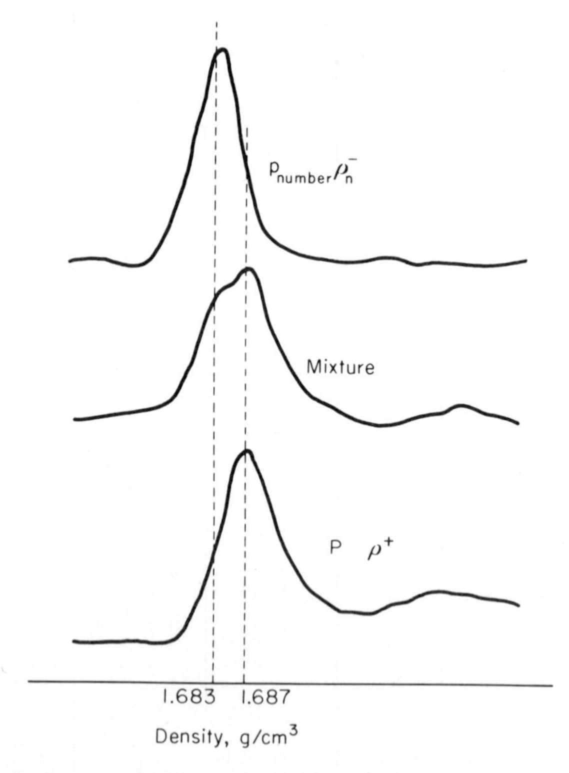

Figure 5. Resolution of mitochondrial DNAs from a petite (p_7 $\rho^-_{\underline{n}}$) and from a grande (P ρ+) by CsCl density gradient (24).

Recently, we have found that the buoyant density of mitochondrial DNA is characteristic (1.687 g/cm^3) of various grandes of different chromosomal genotypes despite variations in the amount of this DNA. We observed the same characteristic constancy of the density of mitochondrial DNA in neutral cytoplasmic petites (1.683 g/cm^3), although its proportion to the total DNA may vary according to the strain.

Therefore, we think that the ρ genetic determinant is identical with mitochondrial DNA. Several fundamental questions arise, however, regarding these hereditary changes in buoyant densities. Such differences can be explained either as a change in the base composition, as a consequence of varying degrees of methylation, or as a result of the presence of an unknown component.

For the first hypothesis, we assume that mitochondrial DNA is a classical, double-stranded DNA with deoxyribose and the four bases A, T, G, and C. The buoyant density in CsCl can be considered to reflect the base composition (37), in which case mitochondrial DNA from a grande or from a chromosomal petite will contain about 23% GC, from a neutral cytoplasmic petite, 21% GC, and from a highly suppressive cytoplasmic petite, 27% GC. Such differences would reflect drastic changes in the sequences of these DNAs and could not result from any conceivable point-mutation mechanism but would fit well the irreversibility of ρ- to ρ+.

The other two hypotheses - namely, methylation and the presence of unknown components - are also conceivable. By unknown components we mean that mutated mitochondrial DNA in ρ- cells could contain high amounts of a different base - e.g., U instead of T - or some sugar moïety absent or different from that present in ρ+ cells. We are now trying to test these possibilities by studying the biochemical properties of mitochondrial DNA by other criteria, such as melting temperature and profile.

In any event, whatever the explanation of the observed differences may be, it is now possible to seek to determine, in terms of mitochondrial DNA, the nature of the interactions between cytoplasmic determinants and nuclear genes. This problem can be dealt with, in part, by hybridization techniques. We can test the extent of homology between nuclear and mitochondrial DNA, as well as the homology between mitochondrial DNA and RNA, to determine whether some RNA is coded specifically by the mitochondrial DNA. At the same time, we may find out more about cytoplasmic information, its autonomy, and its manner of expression.

Lastly, we may speculate about the occurrence of cytoplasmic mutations. The differences in mitochondrial DNA densities may be explained in two ways. We can postulate that ρ+ cells contain a homogenous population of mitochondrial DNA molecules, and, while the ρ+ to ρ- mutation occurs, all the new-formed molecules of mitochondrial DNA change their buoyant density. For example, we can imagine this change as a reflection of a mismatching during replication of mitochondrial DNA in the presence of acriflavine.

The second explanation is that all wild-type cells may contain a population of several types of mitochondrial DNA molecules - those with a density of 1.687 g/cm^3 in great amount and the others maintained in small numbers - in which case cytoplasmic mutation can result from a selection of one type of molecule. In the presence of acridines, the molecule of mitochondrial DNA of density 1.687 g/cm^3 will not be replicated any longer, and a different species of mitochondrial DNA will take over. A study of mitochondrial DNA in diploids resulting from the following cross shows the possibility that such a selection exists.

Cross:	$\underline{P}\ \rho_{\underline{S}}^{-}$	$\underline{P}\ \rho+$
Mit. DNA:	1.695	1.687 g/cm^3
Zygote:	$\underline{P}/\underline{P}$	$\rho_{\underline{S}}^{-}/\rho+$

As we discussed previously, all the zygotes are similar in respect to their hereditary information, but, after many generations, the diploids divide into two classes according to their respiratory phenotype. Most (90%) are petite and the remaining are grande. It was interesting to determine the mitochondrial DNA density for each of these two classes:

1. Petite diploids exhibit a heavy mitochondrial DNA (1.694 g/cm^3) very similar, if not identical, to that of the suppressive petite parent.
2. Grande diploids exhibit a normal mitochondrial DNA (1.686 g/cm^3) similar to that of the wild-type parent.

The occurrence of a selection of molecules is clear in this case, but may not reflect what happens when mutation takes place.

In fact, should molecular selection occur, whether during the induction of cytoplasmic mutation or during the cross with a suppressive cytoplasmic mutant, two mechanisms are possible:

1. Each mitochondrion of a wild-type cell contains a population of different DNA molecules.
2. A wild-type cell contains a population of different mitochondria, each one carrying and replicating one species of DNA. In the first case, the selection could be intramitochondrial, and in the second case, intermitochondrial.

We cannot choose as yet among these hypotheses, but the mitochondrial system enables us to test further the question of the mechanism of cytoplasmic mutation and of interactions between the ρ cytoplasmic determinants and nuclear genes.

REFERENCES

1. Yotsuyanagi, Y. 1962. J. Ultrastruct. Res. 7: 121.
2. Slonimski, P.P. 1956. Proc. Intern. Congr. Biochem. 3rd Brussels 1955, Academic Press, N.Y. 242 p.
3. Galzy, P. 1964. Ann. Inst. Natl. Rech. Agron. 11: 160.
4. Galzy, P. 1962. Compt. Rend. Acad. Sci. Paris 254: 2842.
5. Slonimski, P.P., R. Acher, G. Pere, A. Sels, and M. Somlo. 1963. In "Mécanismes de régulation des activités cellulaires chez les microorganismes," ed. C.N.R.S., Marseille. 435.
6. Sherman, F., J.W. Stewart, E. Margoliash, J. Parker,

and W. Campbell. 1966. Proc. Natl. Acad. Sci. U.S. 55: 1498.
7. Pere, G., L. Clavillier, and P.P. Slonimski. 1965. Ann. Génetique 8: 112.
8. Clavillier, L., G. Pere, P.P. Slonimski, and M. Somlo. 1964. Proc. Intern. Congr. Biochem. 6th N.Y. 1963 IX/S1, 673 p.
9. Sherman, F., H. Taber, and W. Campbell. 1965. J. Mol. Biol. 13: 21.
10. Chen, S.Y., B. Ephrussi, and H. Hottinguer. 1950. Heredity 4: 337.
11. Sherman, F. 1963. Genetics 48: 375.
12. Sherman, F., and P.P. Slonimski. 1964. Biochim. Biophys. Acta 90: 1.
13. Mackler, B., H.C. Douglas, S. Will, D.C. Hawthorne, and M.R. Nahler. 1965. Biochemistry 4: 2016.
14. Sherman, F., and B. Ephrussi. Genetics 47: 695.
15. Ephrussi, B., H. Hottinguer, and J. Tavlitzki. 1949. Ann. Inst. Pasteur 76: 419.
16. Wright, R., and J. Lederberg. 1957. Proc. Natl. Acad. Sci. U.S. 43: 919.
17. Slonimski, P.P., and B. Ephrussi. 1949. Ann. Inst. Pasteur 77: 47.
18. Ephrussi, B., H. Hottinguer, and A.M. Chimenes. 1949. Ann. Inst. Pasteur 76: 351.
19. Yotsuyanagi, Y. 1962. J. Ultrastruct. Res. 7: 141.
20. Jakob, H. 1965. Genetics 52: 75.
21. Ephrussi, B., P.P. Slonimski, Y. Yotsuyanagi, and J. Tavlitzki. 1956. Compt. Rend. Lab. Carlsberg 26: 87.
22. Corneo, G., C. Moore, D.R. Sanadi, L.I. Grossman, and J. Marmur. 1966. Science 151: 187.
23. Guerineau, M., C. Grosse, and C. Paoletti. 1966. Compt. Rend. Acad. Sci. Paris 262: 1901.
24. Mounolou, J.C., M. Jakob, and P.P. Slonimski. 1966. Biochem. Biophys. Res. Commun. 24: 218.
25. Moustacchi, E., and D.H. Williamson. 1966. Biochem. Biophys. Res. Commun. 23: 56.
26. Schatz, G., E. Halsbrunner, and H. Tuppy. 1964. Biochem. Biophys. Res. Commun. 15: 127.
27. Tewari, K., J. Jayaraman, and H. Mahler. 1965. Biochem. Biophys. Res. Commun. 21: 141.
28. Yotsuyanagi, Y. 1966. Compt. Rend. Acad. Sci. Paris

262: 1348.
29. Yotsuyanagi, Y., and C. Guerrier. 1965. Compt. Rend. Acad. Sci. Paris 260: 2344.
30. Mahler, H., B. Mackler, S. Grandchamp, and P.P. Slonimski. 1964. Biochemistry 3: 66.
31. Smith, J.D., and H.O. Halvorson. 1966. Bacteriol. Proc. 34.
32. Marmur, J. 1961. J. Mol. Biol. 3: 208.
33. Meselson, M., F.W. Stahl, and J. Vinograd. 1957. Proc. Natl. Acad. Sci. U.S. 43: 581.
34. Ephrussi, B., H. Hottinguer, and H. Roman. 1955. Proc. Natl. Acad. Sci. U.S. 41: 1065.
35. Ephrussi, B., and S. Grandchamp. 1965. Heredity 20: 1.
36. Ephrussi, B., H. Jakob, and S. Grandchamp. 1966. Genetics 54: 1.
37. Schildkraut, C.L., J. Marmur, and P. Doty. 1962. J. Mol. Biol. 4: 430.
38. Slonimski, P.P. 1958. In "Recent Studies in Yeast." Soc. Chem. London Ind. Monograph 3: 7.
39. Utter, M.F., E.A. Duell, and C. Bernofsky. 1966. In "Aspects of Yeast Metabolism." A.K. Mills, ed. Blackwell Sci. Publ., London.
40. Moustacchi, E., and H. Marcovich. 1963. Compt. Rend. Acad. Sci. Paris 156: 5646.
41. Lacroute, F. 1966. Thèse Fac. Paris.

"Model" Genetic Controls in Bacteria*

John R. Sadler

Department of Biophysics
University of Colorado Medical Center
Denver

What similarities, if any, exist in the regulation of specific enzyme synthesis between bacteria and higher forms is an open question, since the mechanisms of all control systems are obscure at this time. The relevance of bacterial systems to those in higher forms would appear to be mainly in terms of general properties and perhaps in methods of analysis.

At present there is disagreement over very basic questions concerning bacterial systems, such as whether control is negative, positive, or both. There is apparent general agreement on at least two features, namely:

1. Regulation is effected through the action of specific genes distinct from the structural genes controlled;
2. Regulation is effected via the cytoplasmic products of these regulator genes.

*From the Eleanor Roosevelt Institute for Cancer Research and the Florence R. Sabin Research Laboratories of the Department of Biophysics (Contribution No. 284), University of Colorado Medical Center, Denver, Colorado.

The existence of such regulator genes and the proof of their action in the _trans_ as well as _cis_ configuration have been demonstrated in many bacterial systems (e.g., see the review of Jacob and Monod, 1961).

I shall discuss the properties of such regulator genes, particularly that of the _Lac_ operon of _E. coli_, and the results from other systems where they conflict with the _Lac_ system and appear to be well established.

I. POSITIVE VERSUS NEGATIVE CONTROL - THE REPRESSOR HYPOTHESIS

A general feature of most, if not all, well-studied bacterial enzyme systems is the existence of mutants constitutive for the synthesis of the relevant set of enzymes (e.g., Pardee, Jacob and Monod, 1959; Echols et al., 1961; Englesberg et al., 1965). Genetic mapping studies show that in most cases such constitutive mutations are grouped in loci distinct from the structural genes specifying the controlled enzymes themselves. The question immediately arises whether these regulatory loci (as defined by the constitutive mutations) normally produce a repressor, the sole function of which is shutting off structural gene function, or an activator, which in some way is necessary for the synthesis of the relevant enzymes. On these alternative assumptions constitutive mutants would produce no active regulatory product (repressor hypothesis) or a product active irrespective of environmental conditions (activator hypothesis). Hence we should be able to decide the issue by dominance tests with heterogenotes carrying both the constitutive and the wild-type alleles of the regulator locus.

This test was first performed by Pardee, Jacob and Monod (1959) in the _Lac_ system of _E. coli_, utilizing Hfr × F^- crosses to obtain temporary heterogenotes.*

* The _Lac_ operon of _E. coli_ consists of three contiguous structural genes, z, y and a, specifying respectively β-galactosidase, galactoside permease, and thiogalactoside transacetylase. The _Lac_ regulator gene, i, is situated nearest to the z gene.

Their results, as well as those of later workers using permanent heterogenotes, clearly show that repressibility is dominant over constitutivity in the Lac system (Ganesan and Rotman, 1964). Their experiments did create one puzzle which remains today. While the wild-type structural gene for β-galactosidase (z^+) is expressed immediately upon entry into a new cytoplasm, the Lac regulator gene (i^+) is not expressed for nearly 2 hr following injection.

At present the dominance of repressibility over constitutivity is apparently a feature of all well-characterized enzyme systems in bacteria, including several which differ from the Lac system on another crucial point.

This difference arose with the discovery of a second class of mutations in regulator loci, these leading to a loss of, or impairment in, the ability to synthesize the controlled enzymes. Such regulatory alleles exist for the lactose, arabinose, and alkaline phosphatase enzyme systems of *E. coli*. Their dominance relationships with respect to the wild-type and constitutive alleles appear in Table 1.

TABLE 1

System	Dominance relationships*
Lac	$i^s > i^+ > i^-$
Ara	$C^+ > C^c > C^-$
Alk. Phos.	$R_1^+ > R_1^-$, $R_1^+ > R_1C$†

*Derived from data taken from Jacob and Monod, 1961; Willson et al., 1964; Englesberg et al., 1965; Garen and Echols, 1962. The symbols for wild type, the constitutive allele, and the allele leading to the loss of ability to synthesize the enzymes are, respectively: for Lac i^+, i^- and i^s; for Ara C^+, C^c and C^-; and for Alk. Phos. R_1^+, R_1^- and R_1C. These notations are those of the original authors.

†There is no clear dominance relationship between the R_1^- and R_1C alleles.

Although the properties of the i^s mutants are those expected of a repressor altered such that it has lost its affinity for the appropriate small molecule inducer, the other negative regulator alleles C^- and R_1C cannot easily be fitted into a repressor scheme. They are much more easily reconciled with the idea that the regulator gene makes something necessary for enzyme synthesis. These results, though clear and uncontradictory on the simplest assumption of the presence or absence of a gene product, are not necessarily so when we consider that the regulator gene product is probably an oligomeric protein (see below), and when we contemplate the variety of hybrid products which could result from intragenic complementation.

A second and more crucial test is the deletion of the regulator gene in question. The repressor hypothesis predicts the constitutive phenotype will result, while the activator models predict a total loss of enzyme synthesis. Both outcomes are, in fact, observed, the former in the *Lac* system and the latter in the *Ara* system (Jacob, Ullman, and Monod, 1964; Englesberg et al., 1965). At this time the *Ara* results must be considered less than conclusive, because only two deletions have thus far been analyzed and the outcomes fall in the general category of negative results.

Thus, all the data from the *Lac* system are consistent with a purely negative control scheme, while those from the *Ara* and *Alk. Phos.* systems seem equally to require a dual activator-repressor explanation. The decision whether such antipodal control systems do exist in the same organism must await more detailed information on the nature of the products of the regulator genes involved.

II. THE REPRESSOR TARGET - THE OPERATOR AND THE O LOCUS

Closely associated with studies and speculation on the nature of the regulator gene product are the studies and speculations concerning its site of action, the operator. It is necessary to distinguish at the outset between the operator, defined as the point in protein synthesis where repression is applied, and the o locus, the genetic segment either identical with, or specifying, the operator.

The *Lac* o locus is defined by the class of constitutive mutations, termed o^c, which has the distinctive property of being *cis* dominant - i.e., only those *Lac* structural genes on the same genetic element as the o^c mutation function constitutively in the presence of a *cis* or *trans* i^+ or i^s gene (Jacob and Monod, 1961; Willson et al., 1964). The o locus, so defined, is contiguous to, but distinct from, the nearest structural gene of the *Lac* operon, the z gene. This assertion that o is distinct from z rests on three lines of evidence.

1. β-galactosidase from the o^c mutants examined thus far appears to be identical by a number of tests to that from wild-type strains (Jacob et al., 1964; Steers et al., 1965).
2. No known point mutations in z lead to the o^c phenotype (Beckwith, 1964).
3. o^c mutations which are deletions extending into or through the i gene synthesize the *Lac* enzymes at the fully induced wild-type level, while similar deletions extending into z by varying distances synthesize the permease and trans-acetylase at reduced rates (Beckwith, 1964; Jacob et al., 1964).

A large part of, if not all, o^c mutations appear to be deletions. This conclusion results in part from mutational studies by Jacob et al. (1964) indicating that agents known to cause deletions, such as X-rays, are fairly efficient in inducing o^c mutations, while agents known to cause point mutations, such as 5-bromo-uracil or 2-amino-purine, appear not to induce any o^c mutations. If true, this finding separates the o locus sharply from all known bacterial structural genes in which point mutations as well as deletions can abolish function.

The other pertinent fact concerning o^c (z^+) mutants is that their fully induced rate of *Lac* enzyme synthesis is always 100% that of the fully induced wild type, although their constitutive rates of synthesis (in the absence of inducer) may vary between 1 and 100% of that fully induced rate (Jacob et al., 1964; Sadler, unpublished experiments). As yet no o^c mutations are known (excluding those known to extend into the z gene) which adversely affect the function of the Lac genes. This observation, considered with the others already discussed, strongly suggests that the function of the operator is purely negative, i.e., it plays no indispensable role in the function of the Lac genes.

There is no good evidence as to whether the operator per se is DNA, RNA, or protein, or which distinguishes between transcriptional and translational control. Many kinetic, physiological, and inhibitor studies have been done in attempts to resolve this question; the results have been generally inconclusive or contradictory. It is now likely they were predestined to be so, because considerable evidence suggests that in bacteria transcription and translation are normally tightly linked. This evidence results in part from the study of extreme polar mutants (Attardi et al., 1963), in part from studies on the in vitro synthesis of RNA (Bremer and Konrad, 1964), and in part from work with ribosome-depleted bacteria (Naono, Rouviere, and Gros, 1966). In sum, these studies suggest that transcription cannot proceed very far, or persist for long, in the absence of translation, or at least in the absence of ribosome attachment and movement along the m-RNA.

Although the identification of the operator apparently must be postponed until more is known about the mechanism of repressor action, a number of kinetic and inhibitor studies do confirm what was already believed on genetic grounds, that control is exerted at or near the initiation point of transcription or translation. Thus, Inamoto, Morikawa, and Sato (1965) have shown that, following derepression of the Try operon by tryptophan removal, the part of the Try operon m-RNA proximal to the o locus appears first, followed over a period of minutes by the distal portions. After reestablishment of repression, inititation of new m-RNA molecules is blocked, but the extension or completion of those already started is not.

The results of L. Leive (personal communication) are interesting. Using E. coli sensitized to actinomycin she has shown for the Lac enzyme β-galactosidase that a short period of induction terminated by inducer removal permits more enzyme synthesis than does an equal period of induction terminated by the addition of actinomycin - i.e., a transcriptional block at any point along the z gene permits less enzyme synthesis than repression.

Both studies would appear to indicate that control is exerted at the point of transcription initiation and that any m-RNA past this point in its life is immune to repression. However, the data are also consistent with the interpretation that repression blocks ribosome attachment to the m-RNA. Consequently, chain elongation is arrested in those m-RNA molecules not already attached to one or several ribosomes, but allowed to finish in those having some ribosomes attached.

III. THE NATURE OF THE REGULATOR GENE PRODUCT

Most of our knowledge concerning the repressor results from the study of the Lac enzyme and λ prophage systems of E. coli. Since the results obtained from the two systems are congruent on most points, I shall discuss only the former in detail, first summarizing my conclusions concerning the repressor and then presenting the supporting evidence.

1. The repressor is, at least in part, a protein.
2. The rate of enzyme synthesis varies inversely with the first power of repressor concentration.
3. The repressor is growth unstable with a mean lifetime of 1/5 to 1/10 generations.
4. Inducers interact with, and cause structural changes in, the repressor.
5. The synthesis of the repressor itself is not induced.

6. The repressor is composed of subunits, which have sites for combination with inducers.

Many observations point obliquely to the protein nature of the *Lac* repressor. Thus, the specificity of induction (Jacob and Monod, 1961; Müller-Hill, Rickenberg, and Wallenfels, 1964), as well as the possible mutational changes in that specificity (Willson et al., 1964) are phenomena normally associated with enzymes. However, the most direct proof that the repressor is a protein comes from studies on the suppression of i^- mutations (Bourgeois, Cohn, and Orgel, 1965; Müller-Hill, 1966). In these studies, suppressor mutations known to act at the level of m-RNA translation were shown to cause the phenotypic reversion of some i^- mutants (Weigert and Garen, 1965). Additional support for the view that the repressor is, at least in part, a protein has been provided by Horiuchi and Inokuchi (1966), who have shown that the formation of the λ prophage repressor is completely blocked by chloramphenicol. These results do not, of course, exclude the possibility that the repressor includes a second moiety such as a nucleic acid.

The remainder of the conclusions are derived mainly from studies utilizing two types of temperature-sensitive i-gene mutants. These have been described in detail elsewhere (Horiuchi and Novick, 1965; Sadler and Novick, 1965), and it is sufficient to note in one mutant type (TL) the *Lac* repressor is itself heat labile, while in the other type (TSS) the synthesis of the repressor but not the repressor itself is temperature (heat) sensitive. A number of observations suggest that the temperature-sensitive element in the TSS mutants is a monomeric subunit of the polymeric repressor. Figure 1 shows the induced and uninduced steady-state rates of β-galactosidase synthesis for these mutants at various growth temperatures.

The relationship between the differential rate of enzyme synthesis (dz/dB) and repressor concentration (R) was obtained through gene-dosage studies. Earlier investigations by Novick, Lennox, and Jacob (1963) on the *Lac* system, as well as by Gallant and Stapleton

(1963) on the alkaline phosphatase system, had left two possibilities:

1. repression is an inverse, first-power relationship, but the repressor is unstable with a mean life of 1/5 to 1/10 generations; or
2. that repressor is stable, and repression varies as a high power (five to ten) of repressor concentration.

The gene-dosage studies were based on the assumption that a relative increase in the number of i genes in a bacterium gives a corresponding increase in the repressor. This assumption is true for the z gene because an F-genote of type $i^+z^+y^+/Fi^+z^+y^+$ gives levels of β-galactosidase about 2.5 times that of the haploid parent upon full induction, the nonintegral ratio being attributable to the replication of the episomal Lac genes before the chromosomal Lac genes (Sadler and Novick, 1965). A similar gene-dosage effect of 2.5 should exist in i^+ and i^{TL} F-homogenotes versus their respective haploid parents, because a separate study (Novick, McCoy and Sadler, 1965) has shown it is unlikely that i-gene function depends upon the level of repressor present, and because it seems improbable that in i^{TL} strains the fraction of repressor thermally inactivated should depend upon the repressor concentration. In i^{TSS} mutants, however, such an assumption cannot be made, for the heat-labile precursor may be a monomer which must be polymerized to a repressor, in which case the level of the repressor could be elevated much more than 2.5 times the haploid level in F-genotes.

To see the effect of a change in repressor concentration, we must make the haploid to F-genote comparisons at low to intermediate rates of enzyme synthesis where, other things being equal, dz/dB is a function uniquely of repressor level. Table 2 gives the expectations of this test. Comparison is made on the alternative assumptions of an inverse first-power relationship (n = 1) or an inverse higher-power relationship. There is a sharp difference in expectations

TABLE 2

Hypothesis	Expected rate of synthesis Haploid	F-genote	Ratio of rates Haploid/F-genote
$\frac{dz}{dB} = \frac{K}{K + R} \sim \frac{K}{R}$	$\frac{K}{R_h}$	$\frac{2.5\ K}{2.5\ R_h}$	1
$\frac{dz}{dB} = \frac{K}{K + R^n} \sim \frac{K}{R^n}$	$\frac{K}{R_h^n}$	$\frac{2.5\ K}{(2.5\ R_h)^n}$	$2.5^{\ n-1}$

dz/dB = rate of enzyme synthesis per cell = specific activity in the steady state
R_h = repressor concentration in the haploid cell
K = constant

Since the fully repressed or basal rate of β-galactosidase synthesis is about 0.1% of the maximal rate in the wild-type, the level of repressor in such cells = 10^3 K units. Hence, the indicated approximation can be made for low rate of synthesis.

between n = 1, where the haploid/F-genote ratio is unity, and n = 5, where this ratio is close to 40.

The test was applied in two ways: in i^{TL} strains using heat as an inducing agent; and in i^+, i^{TL}, and i^{TSS} strains using isopropyl-thiogalactoside (IPTG) as the inducing agent. The latter was performed with nonleaky y^- (permeaseless) derivatives to ensure that the inducer concentration inside the cells was not raised above that in the medium. In the cases of the i^{TL} and i^{TSS} strains, the tests were conducted at low growth temperatures, where little or no thermal induction of these mutants occurs. The results of two of these tests, thermal induction in i^{TL} strains and IPTG induction in $i^+z^+y^-$ strains, are shown in Figures 2 and 3. It is evident from both results that the haploid/F-genote ratio is between unity and 1.5 and that n is therefore less than 2 and almost certainly unity. The IPTG tests on both i^{TL} and i^{TSS} strains at low growth temperatures also gave ratios very close to unity. From similar experiments on the repression of alkaline phosphatase synthesis, Gallant and Spottswood (1965) have also concluded that repression is a first-power function of repressor level.

The first evidence for repressor instability resulted from experiments with i^{TSS} mutants (Novick, Lennox, and Jacob, 1963). Following the arrest of further repressor synthesis by a shift from a low (30°C) to a high (ca. 40°C) growth temperature, the rise in dz/dB was unaccountably rapid, on the assumption that there existed an inverse first-power relationship between dz/dB and the repressor level (Figure 4). The possibility that this rapid disappearance of repressor represents thermal inactivation is discounted by the observation that heating an i^{TSS} mutant for as long as 2 hr at 42°C under conditions where growth is impossible provokes no appreciable derepression upon resumption of growth. A further demonstration that thermolability is inappreciable in TSS mutants appears in Figure 5, which illustrates the results of temperature shifts of a TSS mutant growing glycerol-limited in the chemostat at a number of widely different rates. Were the repressor appreciably thermolabile, derepression would have been relatively much more rapid in the slower-growing culture (generation time of 15 hr) than in the rapidly growing cultures (generation times of 2 or 4 hr); this is clearly not the case. Evidently the degree of derepression effected is related to the amount of growth at the higher temperature.

The finding in the i-gene studies that repression is first power with respect to repressor concentration appears to force the conclusion that the repressor does indeed disappear faster than we can account for by dilution alone. Thus, the repressor appears to be growth unstable.

It can be shown that the instability of the repressor is not simply a consequence of the temperature shift. In TSS mutants, the synthesis of repressor at high growth temperatures can be stabilized by the presence of IPTG, and repressor synthesis can be arrested by inducer removal with no change in temperature. In this type of experiment, the repressor again shows growth instability, although somewhat less than is evident in temperature-shift experiments {Figures 6(a) and 6(b)}.

Growth instability is not a property unique to the TSS mutants, but can be demonstrated with the wild-type repressor as well. In this case, the arrest of repressor synthesis is achieved through the loss of the i gene carried on a temperature-sensitive episome that fails to replicate at high growth temperatures (A. Novick and C. Gross, personal communication).

Significantly, in temperature shifts of TSS mutants growing rapidly (generation times of less than 70 min), the onset of growth instability is delayed about half a generation - i.e., derepression follows the curve expected from dilution alone (n = 1) and then shifts to a more rapid rise (n = 5). It appears possible, therefore, to uncouple growth and repressor instability to a limited extent.

Whatever the mechanism of growth instability of the repressor, the properties of the TSS mutants permit determination of the relative amounts of repressor following various treatments of the bacterial population. Thus, it is possible to ask and answer the important question of whether regulator genes are themselves regulated. In the TSS mutants, we can estimate the relative amount of repressor from the time required to establish any given degree of derepression following a temperature shift-up, assuming only that the time required is determined by the amount of repressor initially present. In this test two parallel cultures of an $i^{TSS}z^{+}y^{-}$ strain were grown for ten generations, one with and one without sufficient IPTG to maximally induce the Lac operon. They were then transferred to fresh medium lacking IPTG and grown further at 41.3°C. If the inducer had caused an increased synthesis of repressor to any significant degree, it would have been reflected by an increase in the time necessary to derepress that culture. The results indicated that there was at most a doubling in the repressor level in the IPTG-treated cultures, in which the rate of β-galactosidase synthesis was about 1000-fold that of the control culture (Novick, McCoy, and Sadler, 1965). The same sort of experiment can be used to demonstrate that the i^s mutations do not lead to increases in the level of Lac repressor (Willson et al., 1964). TSS mutants have been derived both from the wild-type and from i^s mutants, and, as Figure 4 shows, the two have virtually identical derepression curves following a temperature shift. In $i^{s,TSS}$ mutants the repressor is of the i^s type when present.

In the Jacob and Monod model it is proposed that the inducer interacts with the repressor to bring about an allosteric transition thereby removing its inhibitory effect on the operator (Monod, Changeux, and Jacob, 1963). Two different effects of inducer on the termal properties of the repressor in temperature-sensitive i-gene mutants demonstrate that such interactions do occur.

The first effect, seen in TL mutants, is a considerable enhancement of the thermolability of the repressor by IPTG. Figures 7 and 8 give the results of pulse-heating studies on a TL strain, from which it is apparent the IPTG not only enhances the rate of heat denaturation of repressor, but also abolishes the heterogeneity in thermolability described by Horiuchi and Novick (1965).

The second demonstration of the interaction between repressor and inducer is found in experiments with TSS mutants. In unpublished experiments with $i^{s,TSS}$ strains, Novick, Lennox and Jacob had found earlier that high concentrations of inducer actually decreased the rate of β-galactosidase synthesis during growth at intermediate temperatures. This effect results from an increased production of repressor rather than an enhancement of repressor action, because a considerable period is required after the addition or removal of inducer before its effect becomes evident (Figure 9). Since it is very unlikely that the i gene is induced by IPTG, this result is most understandable on the premise that the TSS mutants synthesize a repressor precursor which is heat labile, but which already possesses the site for an inducer and is stabilized by it.

Although it might seem surprising to find this interaction between inducer and a repressor precursor in an $i^{s,TSS}$ mutant, it has been observed that i^s strains do become induced by very high concentrations of inducer (M. Cohn, personal communication). It appears from these observations that the affinity of the i^s repressor for inducers is greatly reduced but not abolished.

We would expect, therefore, to see the IPTG-stabilization effect at much lower IPTG concentrations in TSS mutants derived from the wild-type than in those derived from i^s mutants. That this is so is shown in Figures 10 and 11, from which we can see that the affinity of the i^{TSS} gene product for IPTG is roughly 300 times that of the $i^{s,TSS}$ gene product. This ratio is about the same as that observed in the concentrations of IPTG required for enzyme induction in the two cases, in agreement with the belief that it is the same interaction of inducer and repressor which is involved in both induction and thermal stabilization.

An analogous effect of 2-nitrophenyl-fucoside has been observed by Jayaraman, Müller-Hill, and Rickenberg (1966). This compound, a competitive inhibitor of induction of the Lac operon, was shown to reduce the rate of β-galactosidase synthesis in leaky i^- mutants and o^c mutants, but not in full i^- mutants. The fact that this compound is effective in o^c mutants suggests that its action is that of an allosteric effector, enhancing repressor action rather than its synthesis.

The assumption that the repressor is polymeric rests on three lines of evidence. First, weak complementation is observed between some pairs of i-gene mutations (first reported by Bourgeois, Cohn, and Orgel, 1965). A similar weak complementation exists between TL and TSS alleles (Figure 12).

Second, as Figure 13 illustrates, the extent of induction of cryptic (y^-) strains rises with the square of inducer concentration (Boezi and Cowie, 1961). From the conclusions given here - dz/dB varies as 1/R and induction is equivalent to the (reversible) inactivation of the repressor - it seems that there are at least two inducer sites per repressor molecule.

Third, these interpretations of the structure and mechanism of synthesis of repressor lead to the expectation that modest increases in the precursor level would cause disproportionately large increases in repressor level in TSS strains at those temperatures where the precursor is significantly thermolabile. Thus, if the heat-labile precursor were the monomer of a tetrameric repressor, then a doubling in the rate of monomer synthesis should cause a 16-fold increase in the rate of repressor synthesis. This test was performed by constructing F-homogenotes of the TSS mutants and comparing their rates of β-galactosidase synthesis with those of the parent haploid strains at various growth temperatures. The results from one test are shown in Figure 14. In both cases, the outcome agrees closely with the expectation, the F-homogenotes synthesizing the enzyme at rates only 1/8 (for $i^{s,TSS}$) and 1/17 (for i^{TSS}) those of the respective haploid parents. From Figure 14 we see that under conditions of maximal induction the homogenote has a rate of synthesis 2.0 to 2.5 times that of the haploid, confirming the higher ploidy of the former. At low growth temperatures, the ratio of homogenotes to haploid approaches unity, the expected condition if the monomer is stable at these temperatures. It should be recalled that TSS homogenote and haploid behave like i^{+} strains during induced synthesis at low growth temperatures. That is, the ratio of rates of enzyme synthesis is near one except under conditions of near maximal induction.

Since it is unlikely from this induction test, and on general grounds, that the TSS mutations alter the basic mechanism of repression, the greatly reduced rates of synthesis in TSS homogenotes indicate a disproportionate increase in repressor level (by a factor of 16 to 34 rather than 2.5). As anticipated, we can explain this occurrence by assuming a polymeric repressor; the results are consistent with the hypothesis that the number of subunits is about four.

One of the long-standing puzzles in the study of the repressor is the long period required for its synthesis, both in the Lac (Pardee, Jacob, and Monod, 1959; Horiuchi and Novick, 1965) and λ prophage systems (Green, 1966), when the cell is initially devoid of repressor. Such long delays become understandable when we assume a tetrameric repressor formed from a small cytoplasmic pool of monomer. If the polymerization were the rate-limiting step, we would expect the onset of repression to be relatively more rapid in slower-growing cells, and this is, in fact, what we see. When cultures of an $i^{s,TSS}$ strain growing at 40°C with generation times of 120, 200, and 300 min are shifted to 30°C, the times required for a 10-fold decrease in dz/dB are about 0.5, 0.2, and 0.1 generations, respectively (Novick and Sadler, unpublished experiments).

IV. DISCUSSION

Many points concerning the structure of the Lac repressor appear to have been clarified. In general, these agree with the hypothesis of Monod, Changeux, and Jacob (1963) that the repressor is an allosteric protein. Thus, inducers interact directly with the repressor, apparently in a cooperative fashion, and the repressor undergoes a change in structure as a result. As predicted, it also seems to be composed of subunits, although there is no evidence that the inducer changes the state of polymerization. These studies assume that the rate of enzyme synthesis is determined uniquely by the repressor level, other things being equal. The consistent results obtained in TL mutants, whether the repressor level is varied by temperature or by inducer, support this assumption and its corollary - induction is no more than the reversible inactivation of the repressor.

The results, however, do not clarify the mechanism of the repressor's action, or whether it does, in fact, have any necessary activator function as has been postulated in the Ara system (Englesberg et al., 1965).

Recent work on the λ prophage repressor (Lieb, 1966; Green, 1966) has revealed two classes of temperature-sensitive regulator mutants apparently analogous to those described for the i-gene: one class requires growth at high temperatures for phage induction while the other does not. On the basis of the properties of these mutants, Green has proposed that λ prophage regulator gene product has dual activator and repressor functions. Working with some of the same temperature-sensitive mutants, Naono and Gros (1966) have concluded that no activator function need be postulated to explain the results. No decision is now possible regarding this controversy.

The conclusion that the repressor is growth unstable is unexpected. Similar instabilities have been found for the repression system for alkaline phosphatase (Gallant and Stapleton, 1963) or can be inferred for the λ prophage repressor (Sussman and Jacob, 1962). That repressor disappearance is usually closely coupled to growth argues against its being simply an unstable protein. Several explanations are plausible, among them the idea that the repressor is a nucleoprotein complex, with the instability an attribute of the nucleic-acid moiety. Again, however, this theory is incompatible with growth instability, as opposed to simple instability. Alternatively, it is possible that the disappearance of the repressor is a consequence of the act of repression. For example, if the repressor attached to each nascent _Lac_ m-RNA strand, thus blocking ribosome attachment, etc., the kinetics of derepression would correspond to the depletion of the repressor pool through the synthesis of m-RNA.

Growth instability could also result, if the repressor were unstable with respect to dilution, in depolymerization to monomeric units as dilution proceeded. To account for the fact that TSS mutants cannot be thermally derepressed in the absence of growth, we would also have to assume that the precursor monomer and that formed by repressor depolymerization differ with respect to thermolability.

ACKNOWLEDGMENTS

This investigation was aided by a grant from the United States Public Health Service (5 R01 GM13383-02) and by a United States Public Health Service Development Award (5-K3-GM-28, 123-02).

REFERENCES

Attardi, G., S. Naono, J. Rouviere, F. Jacob and F. Gros. 1963. Cold Spring Harbor Symp. Quant. Biol. 28: 363.

Beckwith, J. 1964. J. Mol. Biol. 8: 427.

Boezi, J.A. and D.B. Cowie. 1961. Biophys. J. 1: 639.

Bourgeois, S., M. Cohen and L.E. Orgel. 1965. J. Mol. Biol. 14: 300.

Bremer, H. and M.W. Konrad. 1964. Proc. Nat. Acad. Sci., U.S. 51: 801.

Echols, H., A. Garen, S. Garen and A. Torriani. 1961. J. Mol. Biol. 3: 425.

Englesberg, E., J. Irr, J. Power and N. Lee. 1965. J. Bacteriol. 90: 946.

Gallant, J. and R. Stapleton. 1963. Proc. Natl. Acad. Sci., U.S. 50: 348.

Gallant, J. and T. Spottswood. 1964. Proc. Nat. Acad. Sci., U.S. 52: 1591.

Ganesan, A.K. and B. Rotman. 1964. J. Mol. Biol. 10: 337.

Garen, A. and H. Echols. 1962. Proc. Nat. Acad. Sci. U.S. 48: 1398.

Green, M. 1966. J. Mol. Biol. 16: 149.

Horiuchi, T. and A. Novick. 1965. Biochim. Biophys. Acta. 108: 687.

Horiuchi, T. and H. Inokuchi. 1966. J. Mol. Biol. 15: 674.

Inamoto, F., N. Morikawa, and K. Sato. 1965. J. Mol. Biol. 13: 169.

Jacob, F. and J. Monod. 1961. J. Mol. Biol. 3: 318.

Jacob, F., A. Ullman, and J. Monod. 1964. C. R. Acad. Sci., Paris, 258: 3125.

Jayaraman, K., B. Müller-Hill, and H.V. Rickenberg. 1966. J. Mol. Biol. 18: 339.

Lieb, M. 1966. J. Mol. Biol. 16: 149.
Monod, J., J.P. Changeux, and F. Jacob. 1963. J. Mol. Biol. 6: 306.
Müller-Hill, B., H.V. Rickenberg, and K. Wallenfels. 1964. J. Mol. Biol. 10: 303.
Müller-Hill, B. 1966. J. Mol. Biol. 15: 374.
Naono, S. and F. Gros. 1966. J. Mol. Biol. Submitted.
Naono, S., J. Rouviere, and F. Gros. 1966. "Symposium on Ribonucleic Acid Structure and Function." Pergamon Press, London. In press.
Novick, A., E. Lennox, and F. Jacob. 1963. Cold Spring Harbor Symp. Quant. Biol. 28: 397.
Novick, A., J. McCoy, and J.R. Sadler. 1965. J. Mol. Biol. 12: 328.
Pardee, A., F. Jacob, and J. Monod. 1959. J. Mol. Biol. 1: 165.
Sadler, J.R., and A. Novick. 1965. J. Mol. Biol. 12: 305.
Steers, Jr., E., G.R. Craven, and C.B. Anfinsen. 1965. Proc. Nat. Acad. Sci. 54: 1174.
Sussman, R., and F. Jacob. 1962. C. R. Acad. Sci., Paris. 254: 1517.
Weigert, M.G., and A. Garen. 1965. J. Mol. Biol. 12: 448.
Willson, C., D. Perrin, M. Cohn, F. Jacob, and J. Monod. 1964. J. Mol. Biol. 8: 582.

Figure 1. Steady-state specific activities of β-galactosidase in strains carrying the i^{TL}(E), $i^{s,TSS}$ (P) and i^{TSS}(N) alleles of the i gene. (From Sadler and Novick, 1965).

The organisms were grown at the specified temperature for at least 10 doublings prior to sampling for assay. In all cases the medium was a minimal salts-glycerol medium supplemented with amino acids or vitamins as required. Each point represents the average of duplicate assays. β-galactosidase activities are given as Δ O.D.420 × 1000/min. Division by the bacterial density, taken as O.D.350 × 1000, gives the specific activity: This scale is convenient, because wild-type strains give fully induced activities near unity.

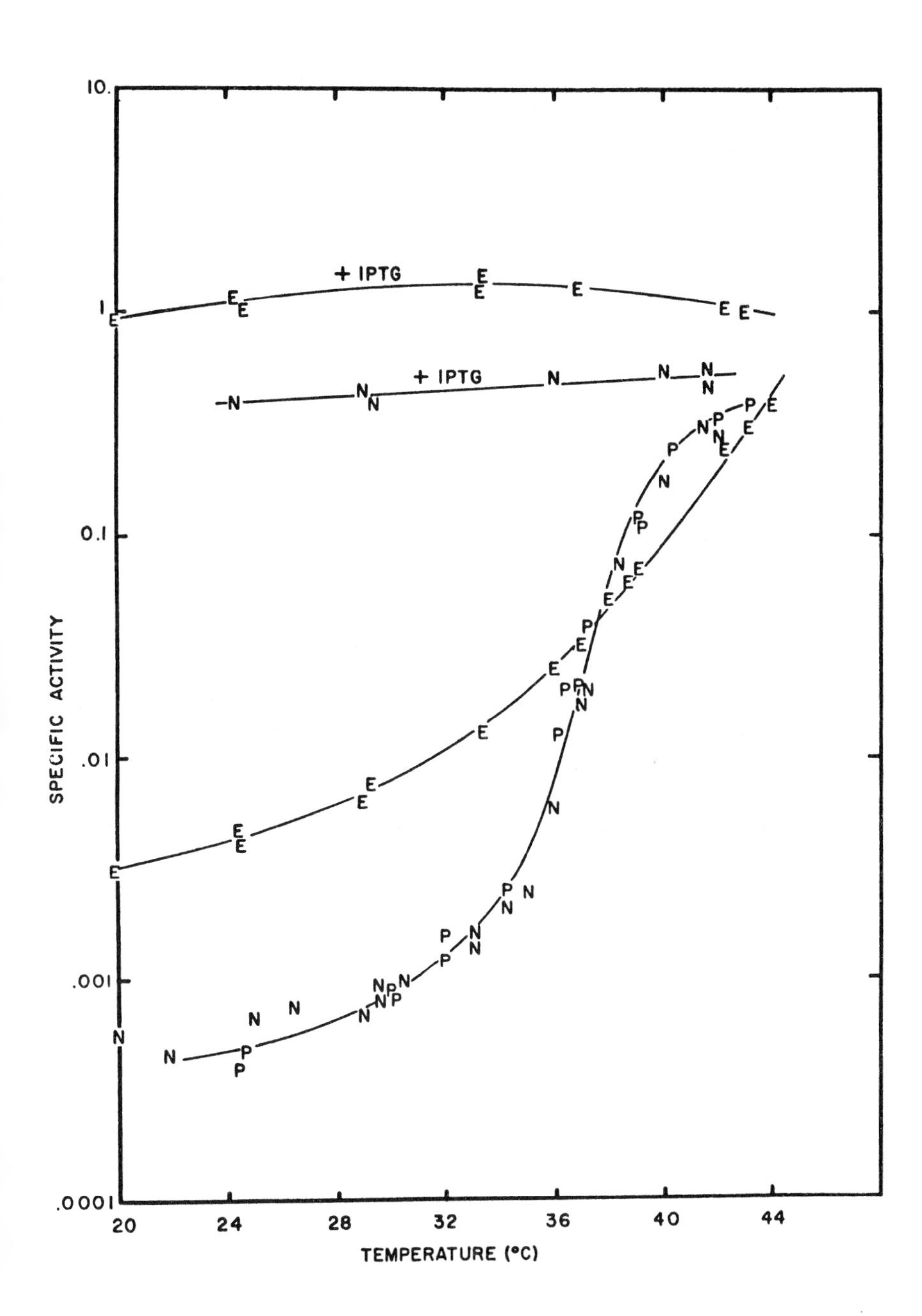
10.
1
0.1
.01
.001
.0001
SPECIFIC ACTIVITY
+ IPTG
+ IPTG
20
24
28
32
36
40
44
TEMPERATURE (°C)

Figure 2. Steady-state specific activities of β-galactosidase in the presence or absence of 10^{-3} M IPTG at various growth temperatures for i^{TL} haploid and F-homogenote strains. (From Sadler and Novick, 1965).

Parallel cultures of the haploid ($i^{TL}z^{+}y^{-}$) and F-homogenote were grown in a minimal salts-glycerol medium for at least 10 doublings prior to sampling for assay. The upper curves were obtained in the presence of 10^{-3} M IPTG. Each point for the haploid (o) and the homogenote (×) is the average of duplicate assays.

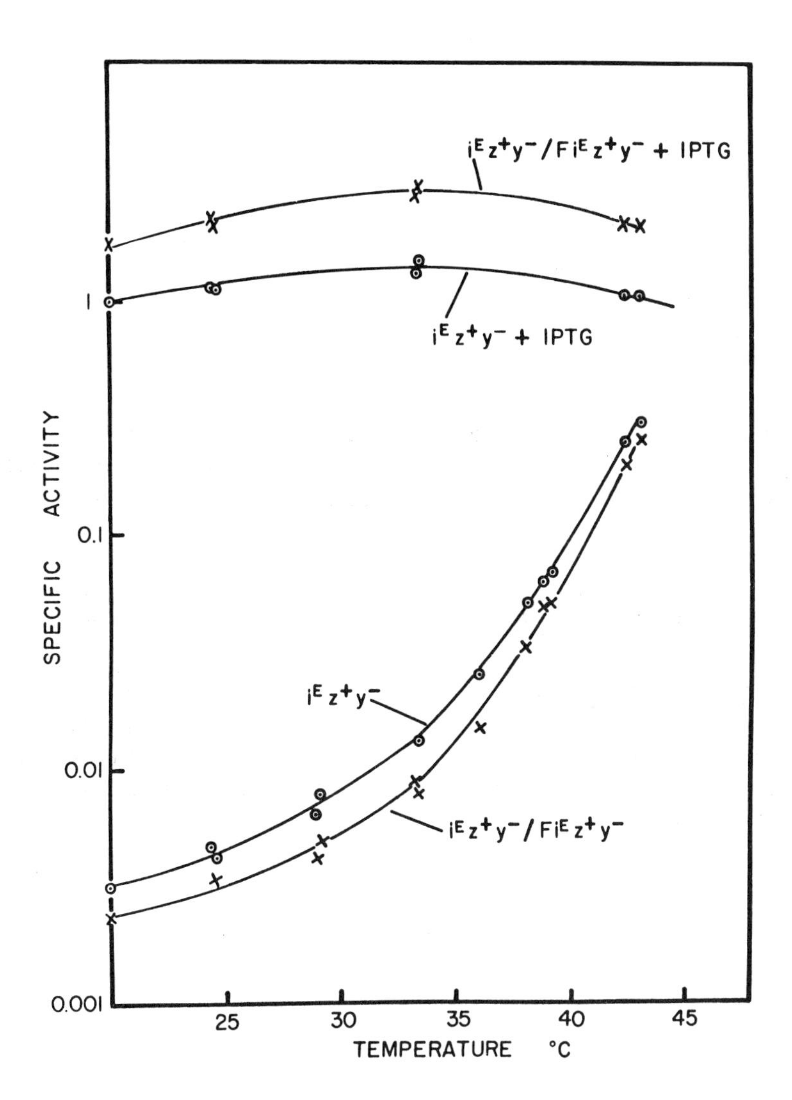
iEz+y−/FiEz+y− + IPTG
iEz+y− + IPTG
iEz+y−
iEz+y−/FiEz+y−
SPECIFIC ACTIVITY
1
0.1
0.01
0.001
25
30
35
40
45
TEMPERATURE °C

Figure 3. Steady-state specific activities of β-galactosidase for i^+ haploid and F-homogenote strains growing in the presence of various concentrations of IPTG.

Parallel cultures of the haploid ($i^+z^+y^-$) and F-homogenote ($i^+z^+y^-/Fi^+z^+y^-$) were grown in the specified concentration of IPTG for at least 10 doublings at 37°C prior to sampling for assay. The medium was a glycerol-salts medium. Each point for the haploid (o) and F-homogenote (×) is the average of duplicate assays on each of three independent cultures. (From Sadler and Novick, 1965).

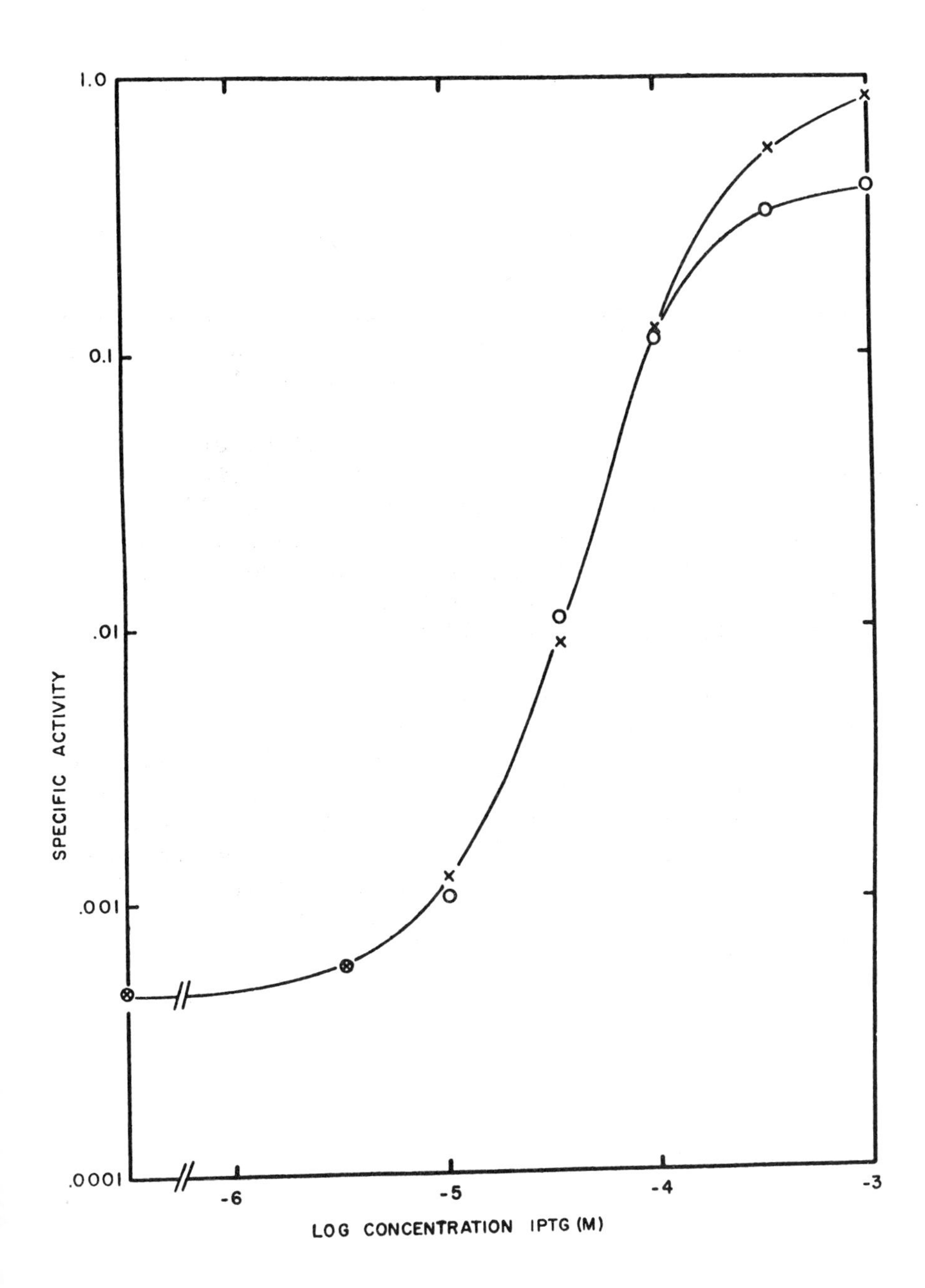
1.0
0.1
.01
.001
.0001
SPECIFIC ACTIVITY
-6
-5
-4
-3
LOG CONCENTRATION IPTG (M)

Figure 4. Kinetics of derepression of β-galactosidase synthesis in i^{TSS} and $i^{s,TSS}$ strains subsequent to a shift in growth temperature from 30 to 41.5°C.

Cultures of the i^{TSS}(N) and $i^{s,TSS}$(P) strains, which had grown for 15 generations glycerol-limited in chemostats (generation times of 5 hr) at 30°C, were shifted to 41.5°C at zero time. At zero time and every 10 min thereafter, samples were removed for duplicate enzyme assay and turbidity determinations. (From Sadler and Novick, 1965.)

The rate of enzyme synthesis, dz/dB, was calculated as $\Delta z/\Delta B$, the ratio of the increments in enzyme and bacterial turbidity between adjacent measurements. The abscissa t/τ gives bacterial growth in generations (e-fold increases) subsequent to the temperature shift. The dotted line labeled $n = 1$ gives the expected rise in dz/dB on the assumption of a stable repressor (an e-fold decrease in repressor for each generation of growth). The dotted line through the experimental points has a slope of about 10.

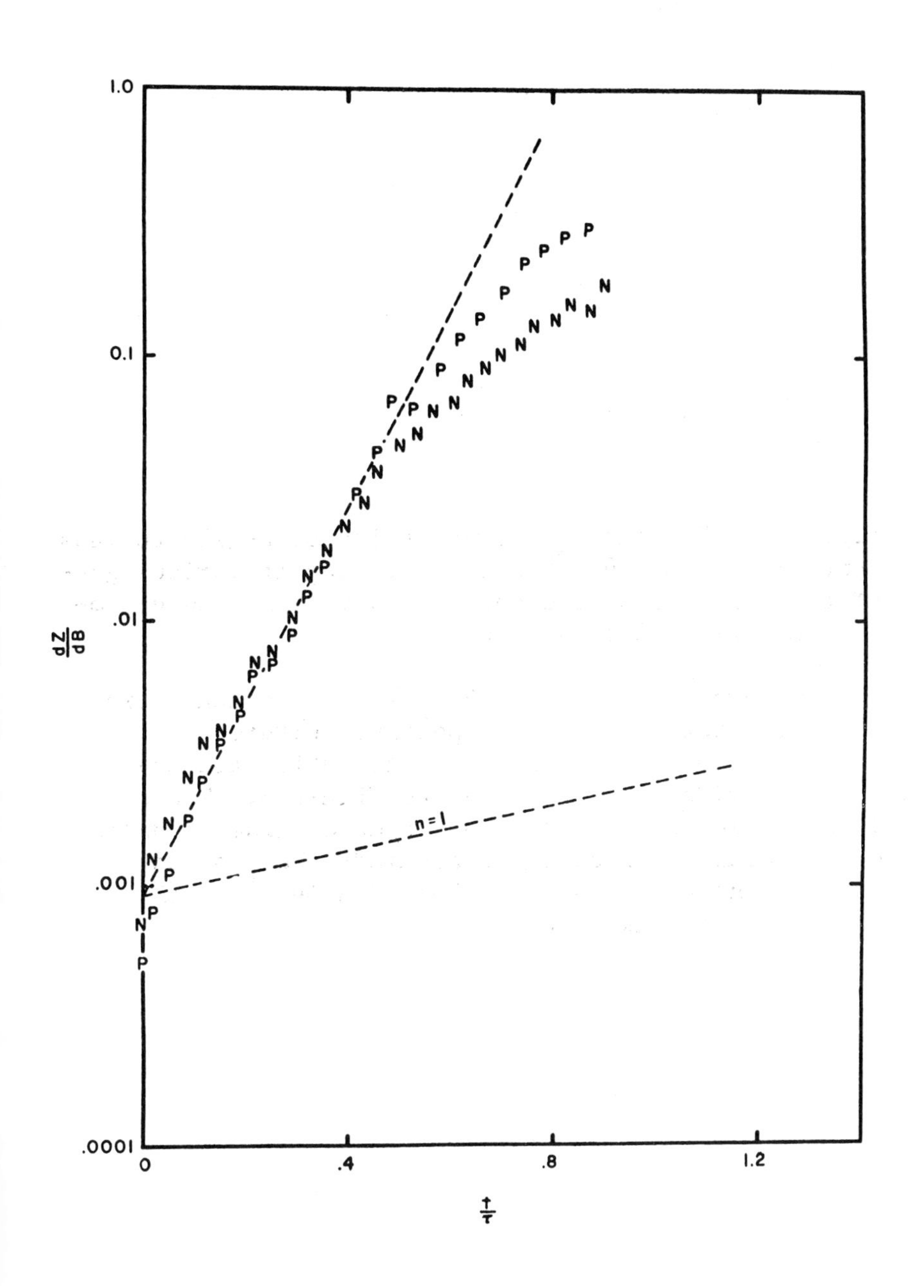
1.0
0.1
.01
.001
.0001
0
.4
.8
1.2
dZ/dB
t/τ
n=1

Figure 5. Kinetics of derepression of β-galactosidase synthesis in an i^{s},T^{SS} strain growing at various generation times, subsequent to a shift in growth temperature from 30 to 41.5°C.

The numbers 15, 10, 4 and 2 refer to the generation times (in hours) of the respective cultures. The conditions of growth and the calculation are the same as those given in the legend to Figure 4. The solid line labeled $n = 1$ gives the expected rise in dz/dB when a stable repressor is assumed. The dotted line through the points has a slope of about 12. (From Sadler and Novick, 1965.)

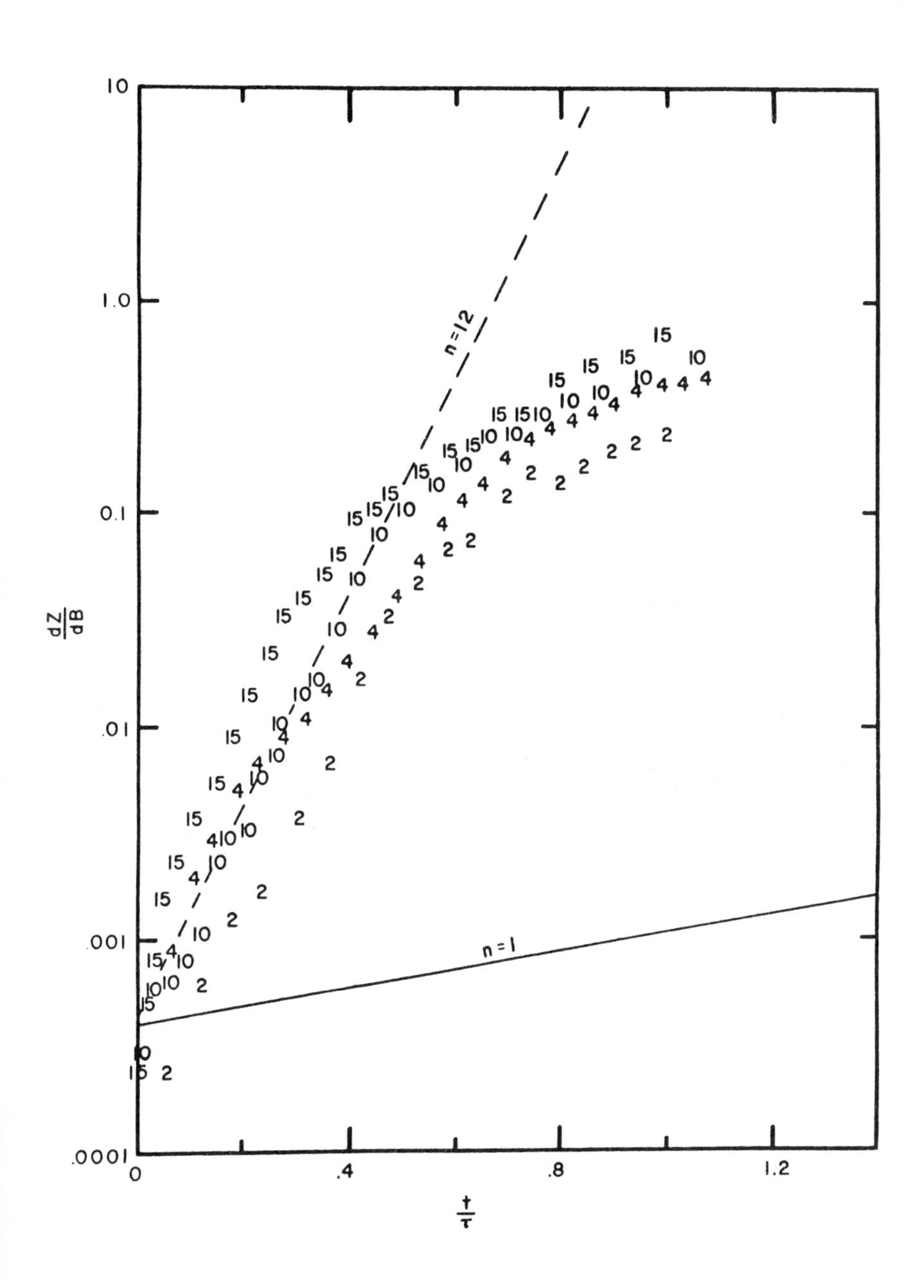
10
1.0
0.1
.01
.001
.0001
0
.4
.8
1.2
dZ/dB
t/τ
n=12
n=1

Figure 6(a). Derepression of β-galactosidase synthesis in an $i^{TSS}z^{+}y^{-}$ strain subsequent to either removal of IPTG at 41°C or a shift in growth temperature from 30 to 41°C.

Parallel cultures which had grown for 12 doublings at either 30°C (•) or 41°C (o) in the presence of 10^{-3} M IPTG were filtered (at the arrows), washed, and resuspended in prewarmed, preconditioned medium lacking IPTG. (From Sadler and Novick, 1965.)

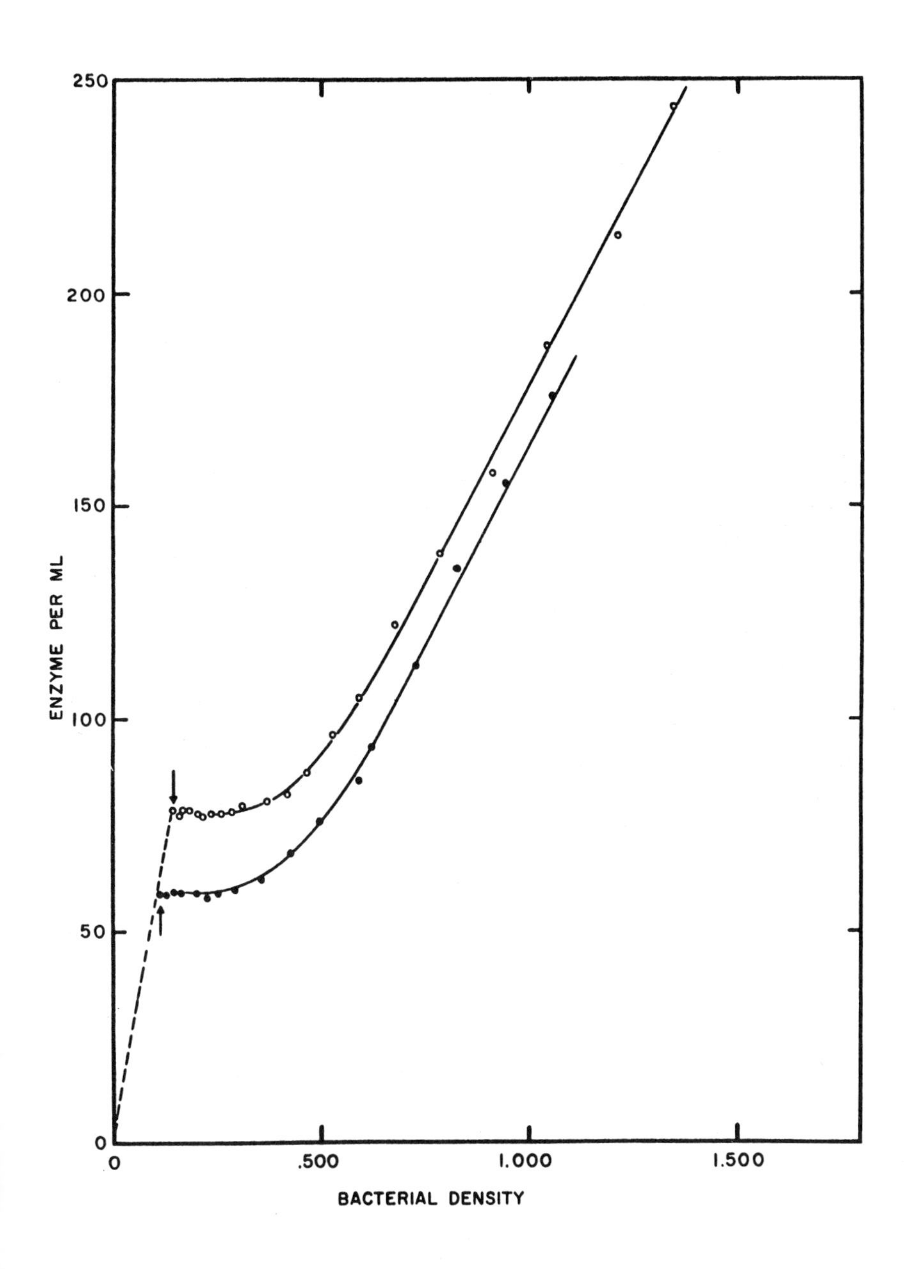
250
200
150
100
50
0
ENZYME PER ML
0
.500
1.000
1.500
BACTERIAL DENSITY

Figure 6(b). Kinetics of derepression in an i^{TSS} strain subsequent to either removal of IPTG at 41°C or a shift in growth temperature from 30 to 41°C.

As in Figure 6(a), (●) refers to that culture growing at 30°C prior to removal of IPTG, and (o) refers to that growing at 41°C prior to filtration. In Figure 6(b), the data shown in Figure 6(a) are given in differential form, i.e., dz/dB is plotted against generations of growth following the shift. The line through the experimental points gives a value of n = 3.3. (From Sadler and Novick, 1965.)

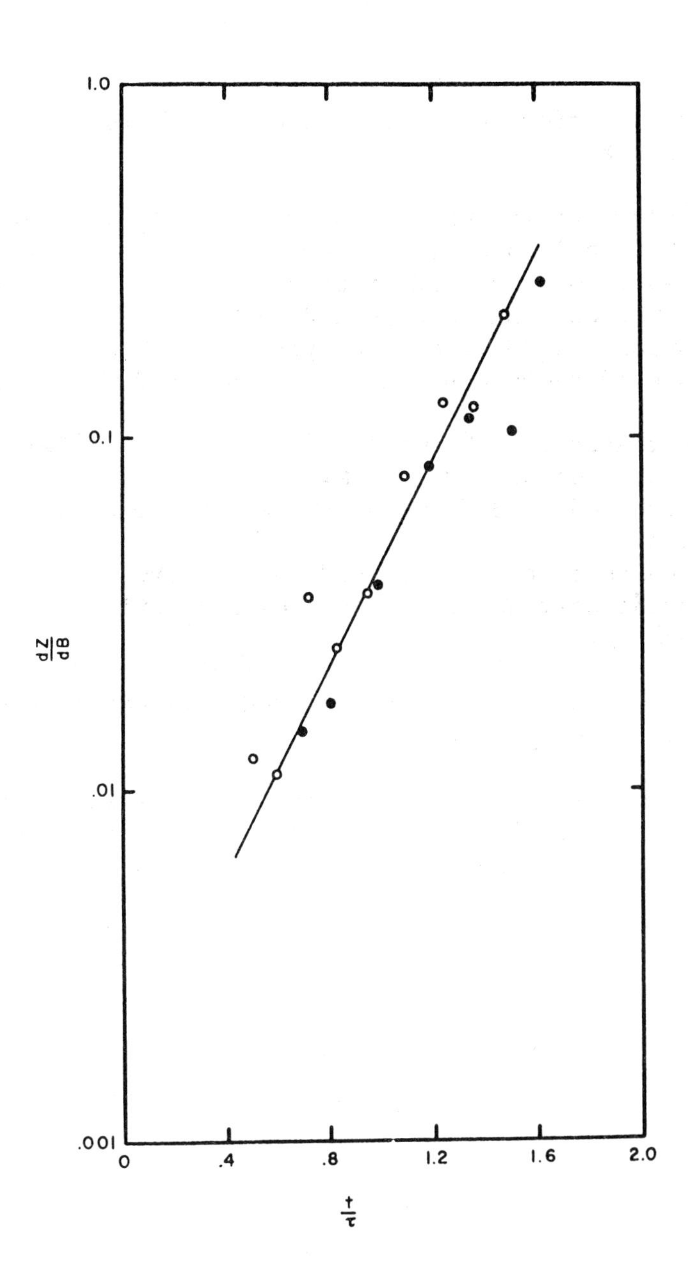
1.0
0.1
.01
.001
dZ/dB
0
.4
.8
1.2
1.6
2.0
t/τ

Figure 7. Effect of IPTG on the thermolability of the i^{TL} repressor.

An $i^{TL}z^{+}y^{-}$ strain, which had grown for approximately 10 doublings in a minimal-glycerol medium supplemented with casamino acids and tryptophan at 25°C, was filtered, washed, and resuspended in buffer containing L-canavanine-H_2SO_4 and 5-methyltryptophan. Various portions of the suspension were then treated as follows:

(∇) incubated at 25°C with IPTG added to a final concentration of 5×10^{-4} M.
(•) incubated at 37°C with IPTG at the same concentration.
(×) incubated at 37°C but did not receive IPTG until immediately before the second filtration and washing.
(□) incubated at 37°C but never received IPTG.
(o) incubated at 37°C and received IPTG during subsequent growth at 25°C.

At the end of 80 min of incubation, all suspensions were chilled in ice, filtered and washed with iced buffer, and resuspended in preconditioned medium containing casamino acids and tryptophan. To one (o) IPTG was immediately added to a final concentration of 5×10^{-4} M. All cultures were sampled periodically for 3 hr for turbidity measurements and duplicate β-galactosidase assays. The dotted lines and numbers refer to the initial rates of enzyme synthesis (dz/dB) following the heat pulse. (From Sadler and Novick, 1965.)

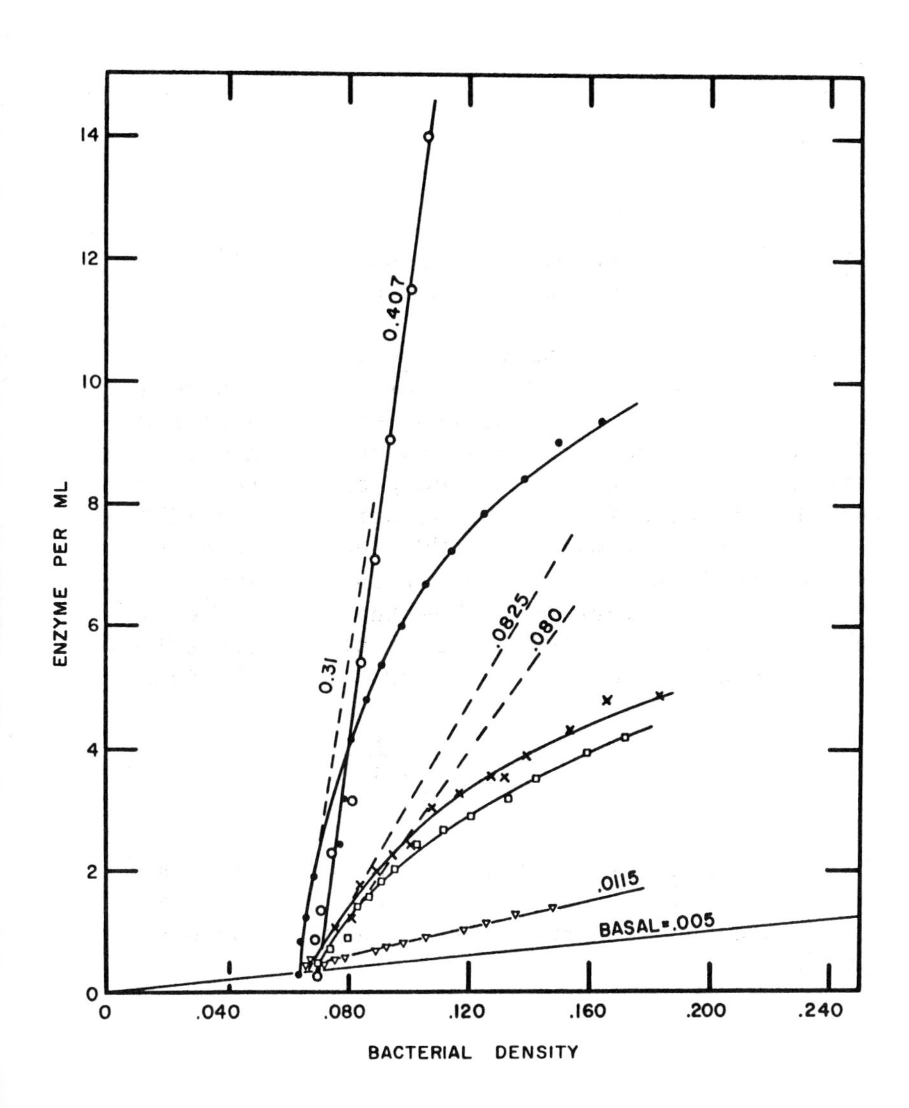
ENZYME PER ML
BACTERIAL DENSITY
0
2
4
6
8
10
12
14
.040
.080
.120
.160
.200
.240
0.407
0.31
.0825
.080
.0115
BASAL=.005

Figure 8. Kinetics of i^{TL} repressor inactivation at 37°C in the presence or absence of IPTG.

Experimental conditions were the same as those described in the legend of Figure 7. The same $i^{TL}z^{+}y^{-}$ strain growing at 25°C was removed into buffer-containing canavanine and 5-methyltryptophan and heated for various periods at 37°C in the presence (•) or absence (o) of IPTG at a final concentration of 5×10^{-4} M. After return to growth at 25°C, each culture was sampled at 10 min intervals for enzyme assays and turbidity determinations. The repressor level was calculated from the initial rate of synthesis following the heat pulse, $(dz/dB)_o$, from the relationship,

$$\left(\frac{dz}{dB}\right)_o = \left(\frac{dz}{dB}\right)_{max} \frac{K}{K + R}$$

where $(dz/dB)_{max}$ was determined on cultures treated identically except that they received IPTG (5×10^{-4} M) during subsequent growth. (From Sadler and Novick, 1965.)

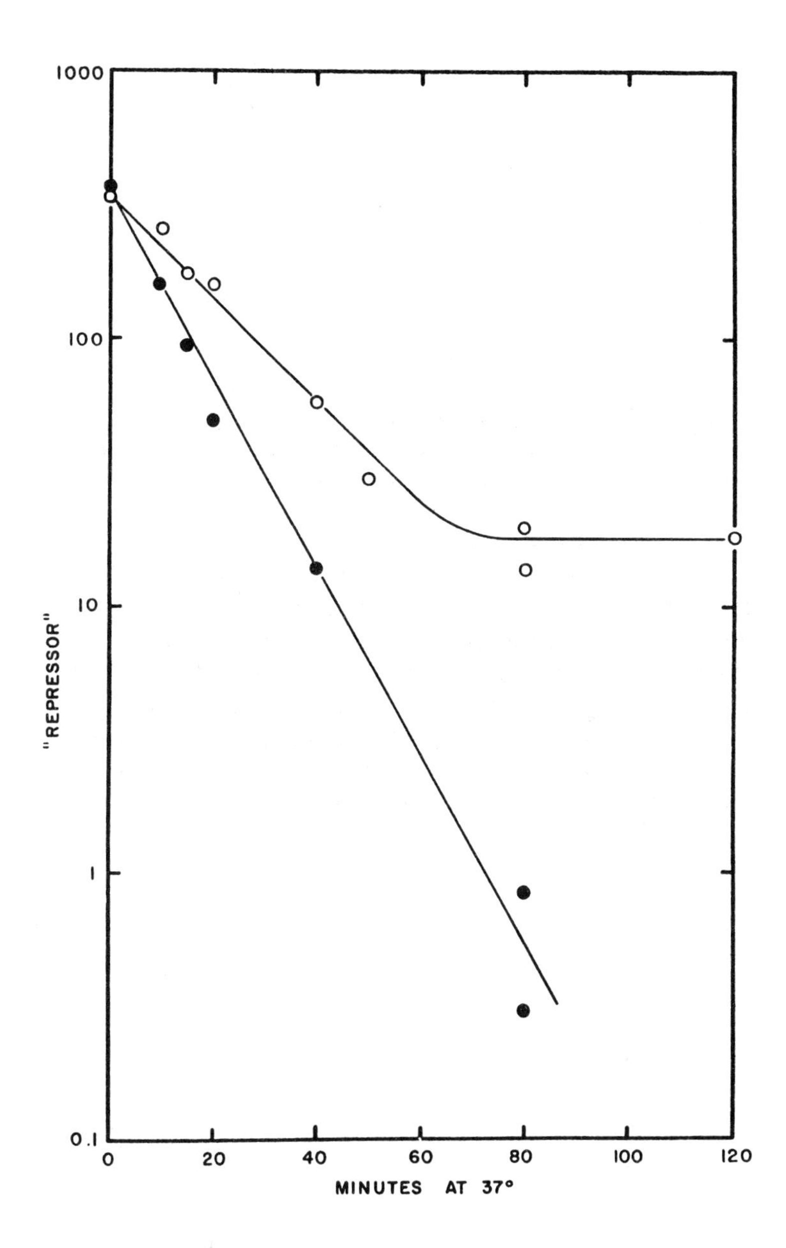
1000
100
10
1
0.1
"REPRESSOR"
0
20
40
60
80
100
120
MINUTES AT 37°

Figure 9. Onset of repression or derepression in an $i^{s,TSS}z^+y^-$ strain following the addition or removal of 0.01 M IPTG. (From Sadler and Novick, 1965.)

Parallel cultures of the $i^{s,TSS}$ strain, which had grown in the presence (Δ, ▲) or absence (○, ●) of 0.01 M IPTG for at least 10 doublings at 38.5°C, were, at the points indicated (arrows), filtered, washed, and resuspended in preconditioned medium. Half of each culture (Δ, ●) received IPTG at the same concentration, while the second half (▲, ○) received none. Samples were removed for enzyme assay and turbidity determinations every 15 min initially and every 30 min thereafter.

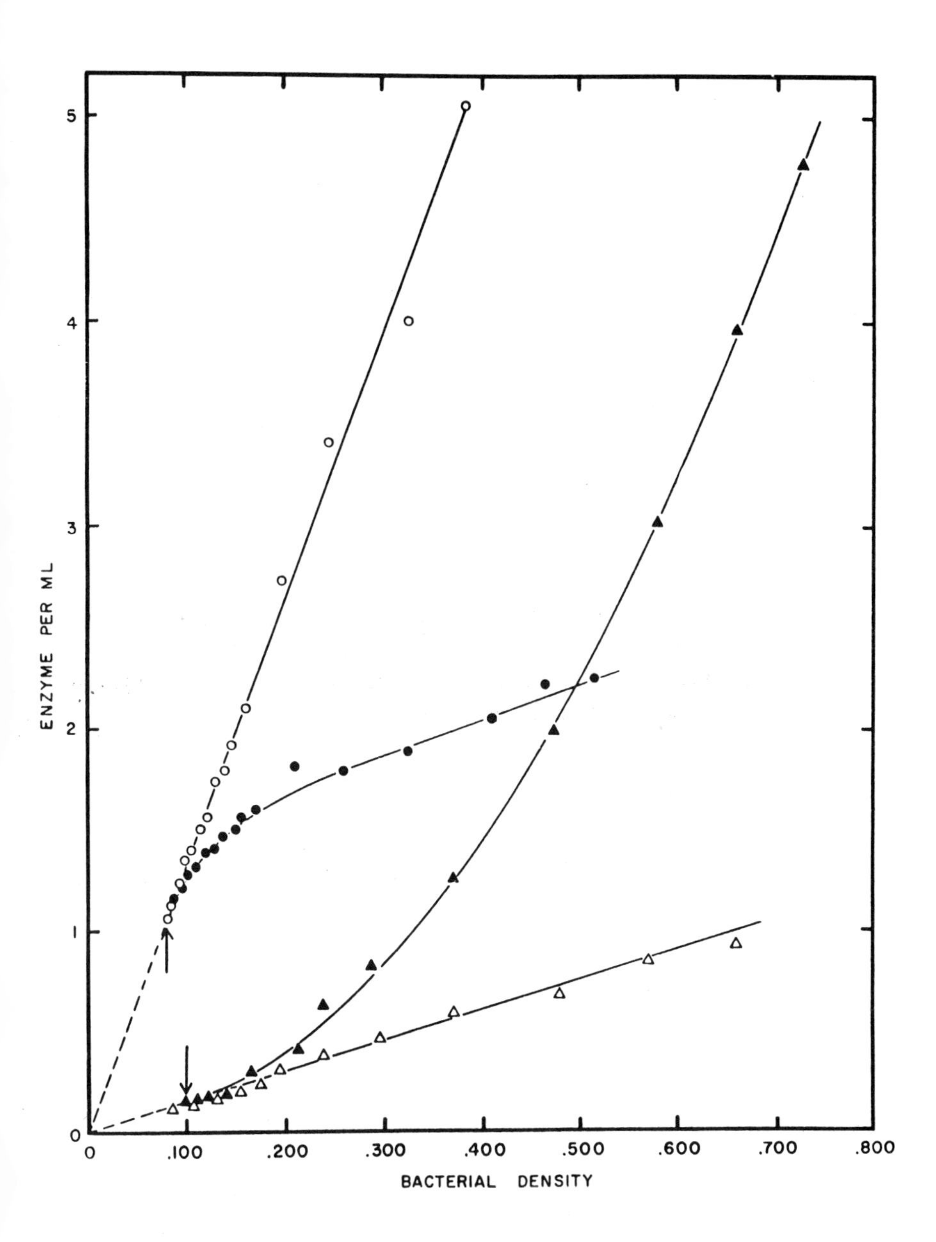
ENZYME PER ML
BACTERIAL DENSITY
0
.100
.200
.300
.400
.500
.600
.700
.800
1
2
3
4
5

Figure 10. Steady-state specific activities of β-galactosidase in an $i^{s,TSS}z^{+}y^{-}$ strain at 38.5°C growing in the presence of various concentrations of IPTG. (From Sadler and Novick, 1965.)

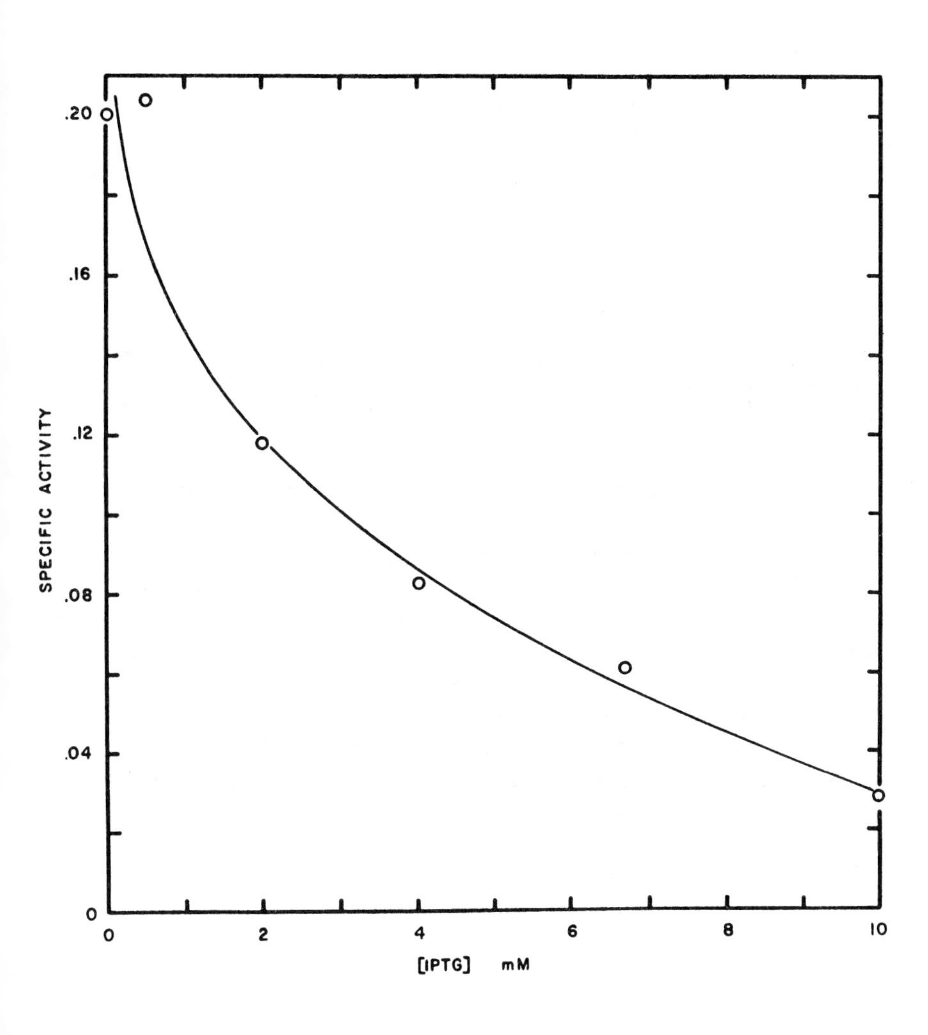
SPECIFIC ACTIVITY
.20
.16
.12
.08
.04
0
0
2
4
6
8
10
[IPTG] mM

Figure 11. Stabilization of repressor in an $i^{TSS}z^{+}y^{-}$ strain by various concentrations of IPTG during growth at 41.5°C.

A series of cultures of the organism were grown at 41.5°C for a minimum of 10 doublings in the presence of IPTG at the concentrations specified. IPTG was then removed by filtration and washing of the cells, always at 40°C. The cells were resuspended in preconditioned medium at 41.5°C, and samples for enzyme assay in quadruplicate and turbidity determinations were removed at 5-min intervals. The initial rate of synthesis (dz/dB) following IPTG removal was determined from enzyme per milliliter (z) *versus* turbidity (B) plots in each case. The error bar for each point indicates the uncertainty in the dz/dB so determined. (From Sadler and Novick, 1965.)

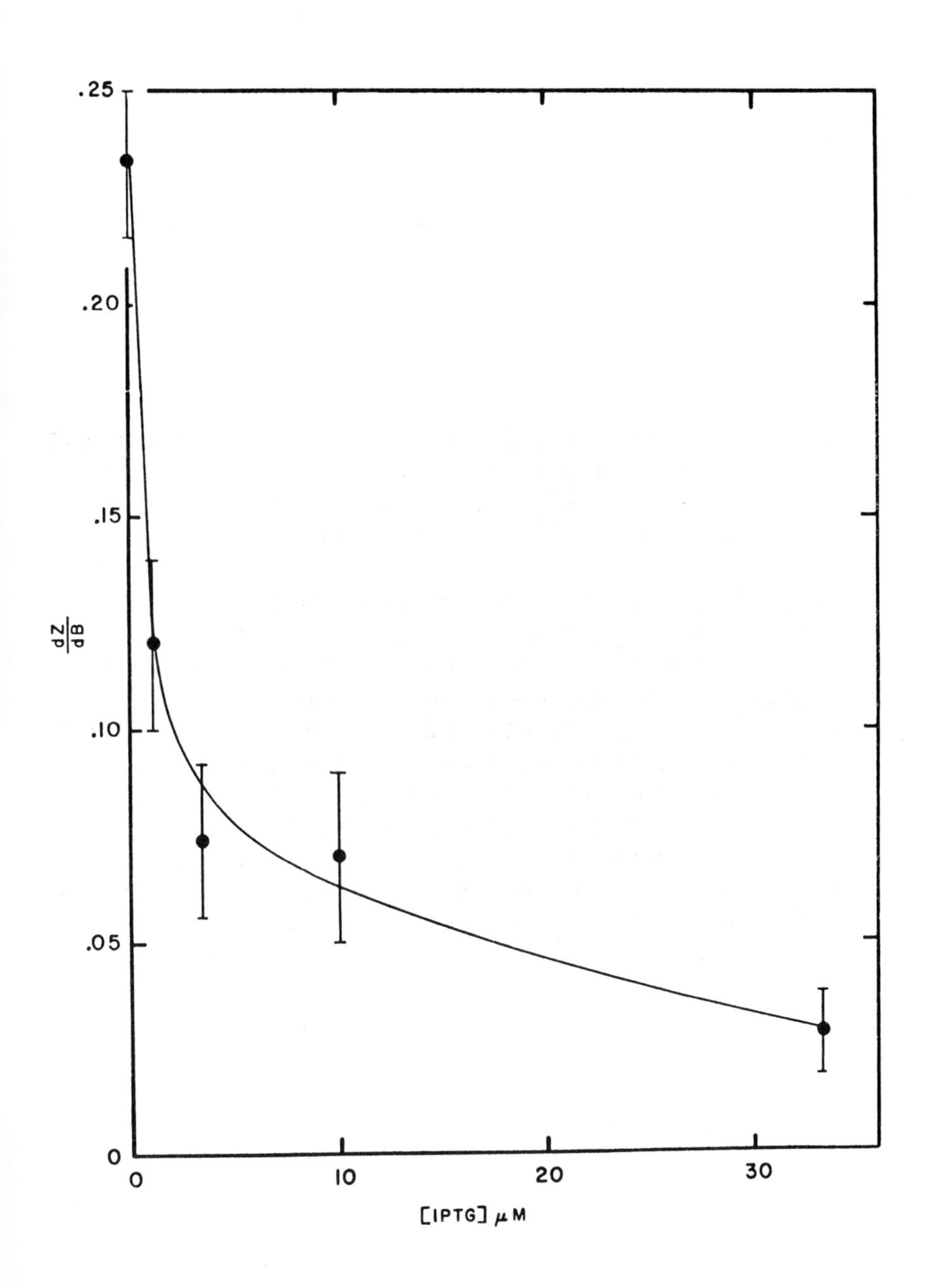
.25
.20
.15
.10
.05
0
$\frac{dZ}{dB}$
0
10
20
30
[IPTG] μM

Figure 12. Complementation between the TL and the TSS i-gene alleles: steady-state specific activities of β-galactosidase in i^{TSS} and i^{TL} F-homogenotes versus that in the $i^{TSS}z^{+}/Fi^{TL}z^{+}$ heterogenote.

Isogenic F_{lac} strains were prepared carrying either the i^{TSS} or the i^{TL} allele on both the chromosome and episome, or the i^{TSS} allele on the chromosome and the i^{TL} allele on the episome. In all cases, the chromosome carried the y^{-} allele and the episome the y^{+} marker, which facilitated scoring of segregation. All strains were grown for at least 10 doublings at the specified temperature before sampling for assay and turbidity determinations. At the same time, samples were plated from each culture to determine the percentage of homogenotic segregants (y^{-}/y^{-}), which was determined to be less than 1.5% in every case.

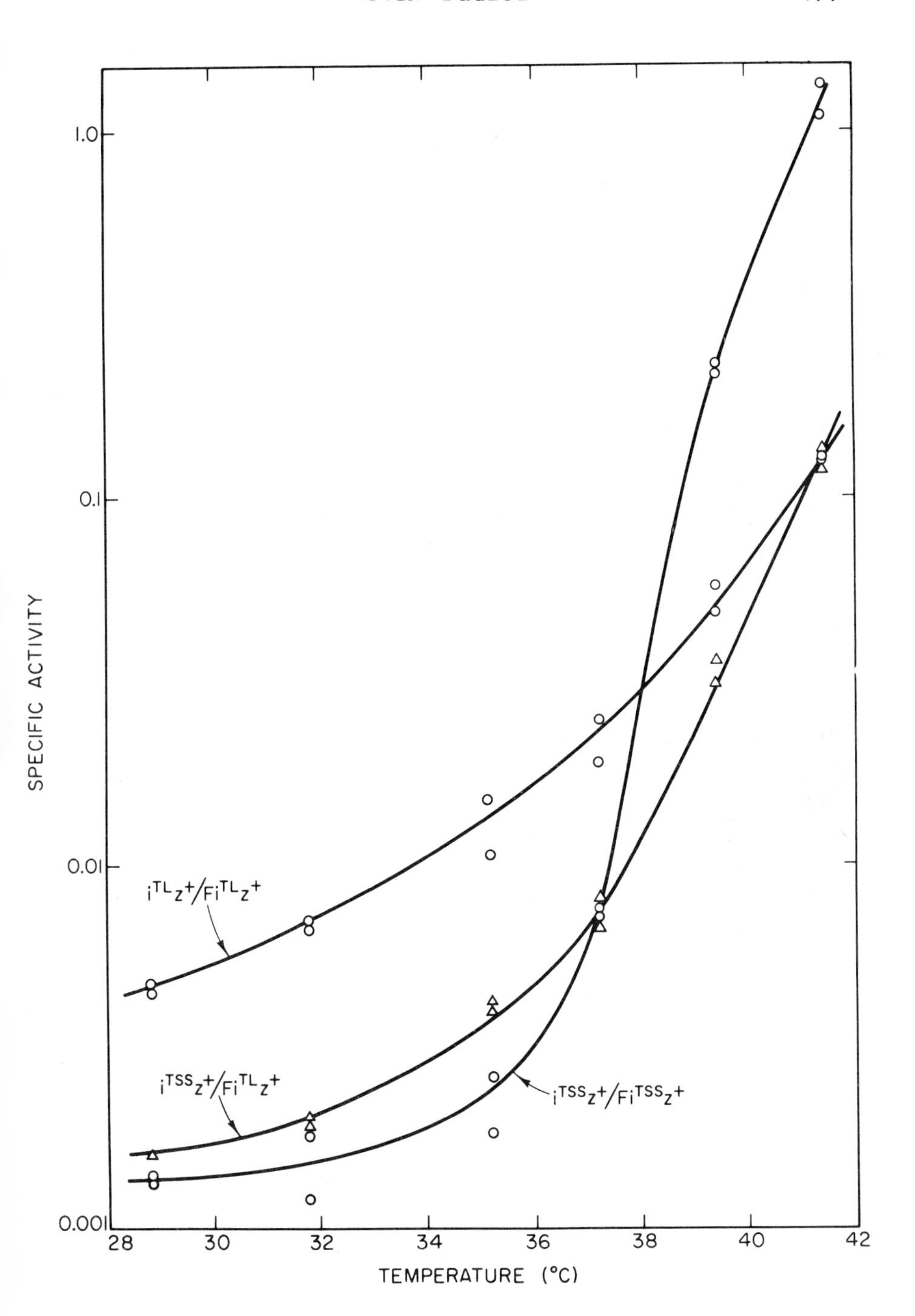
SPECIFIC ACTIVITY
1.0
0.1
0.01
0.001
28
30
32
34
36
38
40
42
TEMPERATURE (°C)
i^TL z+/Fi^TL z+
i^TSS z+/Fi^TL z+
i^TSS z+/Fi^TSS z+

Figure 13. Stoichiometry of induction with IPTG in an $i^+z^+y^-$ strain.

Experimental conditions were the same as those given in Figure 3. The level of active repressor $(R_o - R_i)$ for each concentration of IPTG was calculated on the basis of the equation,

$$\frac{dz}{dB} = \frac{K}{K + R}\left(\frac{dz}{dB}\right)_{max}$$

The total repressor level, R_o, was calculated from the same equation using the basal rate of enzyme synthesis; $(dz/dB)_{max}$ was assumed to equal the steady-state rate in the presence of 10^{-3} M IPTG. The ordinate $R_i/(R_o-R_i)$ gives the ratio of inactive to active repressor at each concentration of IPTG. The dotted line n = 1 gives the expected slope on the assumption that one molecule of IPTG is sufficient to inactivate one molecule of repressor. (From Sadler and Novick, 1965.)

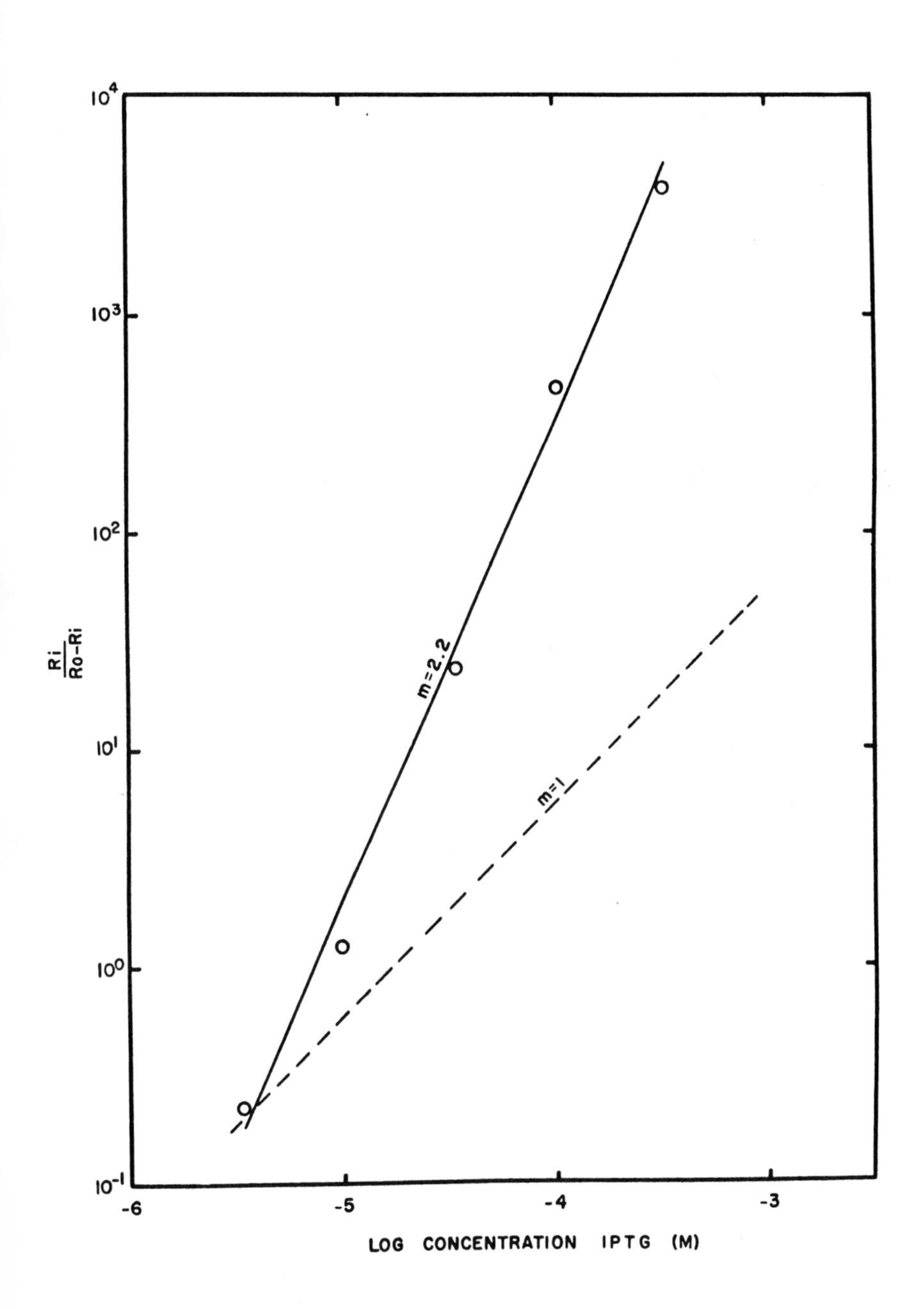

10^4
10^3
10^2
10^1
10^0
10^-1
Ri / Ro-Ri
m=2.2
m=1
-6
-5
-4
-3
LOG CONCENTRATION IPTG (M)

Figure 14. Steady-state levels of β-galactosidase in i^{TSS} haploid and F-homogenote strains growing at various temperatures in the presence or absence of 10^{-3} M IPTG.

Both the haploid and homogenote cultures were grown together in the same shaking water bath to insure identical thermal histories. At least 10 doublings of growth at the specified temperature were allowed before sampling. Each point for the haploid (o) and the homogenote (×) is the average of duplicate assays. (From Sadler and Novick, 1965.)

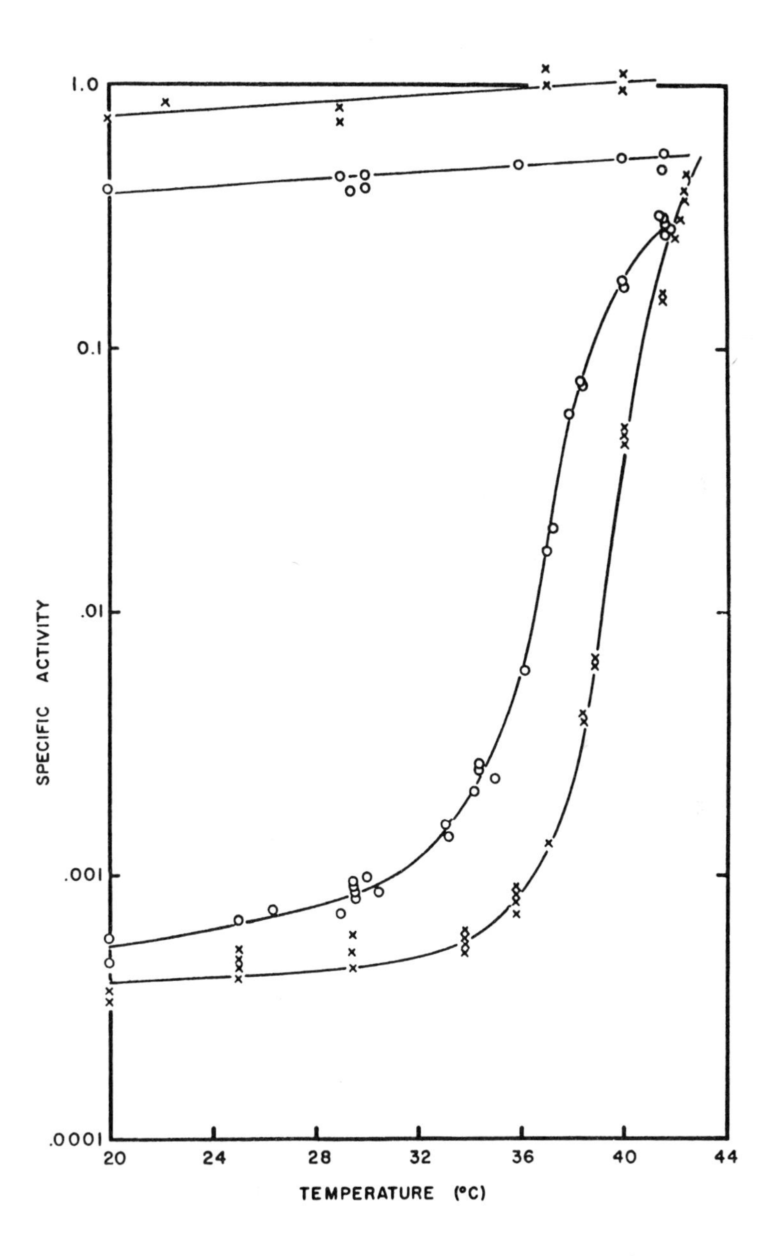
1.0
0.1
.01
.001
.0001
SPECIFIC ACTIVITY
20
24
28
32
36
40
44
TEMPERATURE (°C)

Section V

Conclusion

Concluding Remarks

David M. Prescott

Institute for Developmental Biology
University of Colorado
Boulder

In my own experience with symposia, occasionally as an organizer or contributor but more often as a listener, I have become more and more aware of the difficulty in integrating the presentations. Coordination usually becomes the problem of the individual listener or an appointed summarizer. The papers presented at this meeting, however, maintained a central theme, and thus lessened the problem of integration.

Each of the 15 papers can be related to the interactions diagrammed for a cell in Figure 1. Warner's paper deals with the synthesis of various RNA species in HeLa cells and possible modifications of RNA molecules during their integration into machinery for protein synthesis in the cytoplasm. The audience discussion following the paper raised the question of the function of the rapidly labeled, 90S nuclear RNA. Warner had suggested that such large RNA molecules might be messengers, presumably of a highly polycis-

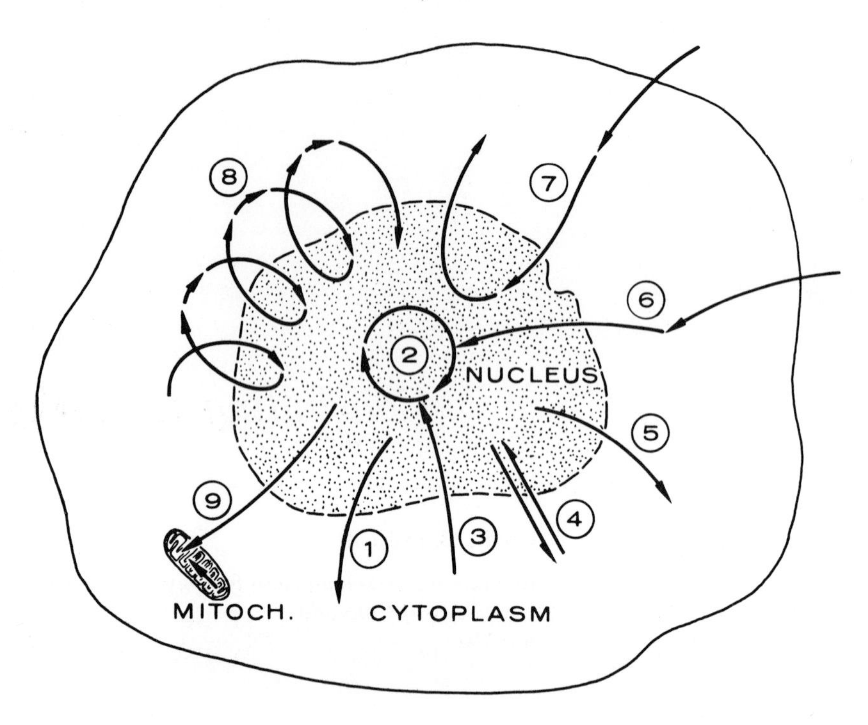

Figure 1.

(1) All classes of cytoplasmic RNA are synthesized in the nucleus and transported across the nuclear membrane.
(2) DNA replication cycle.
(3) Cytoplasmic influence on DNA relication.
(4) Proteins in rapid migration back and forth between nucleus and cytoplasm. (Includes proteins involved in genetic control?)
(5) Gradual displacement of all nuclear protein to the cytoplasm.
(6) Environmental effect on DNA replication.
(7) Cytoplasmically mediated effects of the environment on RNA protein production.
(8) Progression of qualitative change in RNA synthesis through a nuclear-cytoplasmic loop of cause and effect.
(9) Nuclear-mitochondrial complementation.

tronic nature, cleaved at specific points to yield smaller message units before utilization in the cytoplasm. This explanation gains support by analogy with the apparent conversion by cleavage of 45S RNA in the nucleus into two molecules, the 28S and 16S RNA of cytoplasmic ribosomes. Nemer has similarly demonstrated rapidly labeled 70S to 90S RNA in developing sea urchin eggs and embryos, but suggests that such RNA is not premessenger because the proportion between such RNA and m-RNA changes to a degree unexpected for a strict precursor-product relationship. Undoubtedly this fraction of very large RNA molecules will receive the expanded attention it deserves.

At this point in the discussion arose the question of functional ribosomes in the nucleus. Some skepticism was expressed concerning the general occurrence among cells of nuclear protein synthesis. Several times later in the symposium, nuclear protein synthesis was brought up again, implying that critical, unambiguous evidence on this topic was still needed on cells besides those of mammalian thymus and liver.

Dr. Schultze's work is concerned with synthesis of nuclear proteins, but her approach probably cannot give an unequivocal answer to the cytoplasmic versus nuclear site of such proteins. She points out that the short-term rate of nuclear protein labeling is proportional to the nuclear mass in a wide variety of mammalian tissues, and, moreover, that the ratio of nuclear to cytoplasm labeling is the same whether it follows a very short or a relatively long, labeling period. Either nuclear proteins are synthesized in nucleus or the shift of newly synthesized proteins from cytoplasm to nucleus occurs extremely rapidly.

The concept of such rapid shift is not unreasonable, and the work of Goldstein and Prescott on migrating proteins in ameba supports its creditability. If nuclear proteins are derived primarily from the cytoplasm, new protein molecules must be immediately available for migration; the situation contrasts with the delay between synthesis of RNA and its shift to the cytoplasm. At least there are no a priori reasons why all nuclear proteins could not be synthesized in the cytoplasm. In ameba, some cytoplasmic synthesis of the major classes of nuclear proteins has been convincingly demonstrated (see reference (1) in Goldstein and Prescott chapter "Protein Interactions Between Nucleus and Cytoplasm").

In discussions of this type, we still tend to speak of total nuclear proteins, but as our knowledge increases, it will be possible to single out fractions in this heterogeneous mixture of nuclear proteins. If we assume that the nucleus makes only certain proteins (not synthesized in the cytoplasm), we must presume a mechanism for the differential selection of m-RNAs to be used in the nucleus or in the cytoplasm. In addition to describing proteins that migrate rapidly in and out of the nucleus, Goldstein and Prescott also give evidence of the gradual shift of all nuclear proteins to the cytoplasm in ameba.

An influence of the cytoplasmic state on DNA synthesis is clear from Goldstein's experiments on transplantation of nuclei between S and G_2 cells in ameba. The nature of the influence factor or factors is unknown, but conceivably the proteins that Goldstein has demonstrated migrate rapidly back and forth between nucleus and cytoplasm could be involved.

Sadler summarizes the evidence that the repressor substance of the Jacob-Monod model of gene control is at least partially protein in nature. Again, the migrating proteins of the ameba at least have a physiological behavior that might be predicted for the behavior of repressors.

The helices of the ameba nucleus have usually been presumed to represent DNA-protein, but Stevens reports that they contain RNA and migrate through nuclear membrane "pores" into the cytoplasm. She concluded that the helices are concerned with packaging and transport of r-RNA, or possibly m-RNA, to the cytoplasm. The large numbers of nuclear helices found in ameba are not often encountered with regularity in other cell types, but it is reasonable to suppose that the ameba helices reflect function or functions present in all cells, but exaggerated in morphological manifestation in ameba.

In Hennen's studies of nuclear-cytoplasmic interactions in developing eggs of interspecies frog hybrids, cytoplasmic factors apparently can modify chromosomal function. The reversal of such modifications in the case of one type of crossing by back transplantation of a nucleus to an egg of its own species is perhaps not as surprising as the failure to achieve reversal in other crosses. The profundity of cytoplasmic effects on the nucleus in the latter case, clearly demonstrated from the induced gross changes in chromosome number and in karyotype, illustrates that the cytoplasm is not so passive with respect to genetic matters of the nucleus as is often assumed.

Studies by Mounolou, Jakob, and Slonimski, on the interaction of the nuclear genome with function of mitochondrial DNA, raise puzzling new questions about nuclear-cytoplasmic interactions. It is at least clear now that nuclear-mitochondrial interaction does exist.

The papers of Dutton and Finger carried the problem of nuclear activity modification back an additional step to the environment. Although we may still argue at what level (nuclear or cytoplasmic) antigens induce changes in protein (antibody production), it is clear that ultimately a nuclear function - i.e., DNA replication - is initiated or at least enormously intensified. Finger's analysis of the determination of antigen phenotype in _Paramecium_ points up how we might explain the complicated interactions between environment, cytoplasm, and nucleus by current models of genetic control.

The studies of Clever, Nemer, and Bell each bear on the problem of control over RNA synthesis, especially in relation to cell differentiation. Although the ecdysone-directed puff induction in _Chironomus_ larvae demonstrates clearly environmental influence, and we can assume a microenvironmental influence on feather induction in the chicken, the changing pattern of RNA synthesis in early sea urchin development is apparently an environmentally independent progression. The environment of the nucleus is, of course, the cytoplasm, and, from the standpoint of nuclear reactivity, it is inconsequential whether the environmental (cytoplasmic) changes originate in the cytoplasm or outside the cell. If we consider the cytoplasm as the immediately effective environment of the nucleus, we can build a model by which the quality of RNA synthesis may change progressively through a nuclear-cytoplasmic loop of cause and effect (number 7 in Figure 1). Presumably qualitative and/or quantitative changes in protein synthesis form a section of the cytoplasmic part of the loop. The progress of a cell through its life cycle almost certainly must involve a sequential series of such loops.

The switching of a cell into meiosis (Stern and Hotta) cannot presently be related specifically to any scheme in Figure 1, but the control of chromosome pairing with the associated difference (from mitosis) in the timing of DNA synthesis involves nuclear-cytoplasmic interactions.

The diagram in Figure 1 no doubt is redundant, and the indicated patterns of nuclear cytoplasmic interactions probably overlap and interact, but its information is correct, if only in a very generalized manner.

In this symposium, nine different, major groups of organisms are studied in the 15 papers: bacteria, protozoa, yeast, a sea urchin, a dipteran, a bird, plants, mammalian cells, and amphibia. It is indicative of the current convergence in experimental biology that a symposium can be so well-focused and include such a wide diversity of organisms.

Index

N

O

P